# HUMAN VARIATION:

*Readings in
Physical Anthropology*

# HUMAN VARIATION:

## Readings in Physical Anthropology

## Hermann K. Bleibtreu
University of Arizona
Tucson, Arizona

## and

## James F. Downs
University of Hawaii
Hilo, Hawaii

GLENCOE PRESS
A Division of The Macmillan Company
Beverly Hills, California
Collier-Macmillan Limited, London

# Contents

**Chapter Three.   Human Brains, Behavior, and Language          63**

**Chapter Four.   Variation in Human Morphology and Behavior   91**

**Chapter Five.   Inferences About Man from the Non-Human
Primates                                                          111**

**Chapter Six.   Human Biology as a Consideration in the
Study of Prehistory                                               129**

**Chapter Seven.   The Origin of Man                              147**

**Chapter Eight.   The Evidence of Fossil Man                     187**

# Introduction

The primary mission of a textbook is to present a summary of what is known about a given subject. Facts and well established theories are thus more proper material for a text than speculation and commentary. Nor is relevancy to the current social scene and concern with the questions posed by the educated layman a necessary or even desirable feature of a textbook. Textbooks, after all, are schoolbooks to be contemplated in that rarified atmosphere of the classroom, while "pleasure reading" is lighter, usually better stylistically, currently relevant and above all else produces enjoyment. This of course in no way means that it cannot also be highly informative, particularly when the reader has already been through the facts and theories ordeal, thereby permitting him to particularly enjoy the periodical literature. Moreover, a well written, exciting article in a magizine often whets the appetite for a more serious, textbook knowledge of a subject.

This volume is intended to accompany a text in physical anthropology. It consists of articles, most of which come from the popular press, many not written by anthropologists. The editors made this selection because they felt that the most important statements about human evolution and social biology are often best expressed in media other than scholarly books and professional journals. The topical arrangement of this book is similar to that of most current textbooks in physical anthropology. It should really not be much of a surprise that the content of academic physical anthropology is of sufficient public interest that articles about it are quite common in the current periodical literature. Departments of anthropology have no monopoly on the topics of human evolution and human variation. These have been in the public domain long before (and perhaps we should say in spite of ) the organization of anthropology in the schools. An important challenge to the college teacher is to use this great fund of information and ideas to further the education of the students. Hopefully these readings will be helpful in that direction. The articles reprinted here were chosen from hundreds of pertinent items which have appeared in the past few years.

More than anything else anthropology is a way of looking at the world, and an introductory course is an explication of that world view. It is the editors' opinion that a first course in anthropology is no place to avoid the greater implications of textbook facts and theories. Concern with small points and comfortable hedging of social and moral challenges is often felt to be the proper introductory approach "until the student accumulates more knowledge and sophistication." We disagree with that philosophy, partly because students learn with enthusiasm when relevancy is indicated, and because avoiding challenges in the classroom does not make them disappear. Anthropology, in the greater sense of that word, is after all everywhere — in the morning paper, in the magazines at the barber shop, on TV, and in the real world of any city and town. We hope this volume convinces its readers of that point.

The Editors' Notes for each section are not intended as capsules or summaries of the articles that follow. They are simply the editors' thinking on a given topic which prompted the choice of the articles. This does not mean the editors necessarily agree with the message in some of the selections, since it is the mission of the reader to allow fuller exploration of topics generally introduced in textbooks. The editors' stance on these topics is to be found in their text rather than in the selections reprinted here.

# Chapter One

# Anthropology

# and

# Variation

Understanding anthropology, or more colloquially, "really digging its message," is as much a matter of remodeling and casting out established ideas as it is of becoming familiar with new data about human evolution. The "common sense" and many of the predominant philosophical and religious beliefs embodied in the culture of the Western World are incompatible with modern anthropology. Rather than avoiding the conflicts and hedging on the more philosophical extremes of the study of human variation, it is probably intellectually more efficient and certainly more exciting to jump right in and identify the sociocultural implications of the modern view of human biology and evolution.

Unlike a first course in physics or chemistry where you are quite receptive partly because you don't harbor any preconceived value-loaded ideas about electrical charges or elements, you are not a *tabula rasa* when you take that first anthropology course. You have already heard about and have formed opinions on Negroes and intelligence, "missing links," sexual behavior, intelligence, and so on. In some cases your thoughts and those of modern anthropology will coincide, in others you'll be delighted with some new ideas, and in still others you'll be quite upset and remain undecided. At least that's what a good course and a good book on anthropology should do for you. We hope the following readings will have that effect.

1

# ANTHROPOLOGY

*George D. Spindler*

George D. Spindler, a professor of anthropology at Stanford University, is editor of the extensive *Case Studies in Cultural Anthropology.*

   Anthropology is a complex and diversified subject that goes in a number of directions and utilizes a variety of methods and organizing ideas. I shall attempt to describe it by discussing three questions: What is anthropology? What do anthropologists do? Where is anthropology going today?

### What Is Anthropology?

   Anthropology is the study of man and his works. This sweeping subject is divided into a number of major subdivisions.

   *Cultural anthropology* is concerned with the differences and similarities in the many ways of dealing with the problems of existence. Its building blocks are ethnographies—detailed descriptions of whole ways of life in particular places and times.

   *Archeology* is the anthropology of extinct cultures—the study of past ways of life as represented by their own actual remains. Archeologists study artifacts (tools, weapons, houses, etc.), and the traces of man's use of the earth's surface (mounds, terraces, irrigation systems, etc.) in order to reconstruct the cultures of past epochs. Archeology joins forces with cultural anthropology and historiography at many points.

   *Linguistics* is the study of man's language—the distribution of different languages grouped into families and stocks, the internal structure of separate languages, and the relationships of language to other parts of culture.

   *Physical anthropology* studies biological man—the characteristics of different human types through time and in space. In its study of human evolution physical anthropology joins with cultural anthropology, for man creates his own environment with culture and thereby directly affects his own evolution. Physical anthropology and archeology also work together closely, for remains are

Reprinted from the *NEA Journal*, Vol. 52 (Sept. 18, 1963), pp. 28–31. Reprinted by permission of the National Education Association and the author.

often found with the artifacts that were used when the culture was a whole entity.

Anthropology is comparative. Different ways of life are seen in the perspective of the many dramatic forms human life has assumed on this earth. When an anthropologist describes marriage, government, religion, education, or technology for a particular society, he is describing these forms of behavior in the light of his knowledge of other forms quite different.

Sometimes he makes cross-cultural comparison the major purpose of his work, and he has great collections of comparative data available to help him in this purpose. At other times his work is only comparative by implication, but he collects and analyzes his material quite differently than a psychologist or sociologist ordinarily would because of his cross-cultural, comparative point of view.

Anthropology is holistic. Almost always the anthropologist studies one manifestation of the culture in relation to other dimensions of the whole way of life. He sees the structure of the family, for example, as related to the methods of subsistence the people use to earn a living. He studies religious beliefs and concepts of disease causation and cure in relation to patterns of child rearing, because the former are seen, in part, as projections of the latter.

Anthropology is both scientific and humanistic. Sometimes its methods are objective, precise, and rigorous; sometimes they are empathetic, intuitive, and almost literary in quality. Anthropologists agree that one must live as close as possible to the people one is studying and under the same conditions whenever feasible, in order to understand how they feel, and to see life from their point of view. The basic method of data collection in anthropology is, therefore, what anthropologists call participant-observation.

An anthropologist studying a new culture usually establishes residence with the people for a period of time varying from several months to a year or two and tries to maintain a friendly low-pressure kind of interaction with the people. He tries to observe them unobtrusively in the daily round of work and play so that, insofar as possible, they are unaffected by the fact they are being studied.

Anthropologists are strongly committed to the principle that people do not usually know exactly why they behave as they do. Just as the speaker of a language cannot usually describe the grammatical structure of his native tongue, so too is it rarely possible for a parent to tell the inquirer why children are reared as they are, or why the given and time-honored sequence in an initiation rite is followed to the letter or why a seemingly cumbersome and complex system of kinship terms is in use.

The anthropologist's purpose is to examine behaviors and infer the reasons why these behaviors exist in their particular forms, or for that matter, exist at all. For this purpose, the anthropologist, like other scientists, needs theory, for theory provides the logic of inference and, therefore, guides his interpretation of observed behavior. Theory in modern anthropology is undergoing rapid change at the present time, and many anthropologists are just becoming aware of the need for systematic, rigorous theory.

## What Do Anthropologists Do?

In what has been said already, there are some hints as to what anthropologists do. They study human behavior and interpret its meaning. They collect genealogies in order to trace relationships among the present members of the group and their ties with former members. They collect censuses of the population they are studying so that they know its distribution, the relationship between population and subsistence, the composition of households and other small social groupings.

Anthropologists transcribe languages, using phonetic systems, or they store them on tape for future analysis in order that their patterns can be analyzed and compared to other languages. They collect personal documents—accounts of dreams, autobiographies, personal experiences—in order to understand the ways in which culturally patterned experience is interpreted by the individual. And they try to be at least marginal participants in all the important events which take place among the people they are studying and to record observations of these events and the reactions of people to them.

Although anthropologists spend a considerable proportion of their professional lives in the field, the majority have positions in universities or colleges where they teach both undergraduate and graduate students. Their courses bear such titles as Primitive Religion and Philosophy, Social Organization, Culture Change, Personality and Culture, Language and Culture, the Evolution of Man, New World Prehistory. Some courses deal with special fields such as education, law, and medicine, so there are courses called Legal Anthropology, Medical Anthropology and Anthropology of Education.

An increasing number of anthropologists are in demand as consultants, advisers, and analysts for federal agencies that deal with emerging nations and underdeveloped areas of the world. Many anthropologists with positions on university faculties act occasionally as consultants and analysts for industries or governments—

both our own and others—and take temporary leaves of absence from their positions for these purposes.

One of the problems of the profession is that there aren't enough anthropologists to meet the demand. There are only about 900 fellows in the American Anthropological Association at present, and this fellowship is not expected to increase rapidly because of the long period of graduate training—from five to seven years—required for the Ph.D.

### Where Is Anthropology Going Today?

This last question is one of the most difficult ones to answer, for each part of anthropology is generating new ideas, new methods of study, and building new theory. The whole field is in ferment at present.

Human evolution is one of the perennial problem areas that has received special attention lately. Anthropologists realize that man has always been a creature of culture. Every new tool, no matter how crude or how advanced, directly affects the course of human evolution. In the beginning the use of a simple club reduced selective pressure upon the teeth and jaws, so that those of our remote ancestors who had clubs but smaller jaws and teeth could survive better than similar creatures with bigger jaws but no clubs. And since the hand and the brain are intimately related, selective pressure resulted in larger brains that could guide better tools to man's purposes.

Today evolution continues. Man is fast creating a new physical environment through technology. Smog, pesticides, industrial and household pollutants, radioactive wastes, and fallout are new hazards that have already begun to affect the future course of human evolution. Anthropologists are studying these problems armed with knowledge from biology (the field of genetics is supplying new knowledge about the mechanisms of human heredity), and from their study of how culture adapts to man's needs on the one hand and adapts man to its conditions on the other.

Another trend in anthropology today is the emphasis upon cultural change and cultural stability. The concerns range from questions about the sequence of developments that led to the emergence of great urban centers among the Aztec, Maya, and Inca to the minute details of cultural change within a period of a decade in an American Indian tribe, or in a village in the highlands of New Guinea.

Changes in social groupings, in value systems, in technology, in political leadership, in language, and in personality structure as it adapts to conditions of life brought about by cultural transformation are all being scrutinized with new theories and methods of study. One of the particularly interesting problems is what makes cultural patterns persist in the face of what seems to be overwhelming pressure for change.

Sometimes the answer is quite simple—as in the case of the German villagers who bought tractors but continue to do most of the work in the vineyards by hand. Because the terraced hillside plots are too small to use mechanized equipment, the tractors merely replace the cows (yes, really cows, not oxen) formerly used to haul carts full of workers and equipment up to the vineyards. Sometimes it is very complex, as in the case of some American Indians who continue to use native methods of treating illness despite the availability of modern medicine. The reasons the native practices continue in use are tied in with concepts of disease causation that are a part of a world view vastly different from ours.

Anthropologists are currently giving special attention to many other problem areas, but I shall mention only one. They are developing new methods and techniques of research which will make their studies of behavior more precise.

For example, they are using symbolic logic and formal mathematical models to separate and manipulate the elements of observed behavior. They are applying microanalytic methods of study to the use of space between persons in social interaction with each other (the study of proxemics) and to the gestures and bodily movements that communicate content beyond words and that sometimes contradict words (the study of kinesics). They are carrying out rigorous and detailed analysis of the meaning of utterances (parts of whole expressions) in communication. And they are developing new applications of statistics to test the validity of hypotheses about the relationships between variables. Anthropology, in short, is becoming more scientific.

For Further Reading

Brameld, Theodore, *The Cultural Foundations of Education: An Interdisciplinary Exploration* (New York: Harper, 1957). Systematic analysis of the ways in which education and culture interact.

*Case Studies in Cultural Anthropology* (New York: Holt). Separate paperbacks on selected cultures, written with the beginning student in mind.

Cohen, Yehudi, *Social Structure and Personality: A Casebook* (New York: Holt, 1961). Covers socialization and social structure, effect of community systems on personality, social and cultural change.

Foster, George, *Traditional Cultures and the Impact of Technological Change* (New York: Harper, 1962).

Heizer, Robert F., *Man's Discovery of his Past: Literary Landmarks in Archeology* (Englewood Cliffs, N.J.: Prentice-Hall, 1962).

Henry, Jules, *Culture Against Man* (New York: Random House, 1963). Includes novel and significant ways of looking at education and its cultural context.

Honigmann, John, *Understanding Culture* (New York: Harper, 1963).

Howells, William, *Mankind in the Making* (New York: Doubleday, 1959). An excellent and readable treatment of human evolution.

Lasker, Gabriel, *The Evolution of Man: A Brief Introduction to Physical Anthropology* (New York: Holt, 1963).

*Scientific American* Reprints, Vol. 203, No. 3. 1960. These separate reprints include discussion of recent developments in linguistics, archeology, physical anthropology, and cultural anthropology for the layman.

Spindler, George D., *Education and Culture: Anthropological Approaches* (New York: Holt, 1963). Includes sections on the theory of culture and its relationship to education; the educational process in our culture; and education in other cultures.

# PORTRAIT IN SCIENCE: DARWIN'S 'ORIGIN' TODAY

*Gavin R. de Beer*

Sir Gavin de Beer, past director of the Natural History Department of the British Museum, is lecturer in zoology at Oxford University and a professor of embryology at the University of London. Among his books is *Charles Darwin: A Scientific Biography.*

On January 16, 1869, Charles Darwin wrote to his friend Sir Joseph Dalton Hooker: "It is only about two years since the last edition of the *Origin,* and I am fairly disgusted to find how much

From *Natural History,* Vol. 75 (Aug. 1966), pp. 62–64. Copyright© *Natural History* 1966.

I ought to add." On January 22 he continued, "If I lived twenty more years and was able to work, how I should have to modify the *Origin*, and how much the views on all points will have to be modified."

At that time Darwin was seriously troubled by two lines of attack on the *Origin* that appeared to be dangerous and damaging. One was a criticism brought forward by Fleeming Jenkin, who objected that the chances of single variations (that is, mutations) becoming incorporated in a population were infinitesimally small because of the infrequency (in the then current state of knowledge) with which two similar variants could be expected to meet. He also said it was virtually certain that such variants would be swamped and obliterated by interbreeding with the rest of the population.

Jenkin's criticism increased the difficulty under which Darwin was already laboring to account for a supply of variation sufficient for natural selection to work on. Darwin admitted to Alfred Russel Wallace on January 22, 1869: "F. Jenkin argued . . . against single variations ever being perpetuated, and has convinced me." In the new (5th) edition of the *Origin* then in preparation, Darwin did the best he could, which was to lean more heavily on the position that variation was produced as the result—then supposedly inherited— of acquired characters, of the use and disuse of different portions of the anatomy, and of environmental action.

The other attack that Darwin had to meet was from Sir William Thomson, afterward Lord Kelvin, who claimed that the rate of cooling of the earth proved that its age could not be estimated at more than forty million years. This was extremely damaging to the theory that evolution was caused by the natural selection of random variations, and was "opportunistic" because the time available would have been insufficient to allow for the evolution of all organisms from the primordial germ, unless design and direction had been at work. This was a basic and a direct threat to Darwin's constant aim to keep the subject of evolution on a strictly scientific basis, free from metaphysical or theological concepts of providential guidance, which would, of course, have involved supernatural interference with the laws of nature.

That Darwin was shaken by this second blow is shown by a letter he wrote on January 31, 1869. "I am greatly troubled at the short duration of the world according to Sir W. Thomson for I require for my theoretical views a very long period before the Cambrian formation." But Darwin himself as a geologist had devoted prolonged attention to the length of time that must have been involved in the deposition of sedimentary rocks, and he felt justified in writing to Hooker on July 24, 1869, "I feel a conviction that the world will be found rather older than Thomson makes it."

From this standpoint Darwin has been triumphantly vindicated by the discoveries of radioactivity. Today the age of the habitable earth is estimated at some three thousand million years—ample for what Darwin called "wasteful blundering" and blind action of natural selection to have produced what it has. Darwin's fears on that score can be removed.

## The Impact of Mendel

The manner in which Jenkin's attack has been parried may be introduced by quoting a passage in the *Origin* in which Darwin wrote: "The laws governing inheritance are for the most part unknown." Even the 6th edition, published in 1872, contains this passage, which, had Darwin (and everyone else) known it, was already overtaken by events. On February 8 and March 8, 1865, G. J. Mendel had delivered the famous lectures in which he laid down the foundations of the science of genetics, based on his work with generations of garden peas. Mendel's work remained unknown until 1900, when it was unearthed and confirmed but even then the biologists of the day failed to appreciate its significance. Because the character differences then known to obey Mendel's laws were clearcut, the opposition to Darwin's view of gradual and infinitesimal variation saw in Mendel's work a stick with which to beat Darwin.

It remained for Ronald Fisher in 1930 to show the real importance of Mendel's discovery, which was that inheritance is particulate—which means that variance is preserved instead of being "swamped," as had been assumed under the false notion of blending inheritance. Darwin, of course, never knew this, but he need not have worried on either of the scores that troubled him so greatly in 1869. The amount by which the *Origin* has had to be modified to keep it abreast of the present state of knowledge is much less than Darwin thought, from the point of view of theory, and there is much more evidence now available that confirms, extends, and refines its arguments.

## Genetics and the Theory

Confirmation of the validity and reality of the principle of natural selection comes from two sources, genetic and paleontological. Taking the genetic evidence first, it was shown by Fisher that the phenotypic effects of a gene are subject to control by the other genes of the gene complex, and that as the gene complex is reshuffled in every generation by the segregation and recombination of the genes, the resultant individuals show variation of the effects of the gene in question. These effects can be gradually enhanced or diminished, according to which gene complex provides the most efficient adaptation of the organism to its environment.

This is why some advantageous genes have become dominant, and others have become recessive and even suppressed. E. B. Ford showed about 25 years ago that a given gene in the currant moth can be made to become dominant or recessive according to the direction of the selection exerted on different lineages. In other words, there is incontrovertible evidence for selection at the heart of genetics. The phenotypic effects of a gene, clear-cut or not, are themselves the result of selection, and this selection gradually produces results—which is exactly what Darwin claimed.

Heredity is particulate, but this does not mean that evolution is discontinuous or "jerky." In other words, Mendelian genetics and the chromosome mechanism provide exactly what is required to explain evolution by natural selection. A new edition of the *Origin* would say, therefore, that the laws governing inheritance are now known, and that heritable variation arises from the random recombination of segregated, previously mutant genes.

Fisher then showed by a simple demonstration that all attempts to explain evolution as a result of inner urges, fulfillment of needs, effects of use and disuse, stimuli from the environment, orthogenetic trends, or other metaphysical concepts are doomed from the start. Such theories presuppose that there is a "favorable breeze of mutations" leading to adaptively directed and beneficial evolutionary results.

That such a process has no basis in fact is obvious. When a mutation first occurred, environmental conditions that then existed must have been adverse to the mutation. This is why the majority of mutant genes are recessive. This demonstration is so simple that it long evaded attention. But it is inescapable that, in the words of Fisher, "Every theory of evolution which assumes, as do all the theories alternative to Natural Selection, that evolutionary changes can be explained by some hypothetical agency capable of controlling the mutations which occur, is involving a cause which demonstrably would not work even if it were known to exist." Genetics, therefore, shows that natural selection is all-powerful, while the immediate evolutionary consequences of mutation are negligible. It is only after mutant genes have been absorbed into the gene complex (if they become adaptively beneficial), segregated and recombined, and acted upon by selection that mutation plays a part.

## The Zigzag of Evolution

From the paleontological side George Gaylord Simpson has shown that the rate of evolution is not correlated with variability, nor with the number of years occupied by a single generation. Furthermore, in the evolutionary history of such animals as horses, there has been no straight program at all. From the Eocene onward, the trends have zigzagged—first in the direction of many-toed browsers, then of many-toed grazers, and lastly of one-toed grazers. Those lineages that lingered and persisted too long in any of the previous trends of horse evolution paid the penalty of extinction. This, together with the demonstrable adaptation of successful lineages to changed ecological conditions, as revealed by geologic and climatological data, shows that natural selection has been the governing factor in directing evolution. By comparing related marine and terrestrial animals it can likewise be shown that it is natural selection that determines whether evolution takes place rapidly, slowly, or remains stuck, because genetic mechanism can produce either variability or stability—the former because genes can mutate, segregate, and cross over in their chromosomes; the latter because genes mutate only infrequently, they never blend, and they can be linked together in their chromosomes.

It is because natural selection is Darwin's personal contribution to science that his credit remains unblemished. It has sometimes been suggested that as he frequently spoke of "survival" as the prize of victory in selection, he was more interested in longevity than in reproductive capacity; and it has even been held that reproductive selection is "non-Darwinian." This is, however, unjustifiable, for by survival Darwin meant ability "to propagate their kind in larger numbers than the less well adapted." David Lack's demonstration that the *optimum* number of offspring for species survival is not equivalent to the *maximum* is relevant here.

Toward the end of his life, Darwin told his son Leonard that he expected evidence on natural selection to be available in about fifty years. As Fisher's and Simpson's work shows, this estimate was remarkably accurate, and the evidence now available is formidable and constantly increasing. However, only the most salient experimental results can be mentioned here.

## Mimicry and Melanism

In 1936, E. B. Ford showed not only that Batesian mimicry (by which one species looks or acts like another) is a true adaptive phenomenon conveying survival value but also that it has been built up by natural selection of mutant genes. The proof is that where the models are more common than the mimics (in which case predators learn quickly to shun the unpalatable type), the mimetic resemblance is close to perfect, and the variance of the the mimics is small. On the other hand, where the models are relatively infrequent, the mimics copy them only imperfectly and show considerable variance. When a model is less well known to predators, the survival value of resembling it is small, and there is less selection pressure exerted on the mimic to make it copy the model accurately. This is a case in which the close connection between genetics and ecology can be most easily observed.

A second example is furnished by industrial melanism, or color variations. In the middle of the nineteenth century in England, a melanic mutation of the peppered moth appeared, leading to the constant elimination of the melanic variety by bird predators because of its conspicuousness against the natural background of lichens on the trees where it rested. This was a telling case of adverse selection, but the mutation kept on recurring. With the progress of industrialization, the countryside became increasingly polluted by soot, and the trees became black. Now the original, gray wild peppered moth suffered from bird predators in the industrial areas.

This phenomenon is widespread. More than seventy species of *Lepidoptera* are now undergoing melanization in industrial areas, and it has been observed in spiders, as well. Here, then, is a gene that, when it first mutated, was deleterious but that, as a result of utterly unpredictable changes in the environmental conditions, became advantageous and now confers survival value. In fact, the degree of dominance of the gene has increased during the last hundred years. This is one case in which evolution has been under human observation, for the melanic form has been seen to supplant the old gray form in industrial areas, and natural selection has been shown to have directed the evolution.

### Sickle Cells and Malaria

A final example is the mutation that causes sickle-shaped red blood cells among West African indigenes. The gene causes the formation of abnormal hemoglobin, the molecules of which attach themselves to one another end to end, thereby distorting the cells and causing them to look like sickles. These cells are easily destroyed, and in homozygotes (individuals that have inherited only the sickle-cell gene) under conditions of oxygen deficiency, this results in anemia, thrombosis, and death. It is not surprising that the gene is recessive. On the other hand, this abnormal hemoglobin prevents the entry into the red cells of the parasite *Plasmodium falciparum,* which is responsible for a type of malaria. In regions where malaria is endemic, an equilibrium is set up between the number of normal homozygous individuals liable to die of malaria and the number of individuals homozygous for the sickle gene that are liable to die of thrombosis. The heterozygous individuals (who have both normal and sickle genes) get the best of both worlds, for they are more protected from both dangers. But their genetic constitution makes inevitable the production of homozygote offspring of both kinds, who will pay their different kinds of penalty.

In West Africa, the sickle gene is present in about 20 percent of the population. With this percentage, four out of five homozygous sickle children die. The descendants of these populations in the United States, where there is no endemic malaria, show only 9 per cent with sickle genes. This example shows how natural selection, opportunistically, can convert a lethal gene into one that confers survival value under certain ecological conditions. Furthermore, it provides a case of the special advantage enjoyed by heterozygotes, and shows how the percentage of a gene in a population can become changed. The latter is of particular importance because, as a result, evolution can also be defined as a statistical change in the gene pool of a population.

In this way, the theory of evolution by natural selection of heritable variation is established on an experimental basis to an extent that Darwin himself would hardly have imagined possible. Here, then, the *Origin* can be confirmed in theory, expanded in detail, explained in mechanism, and clarified. The same can be said of the fossil record, which by now has provided close series of lineages—in Jurassic ammonites, Cretaceous sea urchins, and Tertiary horses, camels, and elephants—and has also revealed forms that are indicators of the precursors of various classes of vertebrates and of the evolutionary stages intermediate between them.

Advances made in comparative anatomy and embryology since Darwin's day would fill in many chapters in a hypothetical new version of the *Origin*. For instance, I have found vestiges of egg-tooth papillae—similar to those of some reptiles—in embryos of marsupials, despite a hundred and twenty million years of viviparous reproduction. But references in the *Origin* to the Haeckellian theory of recapitulation (in which the succession of embryonic stages in a descendant directly represents the evolutionary stages of its adult ancestors) must be dropped in view of the much more satisfactory principle of pedomorphosis (in which lineages evolve from the youthful stages of their ancestors). Other advances fill out corresponding places in the *Origin:* F. C. R. Jourdain's study of mimicry in cuckoos' eggs; D. Lack's analysis of the taxonomy and ecology of the Galápagos finches (the birds that played such an important part in making an evolutionist of Darwin); and H. W. Lissmann's demonstration that weak electric discharges from muscles in fish can serve, on the principle of radar, to inform the animal of the proximity of other objects, thereby providing an explanation of the initial stages in the evolution of electric organs. The study of ethology at the hands of K. Lorenz and N. Tinbergen has revealed types of behavior that are adaptive and can be traced through related forms.

### The 'Origin' and New Sciences

To bring the *Origin* truly up to date, however, new chapters would have to be provided discussing branches of science that were not even dreamed of in Darwin's day. Here belong serology and immunology, which provide means of measuring the chemical divergence between the bloods and body fluids of different groups of related animals. Biochemistry shows that the affinities of animals can be revealed by the chemical substances built into their systems. Chromosome studies are another new field in which the minute investigation of translocations has enabled T. Dobzhansky to unravel the genealogy of some species of the fruit fly *Drosophila*.

T. H. Huxley, that rigorous puritan of science, always maintained that the final proof of the efficacy of natural selection as a cause of evolution and of the origin of species (not quite synonymous) would rest on whether it resulted in the production of reproductively isolated populations. K. F. Koopman has shown experimentally that *Drosophila pseudobscura* and *D. persimilis* are species that can interbreed, but that even so, matings between flies of the same species produce more offspring than matings between flies of different species.

Another topic that would have to be covered in a new *Origin* relates to population studies that may represent, as Ernst Mayr says, the most important recent revolution in biological concepts. In one sense, Darwin himself introduced population thinking, because instead of regarding a species as a "type" he stressed the variability of individuals within a species—"individual differences . . . frequently observed in the individuals of the same species inhabiting the same confined locality." But he slipped back into thinking of populations as types when discussing varieties and species. It is now necessary to realize that the product of evolution is a population with an adapted pattern of genetic inequality.

Sexual selection is a subject that received only brief mention in the *Origin* and, as Julian Huxley showed, it is in need of revision because some of the cases in which the sexes differ in structure, appearance, and behavior are not attributable to sexual selection, which benefits the reproductive capabilities of individuals of one sex, but to natural selection, which benefits the whole species.

### The Gene Complex

Finally, to bring the *Origin* up to date, a new edition would contain a chapter of agenda for the solution of chief outstanding problems; which are certainly no less numerous than when the first edition appeared. Such an agenda would necessarily include adequate theories of fitness, of sex-ratio control, of variation, and of how the effect of genes is under the control of other genes in the gene complex. This last problem will probably be worked out by the microbiologists—F. Jacob and J. Monod have already found that through chemically interrelated enzymes genes can collaborate to produce a controlling system that responds to changes in conditions. Most important, of course, would be the recognition that evolution must be considered as "dynamic" and not simply as "dynastic."

# THE ROOTS OF HUMAN NATURE

*N. J. Berrill*

N. J. Berrill is a professor of zoology at Swarthmore College. Among his books are *Journey into Wonder, Sex and the Nature of Things,* and *Man's Emerging Mind.*

In this age of explosion of people and atoms man's greatest need, more than ever before, is to understand himself. Why do we act as we do? The question becomes urgent; hence the present intensive

From *The Atlantic Monthly,* June 1966, pp. 92–6. Reprinted by permission of Dodd, Mead & Company, Inc. from *Inherit the Earth* by N. J. Berrill. Copyright © 1966 by N. J. Berrill.

efforts to study other living creatures that most resemble us, to reconstruct from odd-shaped stones and fossil bones the human past, and to search for the beginnings of life on other planets. Institutes for primate research are becoming established in many places, and studies of social groups of apes and monkeys in the wild, before it is too late, are therefore in vogue.

The more we see of the chimpanzee, the more we realize he is one of us. At the emotional level especially, the identity is clear. Young chimpanzees, for instance, exhibit temper tantrums all too familiar to anyone who has brought up children. And an adult chimpanzee becomes intensely disturbed on finding a live worm in its biscuit or on seeing snakes, spiders, and mice—even only the shape of a snake, although the animal may never have seen a snake before. Chimpanzees and people both have this revulsion built into their very being. Fear of the dark is also a common heritage. The sight of toy animals or a model of a human head can be terrifying to a chimpanzee. Toy animals in action can equally terrify a human infant when encountered for the first time. These fears are by no means rational, nor are they necessarily the result of childhood conditioning.

As a rule in this so-called civilization of ours man is a comparatively unemotional being, although, according to D. O. Hebb, the McGill psychologist, only because he is able most of the time to avoid situations which arouse strong emotion. For the most part, he lives in an insulated environment in which his emotional susceptibilities are well concealed, even from himself. In the same way, chimpanzees are placid in their own natural environment, but in close captivity—like a man in prison or an unemployed youth in a modern stone jungle—a chimpanzee becomes unpredictably explosive and often viciously aggressive. Hebb suggests that in the case of men and apes these emotional disturbances reflect a degree of instability which comes with a somewhat overly large brain.

Other qualities in chimpanzees make certain human traits more acceptable and perhaps better understood. Not only chimpanzees but also monkeys will work for hours at solving simple puzzles with no reward other than the satisfaction gained. In fact, a chimpanzee if he likes a learning task will work at it incessantly unless he is hungry, paying no attention to offered food, just as a man engrossed will forgo a meal. This contraverts the tradition that there is an inborn aversion to work, whether mental or physical, and that some tangible reward is required in order for work to be done. What seems to be necessary is not extrinsic reward but intrinsic interest. Just as some birds fly some of the time for the satisfaction of being in flight and some sing for the joy of song as well as to gain a mate or hold a territory, just as boys climb trees and men climb mountains because they themselves are built for climbing, so monkeys and apes and humans enjoy the skill in using their distinctive combination of eye, hand, and brain for what it is worth. Winston Churchill was expressing this when he said, "I like to learn, I don't like to be taught."

In 1964 Adriaan Kortlandt, of the University of Amsterdam, went to the Congo to observe wild chimpanzees. A group of forty-eight chimpanzees which occupied a banana plantation at the edge of the forest were watched from high tree blinds. Previous knowledge of chimpanzees in zoos and in the wild suggested that they normally live in small harem groups of from five to fifteen individuals, with one master of all, and it was assumed that some such state once prevailed in human or prehuman history. Now it seems that this is not so, although it is more or less true for the gorilla.

In the case of chimpanzees on the move, two forms of grouping occur: sexual groups, composed of adult males and childless females, often with a few mothers and children; and nursery groups, composed of juveniles, their mothers, and perhaps one or two adult males, showing no signs of sexual bonds or jealousy. Children up to four years of age are usually carried and are pampered. The young are tolerated and the old deferred to, with seniority conferring wisdom but never tyranny. This general pattern of social life appears to have grown out of the long and intensive care chimpanzees give their young. As a rule, however, chimpanzees in the wild act with the utmost caution, as though aware of weakness rather than collective strength. When a group emerges from dense forest onto a clearing, the adult males are always the first to appear, each looking and listening before emerging from behind a bush or tree. Once out and safe, they chase one another, shrieking, screaming, and stamping, like boys let out to play, although the females remain silent and shy.

A similar combination of sociability, family care, and curiosity has undoubtedly been characteristic of human and prehuman behavior from early times. Why haven't chimpanzees gone further than they have? The answer that they never came down from the trees is simply not true, for they spend much of their time on the ground, walking or running erect in order to see better or to leave hands free for carrying. Moreover, there is good evidence that they use heavy sticks as clubs either to fight off leopards or for display. Gorillas, equally semiterrestrial, are known to use natural weapons in the same way, not to mention a ritual gesturing, stamping, chest-thumping, and vocalizing reminiscent of tribal warriors working up to the excitement and intimidation of a war dance. In both chimpanzees and gorillas the use of weapons is instructive, and it is reasonable to assume that the technique of armed combat emerged among the common ancestors of man and apes many million years ago and is not the peculiarly human vice it has been thought to be. So many subhuman and nearhuman creatures have gone to extinction during prehuman times that the struggle for ascendancy among the various man-apes and ape-men must have been intense.

Kortlandt suggests that it was the early invention of the spear that humanized our ancestors and dehumanized their anthropoid competitors by driving them off the savannas; that although the forest offers the best protection against spears, it has never been favorable to the evolution of the human way of life. He states that chimpanzees seize every opportunity to bring variety into their lives, are fascinated by everything new and unusual; that on one occasion an individual steadily watched an unusually beautiful sunset until almost dark; that "behind their lively, searching eyes one senses a doubting, contemplative personality, always trying to make sense out of a puzzling world." Jane Goodall, accepted as one of themselves by the colony she studied, feels that chimpanzees are truly of the human stock. Somewhere along the line of our own past, apelike creatures ventured out from the fringes of the forest, as hesitantly as chimpanzees, as fascinated by all that was about them, as puzzled and as contemplative, but with a potential determination and decisiveness that carried the day.

The surviving apes are few in kind and far between; monkeys are more numerous and widely spread and are sufficiently akin to apes and men to throw light on our own upbringing. At the Primate Laboratory of the University of Wisconsin, H. F. Harlow has raised infant monkeys with a surrogate mother consisting of a soft cloth-covered wire frame, complete with nursing bottle. Such infants apparently develop normally and show characteristic curiosity concerning their surroundings so long as they can run and cling to the soft mother substitute. As they grow older, they spend increasing amounts of time clinging and cuddling, although taking no more milk than do other infants supplied with the same wire and milk bottle combination without the cloth.

Infant monkeys raised with wire mothers not cloth-covered show no affection for the mother substitute and obtain no comfort;

and they behave like neglected children in or out of institutions. Bodily contact with at least a simulation of the soft reality of the maternal body seems to be essential for normal emotional development. Infants raised from birth for several months with a cloth mother retain their responsiveness long after separation, but those who have known a cloth mother only after the age of eight months lose whatever responsiveness they may have shown immediately after being separated. Freud notwithstanding, the critical need is definitely not the role of the breast or the act of nursing but the clinging of infant to mother and the handling of the infant by the mother. However, it may be comforting for human mothers to know that monkey infants raised with cloth mothers, although seemingly normal as individuals, fail miserably as mothers themselves.

Monkeys also have the eye-hand kind of brain with a very subordinate sense of smell, as in humans and apes. Almost by definition, this means inquisitive fingers and a dominant sense of sight. It is not surprising that a monkey which is in captivity prefers the sight of another monkey, or almost anything that moves, such as a toy electric train, to any other form of satisfaction. There is the story of the psychologist who put a monkey in a room with various inanimate things supposedly of interest and looked through the keyhole to see its reactions, only to see a brown and lively eye peering from the other side. Watching the world go by is a pastime ingrained in us all. Any study of monkey behavior, however, as of children, should be made under natural circumstances, with the observer unobserved. This has been accomplished with baboons in Africa, with an introduced colony of old-world rhesus monkeys on an island off Puerto Rico, and with the elusive forest-dwelling monkeys of Japan.

The Japanese monkeys, with beautiful bright faces and very short tails, live in the forest in troops of up to two hundred individuals, communicating among themselves with vocal sounds relating to emotional state, movement to and from feeding grounds, defense, warning, sex, and infants. The occasional solitary monkey however, makes no sound at all.

Within a troop, social relations become all important. Each monkey apparently knows every other monkey, its rank, status, mother-child relationship, and so on. Some of the infants, for example, are ranked high because they are children of influential mothers. In fact, at the Japan Monkey Center, established for studying these animals, a new troop was organized with monkeys collected from different natural troops. When a newcomer was added to the group, he or she was recognized at once and warmly accepted

by individuals who had come from the same natural troop several
months before. Each monkey troop has its own troop peculiarity
and cultural trend, and each member of the troop differs from the
others in personality and life history. How a distinctive culture is
acquired in monkeys such as these is of considerable human
import.

The Japanese scientists wished to draw their elusive subjects to
a single feeding area where they could be better observed, and to
do so they placed rice and sweet potato through the forest, gradually reducing the food until it was at one locality only, on the
shore of the sea. Then one day a young female monkey, about
eighteen months old, who had been born after the project had
begun, started to wash her sweet potato in the sea before eating it,
a simple action but one with considerable implication concerning
monkey comprehension. Eventually the habit had been caught by
all of the troop except the old and crusty males. In view of this
capacity, it is perhaps suprising that the monkey world has shown
so little enterprise during the multimillion years of its existence.
On the other hand, man himself showed little more until relatively
recent times.

In the earlier studies of both monkeys and apes, altogether too
much has been read into their behavior while in confinement, for
boredom affects these intelligent creatures as strongly and as dis-
turbingly as it affects human beings under comparable conditions.
Sex looms large and often perverse, while personality becomes
lackluster and incurious. The role of the dominant male, polygamy,
and the accentuation of brutishness with age have been over-
emphasized on the assumption that anthropoids in confinement
behave and develop normally. The ancestors of man were outstanding in the literal sense of the word, as venturers into open
country, where danger from predators was enhanced. Of the other
primates now living, only the baboon has left the woods.

Baboons are monkeys, to be sure, but they are comparatively
venturesome monkeys. At some time in the monkey past they abandoned tree life for open ground, although in the last resort they
climb into trees for safety, and invariably do so at night. Their
special interest to man is that as monkeys they have successfully
coped with a new environment of much the same sort, and in much
the same way, as that of the primitive apes whose descendants we
are. Like any grounded monkey, they walk and run on all fours,
and use their forelimbs as arms and hands chiefly when sitting.
Long jaws carry formidable teeth for fighting. Their strength is
primarily collective, and their social organization is one of their
principal adaptations for survival.

S. L. Washburn and I. De Vore studied the behavior of fifteen troops of baboons, troop size varying from thirteen to one hundred and eighty-five, in the Ambolesi game reserve at the foot of Mount Kilimanjaro in Kenya. They found no support for the accepted theory that sexuality provides the most important bond of the primate troop. They found that a troop, viewed at close range, is composed of strongly emotional, highly motivated, and far from neutral creatures. The basic social structure is seen when a troop moves away from the safety of trees and out onto open plains. The less dominant males occupy the van, and the older juveniles follow; in the center of the troop are the females with infants, the young juveniles, and the most dominant males; the back of the troop is a mirror image of the front. Thus, without any fixed or formal order, the females and young are protected. When a predator is sighted, the females and young hurry away, but the males do not, and almost at once a platoon of males becomes interposed. Most animals leave them alone, and only the lion puts them to flight.

Much of the time the members of a troop, like most monkey folk, gather in small groups, sitting and grooming, perhaps two females and young, or an adult male and two females. Newborn infants are a center of attraction, and most dominant males sit or walk close beside a mother. Juveniles play together in groups that persist for several years. If a juvenile is hurt and cries out, adults come running and stop the play. The security of the individual and the survival of the race lie in the strength and diversity of the social bonds. Only the stray or the outcast is vulnerable.

Studies of living apes and monkeys, however much they appear to give insight into our own peculiar nature, are studies of our contemporaries, not our ancestors. The assumption is that man passed through a stage similar to the existing ape, and that earlier both passed through a stage represented by existing monkeys. This may be so, but it is an assumption which needs to be verified or modified by actual evidence from the past. But efforts to reconstruct the human past have always been handicapped by the scarcity of fossil material and by the enormous extent of evolutionary time that we are concerned with. Fossilized remains are, at best, little more than signs along the road. And the primates still available for study as living creatures—four kinds of apes, the old-world and new-world monkeys, the lemurs of Madagascar, the bush babies of equatorial Africa, and the spectral tarsiers of Southeast Asia—are but a remnant of what has gone before. They do represent stages of primate evolution, although each group has had all the time until the present to diverge from a more generalized ancestral type.

The significance of recent discoveries of fossil anthropoid remains can be fully appreciated only when seen in the total perspective of primate evolution. This has been a very long process, coinciding for the most part with the evolution of the other major orders of mammals. To begin with, there was a prolonged phase represented by small primitive mammals, not unlike the present-day shrews, ancestral to all the modern orders and possessing all the particular mammalian characteristics common to mice and men. An arboreal phase followed, beginning with creatures probably similar to existing tree shrews and progressing to larger forms, such as tarsiers and lemurs, more fully adapted to the opportunities, hazards, and general requirements of arboreal existence.

Then came the anthropoids proper, with more handlike feet, better stereoscopic vision, eye-hand type of brain, great curiosity and capacity for mischief, and opportunity to chatter with impunity. There were tarsiers in the Eocene, fifty million years ago, monkeys in the Oligocene, which followed, and apes of many kinds in the Miocene forests, halfway to the present. *Proconsul,* an early Miocene ape of about twenty-five million years ago, a full-fledged ape of a less specialized sort than any of the present survivors, and not too well constructed for arboreal life, may have stood at the parting of the ways. At least he has a fitting name. The final phase, in any case, resulted from the grounding of apelike creatures, from which the specifically prehuman stock took a distinctive evolutionary path.

The key question is, when did this last phase begin?—as early as *Proconsul,* or as late as the beginning of the Pleistocene a million years ago perhaps, when the Ice Age was already imminent, or sometime in between? The debate has been protracted because the evidence, although suggestive, has been too scanty and indecisive. Prehuman creatures appear to have lived in circumstances unfavorable to the preservation of their bones. Their tools are another matter, and discoveries of simple but significantly chipped pebbles have suggested the existence of humanoid beings for a longer time than their bones have indicated. When a stone that more or less fits a human hand has been flaked to a cutting edge for flensing a carcass and is found together with pieces of skull and pelvis, indicative of brain and posture, much can be surmised, and the long-time dead begin to come alive.

Modern man can be traced back only a relatively short way. *Homo sapiens,* self-labeled the wise, includes the Paleolithic mammoth hunters and cave painters of 20,000 years ago, and also, though belatedly admitted, the more stooped and heavybrowed Neanderthal men who lived in Europe during the last interglacial period but were missing when the glaciers finally melted. Other men, such as Peking man, known as *Homo erectus,* erect but not so wise, were tool-makers and fire-makers who were around during the early to middle Ice Age several hundred thousand years ago. Before that, before the initial onslaught of the Pleistocene ice, the trail until recently has been marked only by hand-flaked pebbles. New discoveries in southeastern Africa now push the fossil human story two million years into the past.

The first of these discoveries was made about forty years ago by Raymond Dart, who then and later established the existence and general nature of man-apes known as Australopithecines, about five feet tall and more manlike than apelike, who stood erect with a small, well-balanced head; who ran, hunted, used ready-made but not handmade tools or weapons, and sheltered in caves. They seem to have been widespread through southern lands and to have been closely related to the emergent human stock. That they were not themselves the actual stock is evident from discoveries made during the last few years by the Leakeys, man and wife, who had spent much of their lifetime patiently and persistently digging in and around the Olduvai Gorge in Tanzania.

The Leakeys had been challenged by the earlier discovery of unmistakably manually shaped pebbles found in East African strata of pre-Ice-Age time. At last, they were rewarded by finding remains of two kinds of beings, one of them now identifed as an Australopithecine and the other a tool-maker sufficiently human to be admitted to the rank of *Homo,* as *Homo habilis,* meaning man who is able, mentally skillful, vigorous. The significance of the age of the fossilized remains is that radioactivity-dating methods place them at close to two million years, which puts the human past much further back in time than had been known before. At that time, however, the two kinds of more or less human beings were contemporary inhabitants of the earth, so that to find the true beginnings where human stock departed from the ape, we must now probe into far more ancient periods.

Fossil remains of five individuals were found, one of whom was an elderly woman, one an eleven-year-old child, and a third a young woman aged about twenty years. *Homo habilis* is said to have stood and walked upright. His feet and hands were similar to modern man's. His jaw was roomy enough for a tongue to be used in speech. His teeth show him to have been as omnivorous as we are. And his skull, although small in keeping with his four-foot stature, was shaped much like our own, with room enough for a relatively well developed forebrain superior in form to all but that of modern man himself. Although the Olduvai Gorge is now a desert, during the million years *Homo habilis* appears to have inhabited the area the gorge was part of a wet, tropical region rich in lakes, rivers, fish, and game.

Following the announcement of the first Olduvai Gorge discoveries, John Napier, of the primatology unit of the University of London, called particular attention to the significance of the hand, pointing out that the human hand, which can achieve so much in the field of creative art and communicate such subtle shades of meaning, and on which the preeminence of *Homo sapiens* so largely depends, constitutes, in a structural sense, one of the most primitive and generalized parts of the human body. It is this aspect of the hand which has given support to the almost traditional view that the prehuman forerunners of man were equipped with a hand of essentially human form long before the brain became sufficiently well developed to exploit it. The finding of hands, tools, and skulls at the same site in the Olduvai Gorge makes correlations possible for the first time.

For all its generally primitive structure, the human hand is marvelously made, not only having an opposable thumb and rotating at the wrist, but endowed with two prehensile working arrangements. One is the power grip, such as is employed in using a screwdriver to turn a tight screw, and the other the precision grip, in which the finger and thumb tips take over. The power grip is primitive and is present in some degree in most primates, while the precision grip is the final refinement, present in man but hardly developed elsewhere. The small hand of *Homo habilis* appears to have been capable of a very strong power grip, but the setting of the thumb suggests that the precision grip had not attained its fullest expression. This is in keeping with the fact that their stone implements were little more than pebbles with one or more flakes struck off to produce a chopping stone. Already nearing the goal represented by modern man, the perfecting of the hand apparently kept close pace with the development of the brain.

A small but nearly perfected man inhabiting the earth almost two million years ago not only gives man a tremendous extension of his prehistoric apprenticeship but also gives his prehuman existence a much more extended past. It places the evolution of man from arboreal ape to the Leakeys' little handyman within the long period of the Pliocene when the grasslands and the grassland fauna were evolving as the dominant living feature of the earth.

Man evolved with the creatures he lived with and hunted—not as a Johnny-come-lately pitchforked from the trees into the hostile openness of the plains when the drama of the plains had already reached its climax, but as an early adventurer, aggressive, sharp-witted, and nimble, who took to the ground because of better opportunities and broader horizons. He evolved in company, and in response to the great general environmental challenge of the age. Only his overpowering ascendancy is recent.

# THE EVOLUTION OF HUMAN SEXUAL BEHAVIOR

*Robin Fox*

Robin Fox, a professor of anthropology at Rutgers University, is the author of *Kinship and Marriage.*

Human sexual behavior is as much the end product of evolution as human sexual anatomy. But while we have grown used to the idea that the body has evolved, we are only beginning to understand the implications of extending to behavior the same kind of analysis that has proved successful with flesh and bone. Indeed, it must seem at first glance that this is an impossible task. The evolution of human anatomy can be studied from the various fossil forms that have been discovered and the gradual transition from ape-man to man-ape to true man can be discerned with some accuracy. But we have only the sketchiest idea of what these creatures were *doing,* so how can we ask about the evolution of their behavior?

Nevertheless, we know that there must have been such an evolution. In the same way as there was a gradual transition from apelike to manlike form there must have been a similar gradual transition from apelike to manlike function. Our bodies testify to the first change—as any simple comparison of man with other primates will show. To what extent does our behavior testify to the second?

At least one school of zoologists would claim that the study of the evolution of behavior can be more instructive than that of the evolution of anatomy. The science of ethology—defined by one of its practitioners as "the biological study of behavior"—which has flourished under the leadership of such men as Konrad Lorenz in Germany and Nikolaas Tinbergen in Britain, is one of the youngest branches of zoology. Its stance is "neo-Darwinian" and in essence it points up the fact that natural selection operates on the *performance* of the animal. Structure therefore evolves in order that the creature may function in ways that give it selective advantage in the struggle for survival.

In the case of certain gross motor activities this may seem obvious: Speed enables animals to chase and to flee, etc. But the ethologists have concentrated mainly on the *signaling* abilities of animals, showing how these social signals serve to enhance threat behavior, inhibit aggression, attract mates and so on. The point about these signals, whether they be structural—such as bright coloring—or purely behavioral—such as specific postures—is that they are evolved by the process of natural selection and hence have become part of the genetic "repertoire" of the animal.

When a black-headed gull is defending its nesting site during the breeding season the presence of any other animal is clearly threatening to it. Male and female black-headed gulls look pretty much alike, so even when a prospective mate lands on the site, the male's aggressive instinct of territorial defense is aroused. However, if the female does not stare at the male but turns her head aside, then the male's aggression is inhibited and the preliminaries of mating become possible.

This "looking away" gesture of the gull is only one of many in its total "ethogram" of postures and gestures which are as much a part of its genetic endowment as feathers and wings—and just as necessary to its survival and success. The ethologists have found that by careful comparison of closely related species, they can arrive at answers to the question: "Why does this particular species behave in this particular way?"

Ethologists have, until very recently, confined their attention to lowlier forms of life, such as birds, fish and small mammals. In these the genetically based behaviors are easy to ascertain. But what of the more complex, higher mammals—and what of man?

Some very careful studies of our primate cousins over the past decade have given us much-needed comparative material from closely related species. But these species prove to be much more complex than the little creatures familiar to ethology. It is not that they are without genetically programed predispositions, but that their range of behavior is extended by programing to take more advantage of their learning ability than is the case with lower forms.

At the pinnacle of this development stands man, with the greatest learning capacity of all animals. His behavior has evolved, it is true, but this evolution has been toward greater flexibility. To put it paradoxically, man's greatest instinct is the instinct to learn. It is therefore "natural" to man to be "unnatural"—to go beyond nature and supplement the genetically endowed predispositions of behavior with cultural forms not built into the chromosomes.

This has been regarded by some observers as the ultimate stumbling block to our understanding of human behavior on ethological lines. And it is true that if we stick rigidly to the methods of the ethologists we will learn only a limited amount about ourselves. Nevertheless, things are not so black. What the flexible learning ability of man allows him to do is to extend the range of his behavior, but only within well-defined limits. His genetic behavioral inheritance lays down for him a limited number of things to do, but he can vary enormously the ways in which he does them.

For example, as with many other animals, man prefaces the formation of a stable mating arrangement with some form of "courting" activity. The form of this activity, however, can be extremely varied and consists of a great many postures, gestures and sounds that are traditional rather than genetic. The black-headed gull can "look away" and a few other things, but it cannot write sonnets, dance the frug or wear an engagement ring. The difference can perhaps be expressed in a metaphor: Animal behavior is like filling in a form; in some animals there are a lot of instructions on the form but only a limited space for answers, while in other animals there are an equal number of instructions but the space for answers is large and the range of possible answers is wide. It is not that animals have "instincts" while man does not, but that man can do more things about his instincts than other animals.

If, then, we want to look at the basic sexual behavior of man as the end product of a long process of natural selection, what information have we? We have the fossil record; we have the behavior of related species; we have the behavior of the creature itself. From a judicious survey of the evidence from these three sources we should perhaps be able to reconstruct the evolution of human sexual behavior. (I am confining this analysis to heterosexual behavior.)

It may seem absurd, but perhaps the greatest gap in our knowledge is our lack of information on the "natural" sexual behavior of man. A great deal of our knowledge here is inferential; we know very little about sex despite our seeming obsession with it. But at a fairly gross level we know enough to start with, even if the knowledge is not of the detailed kind that the ethologist would need. What then are some of the main characteristics of human sexual behavior?

There is the striking fact of a lack of an oestrous cycle in the female; she does not go into heat. It is usually phrased as "permanent sexual receptivity" in the human female—which may seem a little extreme and overoptimistic. Such evidence as there is on female receptivity indicates that it is at its height just before and just after menstruation. This is curious in that the peak in other primates comes halfway between menstrual periods—that is, during ovulation. In other words, most primate females are most receptive at the time when they are most likely to conceive, while the human primate female is most receptive when she is least likely to conceive. There may be the evolution of some kind of birth-control device lurking here, but it is difficult to see this as being very efficacious unless the female determines the timing of intercourse according to her own physiological state of readiness—an interesting but unlikely theory.

The lack of heat goes along with the lack of a breeding season. This is not peculiar to man, but it does put him into the category of primates which have continual sexual activity. True, there are "birth peaks" in most societies which show that breeding is to some extent seasonal (in Christian countries the peak comes nine months after Christmas, as a rule), but there is no rutting season as such in man. This year-round activity is probably also connected with another feature—namely, the high level of sexual activity and the drive for novelty and variety in sexual experience. Compared, say, with the gorilla, man exhibits a level of sexual activity which is quite phenomenal.

Insofar as the end product of sexual activity is offspring—and in man this is not always the case—then the "breeding-pair" is the most typical unit for this purpose. Like many fish, birds and mammals which establish "pair bonds," man does not just mate promiscuously and then leave the female to rear the young. Rather, he tends to associate regular sexual activity and at least some degree of emotional attachment with the rearing of offspring.

One way of looking at this—favored, for example, by Desmond Morris—is to see the "pair-bond" phenomenon among animals duplicated in man by the process of "falling in love"—a behavioral mechanism for keeping the pair together. Other observers (including this one) see more of a "contractual" element in the male-female relationship when it comes to the business of forming a family and rearing children. Love and marriage may go together like a horse and carriage, but let us not forget that the horse has to be broken and harnessed.

Strong bonds between mated pairs are certainly common enough in *Homo sapiens*, but this is by no means the whole of the story. These bonds are not necessarily the result of a primitive "pair-bonding" instinct, and indeed seem very variable in intensity. They are primarily an adolescent phenomenon and obviously have to do with giving impetus to the breeding process. But once this is under way the relationship becomes very complex indeed, and the bond between the pair is as much an outcome of their role as "parents" as of their roles as "lovers." The "tenacity of the pair bond" which Morris seems so anxious to establish is as much a tenacity of the parental bond as anything else. There are obviously good evolutionary reasons for this. But the bond is not exclusive; there is no reason why it should be and many reasons why it could not have been.

The starting point for the analysis of the biological evolution of any human social behavior is obvious: the brain. Apart perhaps from the precision grip of the hand and the bones and muscles devoted to the striding walk, this is man's only major biological specialization.

The question we must then ask is a typical one of chicken or egg. Did the growth of the brain lead to the capacity for greater social complexity or vice versa? I think the answer is undoubtedly that as certain kinds of animals developed complex social systems as weapons in the struggle for survival, there was pressure in the direction of selecting out those animals with the best brains. These were the animals better able to cope with the complexities of life in a social group. But in our particular family of animals—the primates—what kind of social system was involved?

Here we must introduce another of our three kinds of evidence:

the social behavior of primates. This is, as we might expect, enormously varied. But certain constant features stand out in those primates which, like ourselves, have an organized social system, and particularly in those which, again like ourselves, have spent a considerable portion of their evolution outside the forest environment in which the earliest primates were nurtured. Typical examples are the baboons and macaques.

A baboon group usually comprises about 40 animals, which wander about in search of food, always keeping together. This cohesion is of enormous advantage to animals like these living in open savanna and subject to attacks from predators. A single baboon is not much of a match for the big cats, but a group of baboons stands a pretty good chance of beating off attacks with concerted action.

The social system, however, is anything but democratic. Power in the group lies with the biggest and most successful of the males. These (never more than about six in number however large the total group) stay at the center with the females and young. Around this central core will wander a number of "cadets"—young males who are candidates for membership in the hierarchy. At the edge of the horde are the "peripheral males"—unsuccessful and immature animals who have not yet made it. Many never will. Some even wander off and become solitaries—the drop-outs of the monkey rat race. These peripheral males act as first line of defense and a kind of living radar for the group. The big males of the hierarchy are the ultimate deterrent, and also they keep order within the group, and are especially solicitous of the welfare of the young.

This is a very sketchy account of a "typical" society of ground-dwelling primates. We must now look at its dynamics. How do young males get into the hierarchy and what is the significance of this? The significance is overwhelming in terms of the evolution of the group because *it is only the males of the hierarchy that do the breeding.* While the cadets and peripheral males may get a chance to copulate with a female during her infertile periods, only the hierarchical males mate with the females at the peak of oestrus—that is, during ovulation. Therefore, only these males are going to pass on genes to the next generation. It is of tremendous significance then to know what characterizes the "successful" males.

Before answering this question we must note that there is another form of terrestrial primate society that has to be reckoned with. This is typical of baboons living on dry desert savanna, as opposed to those living in woodland savanna. The horde is not divided into the components we have just described, but rather into a series of polygamous families in which one male collects a number of females (usually four) and monopolizes these the whole time. Still, however, there are the unsuccessful males at the edge waiting to get in, and we still have to ask how they do it and who succeeds.

Not to put too fine a point on it, we can say that it is the smart ones who make it. But what constitutes smartness? Basically, it is the ability to control and time responses—to understand the consequences of one's actions. The British ethologist Michael Chance has described the process as "equilibration"; thus, an animal caught between the desire to copulate with an oestrous female on the one hand, and the desire to escape attack from a dominant male on the other, must be able to inhibit his sexual response and bide his time. If he fails to do so often enough, he is at worst either going to be killed or driven out, or at best will fail to ingratiate himself with his superiors and be tolerated by them. The stupid animal, then, one that blunders about, following without foresight the dictates of his lustful and aggressive appetites, will never make it to the top. The cunning animal, on the other hand, that can forgo present indulgence in anticipation of future reward, will be more likely to get there.

Of course, he has to have other qualities. He must be sociable and able to cooperate, or the big males will not accept him. He must also be acceptable to the females, it seems, hence his capacities as a baby minder (and the rank of his mother) are important. Besides possessing these charming attributes, he must also be tough and aggressive in order to assert his rights as a hierarchy member. It is easy to see the evolutionary advantages of such a process. It is a breeding system which puts at a premium those qualities in the male most advantageous to the survival of the group.

If this kind of social system was in fact typical of our ancestors, then it gives us some powerful clues concerning the evolution of the brain. Clearly, it was those animals with the best brains which were going to do the breeding, and each generation would see a ruthless selection of the best-brained males, with the dumbest and weakest going to the wall. And it was the *controlling* aspects of the brain which were being so strongly selected. The more the emotions of aggression and lust came under cortical control, the better chance the animal had of surviving and passing on his genes to the next generation.

But the expanding brain had to cope with other things than sex and aggression. Predominant among these were the use of tools and the development of language. Large areas of the cerebellum are concerned with the control of the hand, and growth of this center must have been a response to the demands of tool-making. Control over the emotions was one thing; control of the environment through tools and weapons was, however, equally important. Selection favored the controlled and *skillful* animal. It also favored the animal which could *communicate* best. Up to a point a series of nonlinguistic signals will do, but after a certain point of social complexity is reached, cooperation is impossible without a more flexible code. Large areas of the brain, then, are devoted to speech.

Many commentators have stressed these two aspects of brain evolution, but few have taken the breeding problem seriously. Yet without this component the major puzzle in brain evolution remains unanswered: How did the hominid brain manage to evolve so quickly? About a million years ago, the brain of one of the earliest recognizable hominids (the family which includes man and his extinct relatives and ancestors) was little larger than that of the chimpanzee. Within that million years it trebled in size— an almost unprecedented rate of evolution.

Now, whatever the pressures in favor of a larger "thinking" brain exerted by the demands for better technicians and speakers, the question still remains: By what kind of breeding system were these newly acquired traits so quickly developed? Given that the prespeech and pretools system had, built into it, the breeding mechanisms we have described, then we only have to add that the successful breeders needed to be not only controlled, but also eloquent and skillful. The system would then insure that these were the males who passed on the essential genes, and the rapid (in evolutionary terms) development of the large forebrain would be insured.

This suggests that throughout the evolution of the hominid lines which eventually led to *Homo sapiens*, the social system was one in which the majority of the breeding was done by a minority of the males, with the least successful males being largely shut out of the breeding system. In other words, a system based on the polygyny of the powerful. And note that this polygyny has not to do primarily with sexual appetite. It has to do with dominance and the relation of males to males. The survival value of the system is obvious.

Here we must turn to the most controversial and difficult part of our evidence: the fossil record. We can know that the model of the society of ground-dwelling primates is applicable to our own evolution only if we can show that it plausibly fits our earliest ancestors. We know that the hominid line evolved from monkeylike forms which moved from forest to savanna, and hence must have been in some ways like contemporary savanna-dwelling primates. We also know that those earliest hominids of a million years ago on the East African savanna were elementary hunters, and that this trait increased in complexity and importance as time went by. Hence to the qualities that went into being a dominant male we must add skill in hunting. Indeed, it may have been the pressures of the chase that accelerated the demand for more advanced tools and speech.

Some writers have seized upon the fact that our earliest manlike ancestors were hunters to "prove" many things about the changes from the apelike to the human in sexual behavior. But we must remember that the changes did not occur overnight, and that there was much in the old vegetarian ape that was useful to his omnivorous successor. Some things certainly changed. The female presumably became less and less under the control of the oestrous cycle, and the "permanent sexual receptivity" phenomenon emerged.

It has been suggested that this happened as a result of the pressures exerted by the need for cooperative hunting. Hunters need a fixed home base. The females stay in this base with the young; the males return and provision them—a practice unheard of among vegetarian primates, but common, for example, among hunting carnivores, such as wolves. It has been argued that with such a system the old primate dominance hierarchy could not operate, since this depended on females coming in and out of heat and being monopolized by the top males during ovulation. If the males had to be away a good deal of the time then this would not work, it is argued.

What is more, if the male needed a female to work for him—cooking, skinning, gathering vegetable food, etc.—he would want her "attached" for more of the time than just when she was feeling sexy. Similarly, she would want the constant attention of the

male for provisioning herself and her young. If she were constantly available for sexual intercourse this would be more likely
to happen. The high level of sexuality would make the relationship
more rewarding to the partners and hence keep them "bonded."
Thus many features of "human" sexuality would emerge as responses to the demands of the hunting situation.

This is fine until it is pushed one step further, as it usually is,
and the evolving hominid is credited with instinctive tendencies
to form "monogamous nuclear families." I never cease to be
amazed by the ingenuity that speculative writers resort to in an
effort to prove that deep in man's nature is a *Saturday Evening
Post* family: Dad, Mom and the kids. Their assertiveness on this
point has often a rather frantic air to it, and what they never do is
ask what the consequences would have been if our earliest proto-
human ancestors had allowed fair shares for all in the mating
game. It seems unimaginative, to say the least, to pin these enter-
prising creatures down to dreary monogamy.

The point here is that none of the features of human sexuality
that have developed are incompatible with a breeding system
based on the relative dominance of a few males. If a male can
attach one female to him for the reasons advanced, he can attach
several just as easily, provided he can maintain his harem against
all comers. Insofar as only a minor part of the food intake of hunters is protein and something approaching 80 per cent is vegetable,
then a small army of root diggers and berry pickers may well have
been an advantage to a male.

We can, of course, never know exactly what kind of mating
institutions characterized the transitional man-ape; we can only
ask the question: In order for the critical developments in the
evolution of the brain to take place so quickly, what kind of
breeding system must have been in operation? The answer is:
One that would rapidly select out the animals with the better
brains and pass on their genes to the next generation. And, con-
comitantly, one that would push to the peripheries of the breeding
system animals lacking the qualities of intelligence and control.
Some kind of hierarchical system with differential access to females would solve this problem, and seems to me to be the only
candidate. If every male had been allowed to contribute equally
to the gene pool—as would be the case in a monogamous system—
then we might never have made the *sapiens* bit and been forever
stuck as *Homo stupidus*—promising, with our speechlike grunts
and our crude tools, but not really in the top league.

I have considered only the male contribution to brain development here since this is the most obvious. But lest I be accused of
prejudice we should look at the female's roles. Was she simply
a passive mechanism for passing on the genes of the big-brained
dominant males?

It could well be, but there is a chance that she actively helped
the process along. I have mentioned that the rank of a male's
mother may affect his chances of getting into the hierarchy. The
son of a high-ranking female can be kept near the center of the
group by his mother where the big males will learn to tolerate
him—a help when he comes to make his bid for membership. If
this is a crucial criterion for membership in the hierarchy—and
we are not sure about this—then the qualities that go into being a
high-ranking female, insofar as they involve cortical control of
sex, may well contribute to the development we have envisaged.

They may also help to account for the gradual loss of hormonal
influence over sexual receptivity in the female which led to the
loss of the oestrous cycle. The female was no longer subject to
periodic sexual mania during which she solicited any male in
sight, but gradually came to control her own responses in the
same way as the male. It may well be, in fact, that this permanent
sexual receptivity in the female was a by-product of the general
processes we have been discussing, rather than a result of the
pressures introduced by hunting. To answer this question more
thoroughly we should have to know what qualities went into being
a dominant female. All we can say is that they were not necessarily
the same qualities that went into being a dominant male, with the
exception, perhaps, of bitchiness and bossiness.

We must be wary of taking only one primate system as our
model. Those polygamous primates which live on the arid savannas form "harems" in which several females are permanently
attached to a male which monopolizes them throughout the year,
despite oestrus and seasonal breeding. Some observers have
claimed that the hominids passed through a similar stage of development, since during the forging time of their existence—the
Pliocene—there was extreme drought, and they must have adapted
to these dry conditions in much the same way as contemporary
desert-dwelling baboons. Of course, the creatures we are discussing
were not baboons but man-apes; still, these baboons do rather
knock on the head the idea that there could not have been "stable
family groups" within the protohominid band as long as the

females were subject to periodic sex-mania and breeding was seasonal. There is no doubt, however, that permanent mating of a "human" kind is facilitated by the fact that the human female, in a sense, comes into "heat" at puberty and stays there—at a moderate level of sexual excitement—for most of her life.

There are several forms of breeding hierarchy possible, given an animal which lacks the oestrous cycle, and we cannot know which of these prevailed. Indeed, various groups of evolving hominids may have tried them all. Some may even have tried monogamy. What matters is not the actual institutional form, but the differential access to the females.

The fact that permanently receptive females were more or less permanently attached to dominant males would simply make life harder for the young males who wanted to get into the hierarchy, and would increase the demands for better "equilibration"—for greater control and inhibition. It would be unlikely under these conditions that some males would be absolutely barred from breeding (although it could well happen), but some would be *less likely* than others to contribute significantly to the genetic endowment of the group.

The criteria of dominance would of course differ as the animal became progressively more "human," but they would be basically much the same as among the primates. Hence the successful male would have to be controlled, cunning, cooperative, attractive to the ladies, good with the children, relaxed, tough, eloquent, skillful, knowledgeable, and proficient in self-defense and hunting. Depending on the nature of the group, some of these qualities might have been emphasized more than others.

With the advent of agriculture and the frighteningly rapid growth of population densities over the last 10,000 years, things have changed. But the animal coping with these changed conditions is the end product of hundreds of thousands of years of intensive selection in which, if this hypothesis is right, differential access to mates was of crucial importance. And this *must* have left its mark on our behavior.

We should look briefly at the incest taboo to complete our roster of current sexual facts and their evolution. Many observers have put the taboo on incest at the heart of our social development. Animals are incestuous; man is not. This then is the great breakthrough. Many reasons have been given for this, and all assume that the taboo is *imposed*. But it is highly probable that it is, in fact, a natural development.

As far as we can tell from primate evidence, there is, for example, no incest between mother and son. The mother is to her son a "dominant" animal, and mating requires that the female partner be "subdominant." If a young male manages to get into the hierarchy, he may cr may not mate with his sisters. On the other hand, the possibility of fathers mating with daughters is quite high. The frequency of occurrence of incest in human society is exactly parallel. This fits our picture of sexual relations evolving in a "dominance" framework.

It follows that with the stabilization of mating relationships equilibration would have been more in demand. Particularly in the case of the growing "boy," it would have been important to control any sexual approaches toward mothers and sisters who were under the control of a dominant male or males, and he also had to inhibit aggressive advances toward the latter. Hence neural mechanisms evolved to this end.

The young hominid met his first and most intensive trial of "controls" in the immediate family circle, but he was learning them as they applied to *all* dominant males and their females. Freud, although perhaps right about some of these evolutionary processes that led to incest taboos, was wrong about locating them exclusively in the nuclear family. The "Oedipus complex" has to do with the relationship of "young subordinate males to older dominant males"—not just sons to fathers.

The sum total of all these processes was to produce a creature capable of control and of guilt—the mechanism that lets the individual know it has broken rules. As the controlling elements of the brain came to dominate the appetitive elements, the evolving hominid could depend less on "instinct" as a guide to action. D. H. Lawrence, it seems, was wrong: Sex really is in the head.

If "differential access to mate" is the secret of it all, how does this help us to understand our own behavior? It has been argued that man is tenaciously monogamous, but the monogamy, if we are honest, is more apparent than real. It is very rare for men of power, wealth and influence to confine their sexual activities to one woman. Although the majority of males in a population are confined to one woman at a time, those in a position to do so seem to accumulate more. These may be straight "wives," as in in overtly polygamous societies, or they may go under other names. A "big man" is one who has access to many females, or is credited with such access, or who controls a large number. They may not be mates, but we know that only a high-prestige man can run even a chaste harem. How far up the pecking order is a man with one wife, two full-time secretaries, 20 typists, and a girl who comes in to do his manicuring? I think of professors with a modest haul of, say, one wife, one secretary, one research assistant, two teaching assistants, several members of a research team and four part-time typists. The gathering unto us of females as a sign of status must surely be deep there in the cunning brain.

Another factor that must be an end product of the processes discussed is the difference between male and female sexual behavior in *Homo sapiens*. Because the equilibration process was predominantly directed toward the male, we might expect that he is more readily conditionable in matters of sex than the female— that most males are more easily made to feel guilty about sexual matters.

Men are caught between their inherited tendencies to promiscuity and dominance and the necessities of regularized mating; women, between the same promiscuous tendencies and the pulls toward security for self and offspring that can usually be obtained only by at least a show of fidelity. Again, we see a product of the dominance process wherein the status of the male is measured by his control over females.

If this control is challenged, then the "owner's" self-esteem suffers. It is noticeable that it is usually women who are *punished* for unfaithfulness. Thus the other curiosity of male behavior— sexual jealousy—is part and parcel of the scheme.

In any event, the doctrine that male and female differences in sexual behavior are simply the result of the learning of different sex roles needs careful examination in the light of the evolutionary evidence. Also the notion that male-female relationships can be totally explained by "pair bonding" tendencies that never quite evolved properly (Desmond Morris again) should be treated skeptically.

The point here is that human sexual behavior is the product of enormously complex evolutionary processes. It is no good taking fragments of this behavior and trying to "explain" them by *ad hoc* hypotheses, however entertaining. The only theory worth aiming at is one that will account for *all* the basic emotions—dominance, love, guilt, tenderness, parental affection, jealousy, security, lust, fidelity, novelty and many others. Such a theory must take account of the difficult evolutionary problems that we have raised.

There are obviously many confused issues here. I have been able to outline only a fraction of the complexities, and have glossed over many extremely complicated issues and missed others completely. So, if nothing else, perhaps I have put the interested reader on guard against those who seek to exploit the obvious interest of this topic by offering intellectual shortcuts to solutions. As I have said, some things we can never know and it is dishonest to pretend that answers are possible, but other things can be settled with a fair degree of approximation to the truth— given time, patience and hard work.

## MEN OUT OF MONKEYS, OR MONKEYS OUT OF MEN?

*Sara Murphy*

There we were, arguing in a Little Rock courtroom on April Fool's Day about whether the Darwin theory could be taught Arkansas school children. When the spectators laughed, Judge Murray O. Reed admonished them sternly; merriment would not be tolerated.

The court action was brought by a Central High School biology teacher who sings in a Presbyterian Church choir, Mrs. Susan Epperson, who sought a declaratory judgment on the constitutionality of Arkansas Initiated Act I of 1928. This law, approved two-to-one in a referendum, provides for a $500 fine and loss of job for any teacher advancing the theory that man is descended from a lower form of life. It was passed in the emotional wake stirred up by the famous 1925 Scopes "monkey" trial in Tennessee. Mississippi is the only state besides Arkansas and Tennessee which still has an antievolution law on its books.

As theatre, the trial was a flop. It lasted two hours and 20 minutes. State Attorney General Bruce Bennett called Nietzsche "Nitsky" and spelled a few of the scientific terms he couldn't pronounce, but the judge held him firmly to the constitutional issue: does the law infringe on Mrs. Epperson's freedom of

From *The New Republic*, May 7, 1966, pp. 9–10. Reprinted by permission of *The New Republic*, © 1966, Harrison-Blaine of New Jersey, Inc.

speech? The question of whether it collides with the fundamentalist interpretation of the Bible was not allowed before the court, although Bennett tried repeatedly to put it there. He also asked several questions about *Modern Biology* by James H. Otto and Albert Towle, the book used in Mrs. Epperson's class; for example, did Mrs. Epperson believe a protozoan was an "infinite cell"?

"I believe it is finite," said Mrs. Epperson. There was no question about it—the attorney general was flunking tenth-grade biology.

Arkansas politicians, having worn the racial question threadbare, are shopping around for a new emotional issue. Bennett did his best to set up evolution, as he had done in the past, more successfully, with race and Communism. The Osceola (Arkansas) *Times* had pointed out that "political figures may be made or broken on whether man has any relation to the monkey." Orval Eugene Faubus, who has said he will not be a candidate for governor again, appeared before a Baptist Sunday School class to declare that if man has evolved from a lower form of life, then the Resurrection is a myth. Theologian Faubus added that he was not in favor of repealing the Bible and that Judge Reed had been unduly hard on Attorney General Bennett. Faubus did not reach these conclusions independently; his mail was running eight-to-one against the teaching of evolution in public schools.

Although much of the state's press is in favor of doing away with the law, *The Green Forest Tribune* speaks for those who aren't: "Such a theory taught to a group of sensitive young children by an instructor or a person who has no personal knowledge of God, could have a damaging influence upon the young minds. Without restriction there would be nothing to prohibit a teacher from instructing pupils in the theory of Charles Darwin, with no mention of the Biblical story of the creation of man."

I would not have become concerned about the political potential of evolution had I not been seated at the trial beside an amiable young man who had left his television repair business to attend. He teaches a Sunday School class at a local Baptist church and is genuinely alarmed; if such a dangerous theory as evolution is taught, the churches will be done in once and for all. He reasons that no mere accident could fit together all the parts in a television set so that they would produce a picture; by the same token, no accident of nature could produce so complicated a being as man. For a while I was making some headway in replying to his arguments, but by the end of the trial he was reduced to an angry incoherence.

The Epperson case is now in the hands of the judge. He is expected to render a decision sometime before the summer primaries.

## MONKEY TRIAL, 1968

Back in 1925, a young biology teacher named John Scopes dared challenge the Biblical version of creation in the schools of Dayton, Tenn., and earned for himself a chapter in the evolution of the U.S. The immediate effect of his trial was to spur passage of antediluvian, anti-darwinian "monkey laws" in Arkansas and Mississippi as well. But biology and the Bible are uncomfortable bedfellows, and finally last week, 43 years after Scopes's conviction, the Supreme Court struck down one of the monkey laws.

The High Court acted on the challenge of yet another biology teacher—pretty, 27-year-old Mrs. Susan Epperson of Little Rock, Ark. As it turned out, Arkansas had inadvertently violated its own law three years ago by revising public-school biology textbooks to include a chapter on evolution. At the urging of the state's Education Association, Mrs. Epperson then filed suit to get the monkey law off her back.

Church and State:

In a unanimous decision that sidestepped the delicate issue of state control over curriculums, the Supreme Court found that the Arkansas law permitted the teaching of only the Biblical version of creation. Justice Abe Fortas, who wrote the decision, ruled it thus violated the First Amendment because it constituted "an establishment of religion."

"Children can believe whatever they like about evolution," a relieved Mrs. Epperson remarked, "but they have the right to hear about it." To which the man who started it all, 68-year-old John Scopes himself, could only add, "It is what I have been working for all along."

From *Newsweek* Magazine, Nov. 25, 1968, pp. 36–37. Copyright Newsweek, Inc., 1968.

# Chapter Two

# The Special Case of Human Evolution

In man, and evidently in some other animals, there is a feedback between the niche in which the animal lives and the behavior of the animal itself. A population responds, over time, to changes in the niche (i.e., the animal adapts), and in turn, the behavior of the animal modifies the niche. The famous case of tool use in the chimpanzee is an example of an activity that is not genetically specified, but is a consequence of the general capacity to learn and occasionally improvise. The use of a stick changes the chimps' niche by expanding it. For man, the enormous flexibility provided by learning (a mental capacity probably originally evolved for quite specific reasons) has vastly altered his niche. This means that man is subject to the diversity of effects of his varied niche.

Evolution, far from having ceased for man, now comes about by feedback from an environment constantly changed by man himself. The magnitude of this phenomenon is what makes man unique among animals. Altering the environment at a rate much greater than genetic adaptation can occur, he has committed himself to ever greater dependence on culture, until culture itself has become his niche. The evolutionary consequences of this environmental tampering are not always considered desirable in terms of cutural values. For example, without medical therapy the genes that predispose their carriers to diabetes would drop out of the human gene pool—

43

a simple example of natural selection. Instead, of course, the genes are increasing because therapy is now an established part of the cultural niche. Although the therapy does not cure the disease it does prevent its expression. The eventual working of natural selection would not have cured the disease either, but it would eliminate the genetic disposition at the cost of the carriers—a fate which culture avoids.

The point is that culture often simulates natural selection and other processes that occur naturally in other animal populations. The diabetes example is rather straightforward, but culture also simulates more complex natural processes such as the limitation of population size.  In man we evidently must rely primarily on conscious, deliberate social methods to effect control. "Letting nature take its course" is in most cases culturally unacceptable when an exercise of will can achieve similar ends by what are considered more immediate humane means. One such commitment builds on the next, until the cumulative effect on human evolution is overwhelming. Man finally realizes, like it or not, that he is responsible. Having begun to control nature during his prehistoric past he is now committed to ever increasing control. Few Natural processes remain untouched by culture. Because of this, man is unique among animals.

# EVOLUTION—ORGANIC AND SUPERORGANIC

*Theodosius Dobzhansky*

Theodosius Dobzhansky is a professor of zoology at Columbia University. Among his books, *Mankind Evolving* is of particular interest to anthropologists.

Science should be anthropocentric or relevant to man, but in the broadest sense. Thus knowledge and understanding of subatomic

From *Bulletin of the Atomic Scientists*, Vol. 20 (May 1964), pp. 4–8. Reprinted by permission of *Bulletin of the Atomic Scientists* and the author.

particles, of atoms and molecules, of organisms high and low, of mountains and oceans, of planets and suns and galaxies, assist man in his quest to understand himself and his place in the universe. What is man, whence came he, and whither is he going? It is debatable whether science alone can hope to answer these questions. However, even the best intellects are plainly powerless to face up to them in the absence of scientific knowledge. Omar Khayyám expressed this powerlessness most poignantly some eight and a half centuries ago.

> Into this Universe, and Why not knowing,
> Nor Whence, like Water willy-nilly flowing,
> And out of it, as Wind along the Waste,
> I know not Whither, willy-nilly blowing.

Darwin complained that, as he grew older, he lost the capacity to enjoy poetry. He may or may not have been familiar with the great poet of Persia, but he sketched a rough draft of possible answers to some of Omar Khayyám's queries. Biologists have been working on this draft for a century since Darwin. There has been notable progress, but a vast amount of work remains to be done. Man is the outcome of a long process of evolutionary development. He is kin to all that lives. Not only has he evolved; he is evolving. The direction of his evolution is unknown.

Another poet, Nietzsche, has dared to suggest a solution: "Man is a rope stretched between the animal and the Superman—a rope over an abyss. Thus spake Zarathustra." This is a fine statement of the direction which the evolution of man *ought* to take. Strange to say, Nietzsche had only contempt for that "English shopkeeper," Darwin, even though in Nietzsche's own great work there is as Brinton justly notes, more Darwinism than Zoroastrianism. But is mankind really evolving toward some sort of supermankind? Let us not forget that the Nietzschean "rope" leading from animal to superman hangs over an abyss. There is no assurance that the passage over the rope will be accomplished safely; to many of our contemporaries, the abyss seems mankind's likeliest destination. That atomic energy, which used wisely could benefit mankind enormously, may become the instrument of suicide of the human species is probably not the gravest danger. There is no biological law, nor any other law of nature, that guarantees either evolutionary progress and betterment or deterioration and downfall to the human or to any other species.

Evolution

Man is, however, an extraordinary creature. The human species has already moved some distance along the Nietzschean "rope," away from simple animality. Man, and he alone, has it within his potentialities to refuse to accept the evolutionary direction of blind forces of nature. He may be able to understand, to control, and to guide his evolution. The fundamental fact about human evolution is that mankind is simultaneously engaged in two kinds of evolutionary developments—the biological and the cultural. Human evolution can be understood only as a product of interaction of these two developments. Yet so strong is the craving of the human mind for either-or categories that time and time again either the biological or the cultural component has been underrated or neglected. I suspect that a history of human error could be interestingly written in terms of this neglect of one or the other component of man's nature.

Heredity

On the biological side, man is one of the two million or more species now living on earth. He is a primate, a mammal, a vertebrate, a sexually reproducing multicellular animal. Man's biological nature resides in the same wonderful stuff, the deoxyribonucleic acid, DNA, as does the nature of a mouse, a fly, a corn plant, or a microbe. Human DNA has merely a different arrangement of the four nucleotides, the four "letters" of the genetic "alphabet," which compose also the DNA of a fish, an insect, or a plant.

Inescapably, man's nature is in part biological nature. But man is more than DNA's way of making more DNA of a particular kind. There seems to be nothing especially remarkable about the chemistry of human DNA, nor even about the structural and physiological machinery of man's body. Man receives and transmits, however, not one but two heredities: the biological and the cultural. Man's biological heredity, like that of any other organism, is encoded in DNA, carried mainly in the chromosomes of cell nuclei, and transmitted by parents solely to their children and to progeny in the direct line of descent. Cultural heredity, or simply culture, is transmitted by teaching, imitation, and learning, mainly by means of the symbolic processes of human language. The transmission of culture is, at least in principle, independent of descent relationships, and does not even require that the transmitter and acceptor come together in space or in time. We are all inheritors from Newton and Darwin and Pasteur, whom we have never seen and who died before most of us were born. Man's most subtle yet most fundamental attribute is self-awareness; he is conscious of his own being and of the cleft between himself and the world in which he is simultaneously an actor and a spectator.

The key problem, and one about which dissension is rife, concerns the relationships between man's biological and cultural evolution. One extreme is a thoroughgoing genetic determinism. A distinguished biologist has written that "the materials of heredity contained in the chromosomes are the solid stuff which ultimately determines the course of history. . . . The structure of society rests on the stuff in the chomosome and the changes it undergoes." This extreme is rather easily refuted; historical and social changes are sometimes far too rapid to be merely manifestations of genetic changes. Our generation, that of our parents, and that of our grandparents have witnessed prodigious amounts of change, but the differences between these generations are cultural rather than genetic. Man is, after all, something more than an elaborately contrived bag of DNA.

## Consciousness

The opposite extreme is represented by views which relegate biology and culture to different insulated compartments. One of these views is really an astute modern version of antievolutionism. It holds that while the descent of man's bodily frame from animal ancestors is a credible hypothesis, culture and consciousness are not offshoots of the same process. The basis of this view is a genuine philosophical difficulty which remains unresolved in modern evolutionism. Consciousness and self-awareness we can experience as unquestionable realities solely in ourselves, by introspection. It is only by analogy with my own experience that I infer consciousness also in other persons whose behavior I observe. Extending the analogy still further, I assume consciousness also in other people whom I have not met personally. But where is the extension of the analogy to stop? Are consciousness and self-awareness attributes only of the human species? If so, have they appeared suddenly and fully fledged at some particular spot in man's phylogeny?

Evolutionists as different in their general philosophies as Teilhard de Chardin and Bernhard Rensch saw themselves compelled to assume that rudiments of consciousness are omnipresent in nature, not only in living beings down to the simplest but in inorganic systems as well. The considerations that drove Teilhard and Rensch to these uncomfortable expedients are of the same kind that made as eminent a philosopher as Whitehead assume that there could be no life or consciousness in men unless there were rudiments of life and consciousness everywhere, down to the atoms and, presumably, to subatomic particles.

Not being a philosopher, I expose myself to criticism by saying that I fail to see why life and consciousness, or rather their first rudiments, could not have originated at some stages of the evolution of the universe, and then developed to their present conditions. I fear that Whitehead, Teilhard, Rensch, and others have in this matter chosen the same path of reasoning that led in biology to theories of preformation or the assumption that a miniature image of the adult body exits in the sex cells from which the body develops. Evolution is, however, not simply an unfolding of preformed shapes and structures any more than embryonic development is mere expansion of a preexistent body frame. The process of evolution is capable of producing real novelties.

## Transcendence

Cosmic evolution has transcended itself in producing life; the origin of man transcends biological evolution. The highest achievements of the human spirit involve self-transcendence. Now "transcendence" is a dangerous word which is liable to be misunderstood but I can find no other word to express an idea which must, I think, somehow be brought to the attention of biologists as well as of philosophers. To me, transcendence does not mean injection of a novel species of energy. The statement that life transcends the limits of inert matter does not imply that biological phenomena are manifestations of some special vital force; human consciousness and culture transcend the limitations of animal life without any addition of a nonbiological energy. Transcendence does mean the emergence of systems or phenomena subject to regularities which are meaningless without these systems or phenomena. Mendel's law does not apply to chemical reactions, and poetry makes no sense to a mouse; this does not prevent the units, the behavior of which is described by Mendel's law, from being chemical compounds, and poetry uses words and concepts used also in ordinary language.

Feedback

Although analogies between evolution and individual development are slippery, the gradual emergence of self-awareness in a
child may be a good model of human evolution transcending biology. Rensch admits that the human self "is nothing but the result
of the connection of psychic processes by one central nervous
system." My self came into being gradually; not even my genetic
potentialities existed before the meiosis in the germ cells of my
parents or before the union of two of these cells in fertilization.
This neither leads me to doubt that I exist at present (remember
Descartes' cogito ergo sum) nor forces me to assume that I was
somehow present in the primordial virus in which biological evolution presumably took its rise.

Unreconstructed nineteenth-century-style reductionists see
nothing but agitation of molecules in life and in man. Theological
fundamentalists are, however, not alone in contending that the
cosmic (inorganic), biological, and cultural evolutions are separated by unbridgeable gaps, instead of being integral parts of the
grand process of evolution of the universe. Strangely enough, they
are bedfellows with Marxist theoreticians, who proclaim that the
biological evolution of mankind ended when it produced a being
capable of "working." Henceforth, social or cultural evolution has
taken over. Ways of thinking only a little less extreme than these
are accepted by many social scientists, including anthropologists.

Man is not a molecule, and though he is an animal he is a very
special kind of animal. But the idea that there is a feedback relationship between the biological and the cultural evolutions of mankind must, I think, be maintained. The big problem is evidently
how this relationship operates and where it is taking the human
species. Let no one mistake it—there are no easy answers here.
This matter needs careful rethinking in the light of present knowledge, and even more, it needs further research.

The main premise that cannot be stressed too often is that what
heredity determines are not fixed characters or traits but developmental processes. The path which any developmental process
takes is, in principle, modifiable both by genetic and by environmental variables. The degree of the modifiability or plasticity is,
however, quite different for different developmental processes. As
a general rule, the processes whose consequences are essential for
survival and reproduction are buffered against environmental and
genetic disturbances. Two eyes, a four-chambered heart, ability to

maintain an approximately constant body temperature, suckling instinct in the infant and sexual drive in the adult, capacity to think symbolically and to learn a symbolic language—all these "normal," or species, or group characters develop in almost every human. Conversely, plastic characters are generally those in which a variability is advantageous. Suntanning and shade bleaching are examples. Fixity or plasticity of a developmental process is itself genetically determined. They are set by natural selection usually at levels advantageous to the species.

## Culture

For a human being, membership in a culture is vital. Lack of a capacity to acquire a culture makes an individual a low-grade mental defective. A fixed capacity to acquire only a certain culture, or only a certain role within a culture, would, however, be perilous; cultures and roles change too rapidly. To be able to learn a language is imperative, but a restriction of this ability to only a certain language would be a drawback. Insect behavior is largely, though not wholly, stereotyped and genetically fixed; human genotype brings about a comprehensive plasticity of behavior. This plasticity is adaptively essential, because culture is wholly acquired in every generation, not transmitted through genes. The connection between genetics and culture is often imagined to consist of the possession by some human populations of genes for this or that cultural trait, or the possession by the human species of genes for this or that "cultural universal," but that is sheer misconception. The biological success of the human species has been due precisely to the genetically secured capacity of every individual free from overt pathology to acquire any or all cultural traits or universals.

But does it follow that for virtually all propositions in the analysis of culture or culture history, genetic constitution of individuals or of populations can be taken as constants? This "proposition" seems to be fairly representative of the views of many social scientists. Now, if it asserts that the capacity to acquire a culture is not a property of only some races and populations, but is vouchsafed to all nonpathological human genotypes, this is warranted. But it must be qualified in at least two ways. First, the cultural capacity of the human species did not appear suddenly, but arose gradually in evolution, and its origin is a biological as well as a psychological and social problem. Secondly, and even more important, this capacity is not a constant, not some sort of a single quantum, but varies quantitatively and probably also qualitatively in time, in space, and from individual to individual.

Here some biological considerations are in order. Modern biology is breaking away from the typological modes of thought. The concept of species representing a "type," of which individuals are more or less imperfect manifestations, is being replaced by the concept of a Mendelian population composed of genetically different and usually unique and unrepeatable individuals. The genetic variations among individuals of a population, or among populations of a species, is not an accident or a sad imperfection of nature. Quite the contrary, much of this variation is adaptive in the environments in which the species lives, and it is kept up by natural selection. Perhaps the most interesting kind of variation is polymorphism, the presence of two or several more or less distinct genetically conditioned forms, polymorphs, in the same breeding population. The polymorphs are usually adapted to exploit most efficiently different facets of the environment, different ecological niches, or different ways of life.

Man is genetically a highly variable and polymorphic species. The variability affects behavioral traits no less than physiological and structural ones, and it is false to imagine that these three categories are clearly separable. The chief reasons why so many people are loath to admit the genetic variability of socially and culturally significant traits are two. First, human equality is stubbornly confused with identity, and inequality with diversity, as though to be entitled to an equality of opportunity people would have to be identical twins. Secondly, it is futile to look for one-to-one correspondence between cultural forms and genetic traits. Cultural forms are not determined by genes, but their emergence and maintenance are made possible by the genetically conditioned human diversity. The division of labor in many societies is, indeed, largely a cultural phenomenon and is only to a limited extent genetic. But could it be sustained in a population consisting of persons as similar as identical twins? This is not entirely an empty question, since at least one great geneticist has recently envisaged the possibility of bringing about such genetic uniformity.

The fact that radical changes in the ways of life of our generation and those of our parents and grandparents must have been cultural rather than genetic only proves again the absence of one-to-one correspondences between genetic and cultural changes. It does not, however, prove that the biological evolution of mankind has stopped or that it is irrelevant to the cultural evolution. On the other hand, it is difficult to demonstrate that mankind has changed biologically even since, let us say, the days of the ancient Greeks and Romans, if by "proof" is meant the ascertainment of sizable gene differences. We cannot test the genes of Pericles, Caesar Augustus, and their contemporaries. But neither was Darwin able to "prove" organic evolution in this sense. The evidence is indirect, inferential, but nevertheless, I think it is conclusive.

Variants

Paradoxically, it is precisely because we know that mankind changes so greatly in cultural aspects that we can be reasonably confident that it also changes to some extent genetically. When the environment changes, the only other necessary condition for the occurrence of genetic evolutionary change can be defined. This is the presence in human populations of genetic variants, some of which confer upon their carriers a higher fitness. Despite all the inadequacies of our present knowledge of human genetics, this can scarcely be doubted. What is more, since the environment in which man lives is in the first place his sociocultural environment, the genetic changes induced by culture must affect man's fitness for culture. The process thus becomes self-sustaining. Biological changes increase the fitness for, and the dependence of, their carriers on culture, and stimulate cultural developments. Cultural developments in turn instigate further genetic changes. This amounts to a positive feedback relationship between the cultural and the biological evolutions.

Positive feedback explains the great evolutionary change, so great that it creates the illusion of an unbridgeable gap, that transformed our animal ancestors into man. Human evolution is the outstanding example of what Simpson has termed quantum evolution, a rapid passage to an entirely new way of life. The rates of evolutionary changes tend, however, to be variable rather than constant. The evidence of paleontology shows that bursts of evolutionary activity are often, and even usually, followed by periods of an at least relative quiescence. Those who believe that man no longer evolves biologically might contend that our species has entered upon such a period. Here we must, however, proceed with the greatest caution. The potentialities for rapid evolution of the human species have not been depleted, since the environment continues to change and the genetic variance remains apparently as plentiful as ever. What may be happening is, however, that the direction in which the evolution has been proceeding may be altered, and altered on a pernicious course.

Mankind is faced with a cruel paradox—it is the outstanding success of both the biological and the cultural evolutions of our species that gives rise to dangers and may even sow the seeds of its destruction. Consider that one of the criteria of biological success, maybe even the chief criterion, is increase of the population size, especially when combined with an expansion in space and capture of new opportunities for living. *Homo sapiens* is unquestionably successful in the light of this criterion. Unfortunately, the "success" of the human species has culminated in a population explosion. This tale is too well known, and has been told too many times, to need another recital. I wish only to stress that the uncontrolled population growth entails both genetic and cultural hazards, and here again it is wrong to imagine that these hazards are neatly separable.

Neither do I need to retell here the story of the alleged relaxation or suspension of natural selection in civilized mankind. The dangers from this source, although not necessarily exaggerated, have often been presented in a wrong perspective. True enough, the advances of obstetrics have reduced the selective pressures against difficult childbirth; dentistry has made the genes for weak teeth lose a part of their selective disadvantage; oculists can alleviate the drawbacks of some forms of weak eyesight. On the other side of the ledger, selection for some traits has probably increased in intensity. The genotypes that enhance the ability of their carriers to withstand the stresses of crowding, of the enervating "tempos," of the anxieties and insecurities, have become selectively more advantageous than they were. Surely, then, natural selection does not work in modern mankind as it did in the primitive or the precivilized man. But this is both inevitable and desirable. Natural selection is the agency which translates the environmental challenges into genetic alterations, and civilized environments present challenges utterly different from those of the past. We wish to be fit to live in today's environments, not in those of the middle ages, or preliterate societies, or the stone age.

The most mischievous error, however, is the notion that the progress of mankind would be safe and irresistible if only natural selection were permitted to operate unobstructed by civilization. Natural selection does not guarantee even the survival of the species, let alone its improvement. Dinosaurs became extinct even though their evolution had been piloted by natural selection quite

unhampered by culture. Natural selection is automatic, mechanical, blind. It brings about genetic changes that often, though not
always, appear to be purposeful, furthering the survival and op-
posing the extinction of the species. And yet, natural selection has
no purpose. Purposes are human prerogatives.


Choice

Man, if he so chooses, may introduce his purpose into his evolution. The biological predicament is not that natural selection has
ceased to act; it is that the selection may not be doing what we wish
it to do. Man is the only product of evolution to have achieved the
knowledge that he came into this universe out of animality by
means of evolution. He may choose to direct his evolution toward
the attainment of the purposes which he regards as good, or which
he believes to represent the will of his Creator.

Here again, let us not delude ourselves with easy answers. One
such answer is that a superior knowledge of biology would make
it unmistakable which plan is the best and thus best followed.
Another is that biological evolution has itself implanted in man
ethical ideas and inclinations favorable for the continued progress
of evolution. Now, I would be among the last to doubt that biology
sheds some light on human nature, but to plan even the biological
evolution of mankind, let alone its cultural evolution, biology alone
is palpably insufficient. Waddington has shown, I think clearly,
that our biological evolution has instilled in us no ethics and no
ability to discriminate between good and evil. What evolution has
done is to make us "ethicizing beings" and "authority acceptors,"
particularly in childhood. But what ethical principles, purposes, and
goals we accept and work out for ourselves come from our superorganic inheritance, from our culture.

In man, organic evolution has transcended itself by producing
the superorganic. It is in order to serve as the foundation for the
further advancement of the superorganic that the biological nature
of mankind must not only be maintained but improved and en-
nobled. In planning human evolution, including biological evolution, biology must be guided by man's spiritual and cultural heritage, by what Aristotle meant by "poetry" when he wrote that "It
is not the function of the poet to relate what has happened, but
what may happen—what is possible according to the law of probability or necessity."

Human evolution has forced mankind to a crossroad from which
there is no turning back and no escape. Our animal past is irre-

trievably lost—we could not go back to it even had we wished. The choice is between a twilight, cultural as well as biological, or a progressive adaptation of man's genes to his culture, and of man's culture to his genes. I am optimistic enough to hope that the right choices will be achieved before it is too late. The grounds for this optimism cannot be put better than in the words of Albert Schweitzer: "Because I have confidence in the power of truth and of the spirit, I believe in the future of mankind. Ethical world- and life-affirmation contains within itself an optimistic willing and hoping which can never be lost. It is, therefore, never afraid to face the dismal reality, and to see it as it really is."

# TECHNOLOGY, ADAPTATION, AND EVOLUTION

Hudson Hoagland

Hudson Hoagland, President of the Worcester Foundation for Experimental Biology, is editor of *Evolution and Man's Progress*, and *Hormones, Brain Function and Behavior*.

Adaptation to the environment is necessary for the survival and health of the individual and of the species. Science and technology, however, have wrought rapid and major changes in both our physical and social environments and have so strained our adaptive capacities as to produce a number of serious social maladjustments.

The two most serious of these various maladjustments, brought to an increasingly inflamed state by rapidly advancing science and technology, are the so-called population explosion, primarily resulting from the impact of modern medicine and public health on underdeveloped countries since World War II; and the nuclear weapons and their delivery systems that are the result of advances in physical science and technology.

From *Bulletin of the Atomic Scientists*, Vol. 25 (Jan. 1969), 27–30. Reprinted by permission of *Bulletin of the Atomic Scientists*.

High birth rates and low death rates have generally been regarded as desirable, and nations have felt secure behind their
weapons of defense so that neither big families nor big armaments
have traditionally been thought of as evil. However, the appalling
upsurge of numbers of people in poverty-stricken countries is a
grave threat to world stability, and nineteenth-century concepts of
national sovereignty and balance of power have always led to war.

These power concepts have produced two devastating world
wars in my lifetime; a third one, with nuclear weapons, would
destroy us. World war to advance national ambitions became obsolete in 1945 when we atom bombed Hiroshima and the kind of
frenetic nationalisms we see everywhere today, fed by emotions
of superpatriotism inflamed by communist, fascist, and militarist
ideologies, are exceedingly dangerous in this crowded world of
hydrogen bombs and chemical and biological weapons.

Vietnam is typical of the kind of vicious, escalating violence that
is integral to competitive sovereignties torn by conflicting ideologies and uncontrolled by law to prevent war. I believe that more
Vietnams are bound to recur frequently under the present system
of irresponsible nation states in which hates develop between
peoples, creating tensions that demand relief. The Israeli-Arab
War, the Pakistan-India war, the Korean war, as well as the current
Berlin blockade by East Germany and the invasion by the USSR of
Czechoslovakia are other examples, any of which could escalate
to World War III.

Richard Barnet in a review of Ralph Lapp's book *The Weapons
Culture* (*Science*, April 19, 1968), wrote:

Military power is less and less relevant to the real threats to
national security in a world undergoing political revolution, and
its ineffectiveness to achieve useful political results is being demonstrated around the world, most notably in Vietnam. The plain truth
is that, after spending $1,300 billion since 1945 on defense, the
Pentagon cannot prevent the nuclear annihilation of the United
States. . . . Each year the people of the United States pay a stag-
gering national security bill and end up with less security than they
had the year before. It is not surprising that the military establishment seeks to justify a bad bargain in mystical or heroic terms,
for the defense budget would not stand the test of practical social
or political accounting. . . . As long as the premise undergirding the
military establishment—that more weapons mean more security,
more power, and more prosperity for the American people—is
immune from political debate, we will continue to finance the
"weapons culture." Public discussion of substantive issues of defense, in which the military establishment is challenged to defend
its budget in terms of specific national priorities, would be useful.

But the military will always come up with a plausible argument for more until the very assumptions of the arms race are rejected by the electorate and the great bureaucracies that feed on the defense budget are recognized for what they are: a threat to the national security.

All organisms must adapt or perish, and our environment changed drastically following Hiroshima. Plans for antiballistic missile defense show it to be frightfully expensive, provocative, dangerous, and ineffective. Modern nuclear, bacterial, and chemical weapons render obsolete the traditional view of national sovereignty as a way of protecting the security of a people by recourse to war when diplomacy fails.

Diseases we personally suffer may be regarded as the result of inability to adapt to stressful environmental changes. Such changes may swamp our internal mechanisms of defense and homeostasis necessary for health. Thus severe or prolonged stress may produce chronic disabilities, including neuroses, a variety of psychosomatic disorders, cardiovascular damage, and other degenerative ills, and increased susceptibility to infections. Much research has dealt with these matters and we know much more than we did a generation ago about our defenses against stress and how adaptation may let us down. Yet adaptation is necessary for the survival and evolution of all living organisms as well as for social systems and institutions.

We, like all other forms of life, are a result of biological evolution by natural selection. In the short span of roughly a million years, our ancestors evolved a very elaborate and enlarged cerebral cortex, together with an earlier development of an upright position that freed the forefeet from the ground so that they could be used as hands to manipulate objects and make tools and weapons. The rapidly enlarging cerebral cortex made possible language—the use of words as symbols for ideas to pass on information to one's fellows and offspring. This ability to transmit information rapidly from leader to followers and from generation to generation, combined with a very long childhood dependency, made possible a new kind of evolution—psychosocial evolution—which is roughly a thousandfold faster than biological evolution. Psychosocial evolution has a feedback further to facilitate brain development and intelligence.

Thus our ancestors invented agriculture about 12,000 years ago and city-states 7,000 years ago. All our institutions of law, education, business—of weapons, transportation, and communication—are products of social evolution. Modern science, our most powerful tool to advance psychosocial evolution, is only about 300 years old and has brought about more changes in the human condition during the past century than occurred in the 40 preceding centuries.

There is an analogy between biological evolution by genes and social evolution by ideas. New ideas, it has been pointed out, are analogous to new mutations of genes. Most genetic mutations are lethal, harmful, or worthless; a very few, one in a thousand, constitute the basis of advancing biological evolution by appearing at a time when the environment happens to confer an advantage to the organism possessing that particular mutant gene. It is also true that most ideas do little to advance social evolution. There is environmental selectivity not only to favor the viable gene mutation producing biological progress, but also social environmental selectivity to favor certain ideas contributing to social progress. Like mutant genes, an idea may be "before its time," that is, the social climate may not be right for its acceptance, and many ideas are harmful and may even be lethal to the individual and to society. Here one might mention Nazism and the militant ideology of prewar Japan and other chauvinistic nationalisms. Just as many mutant genes may be lethal for a species, so ideas that produce nuclear war can be lethal for our species unless our political phenotypes are suitably controlled.

What a future man can have if he learns to control his propensity to overpopulate the earth and control his instinctive aggressions and parochial hates and fears, and thus refrain from committing nuclear suicide and becoming another extinct species.

## Overpopulation

Crowding of animals in the natural state as well as in zoos and laboratories has been shown to create serious stress. At critical levels of crowding, the social organization of groups is disrupted and this is accompanied by fighting, reproduction failure, cannibalism, and increased death rates. Postmortem examination of the animals shows evidence of overactivity of the pituitary adrenal axis with signs of adrenocortical exhaustion. Crowding of people in concentration camps is highly stressful and has resulted in pathology and deaths with evidence of exhaustion of the adrenal cortex. Increased atherosclerosis, psychoses, neuroses, crime, delinquency, and reduced fertility may accompany the stress of crowding in slums and ghettos, although direct evidence for stress as a causal factor and for adrenocortical involvement has not been studied.

I regard the population explosion as a serious social disease. It is especially ironic that the humane practices of medicine and public health aimed to reduce physical suffering and prolong healthy lives should be the primary cause of this affliction. The unprecedented increase in the world's population is occurring in economically underdeveloped countries least able to afford it. Prior to World War II, for about 100 years following Pasteur and the development of bacteriology and immunology, the European population growth rate increased slowly as a result of the conquest of infectious diseases and improvements in public health, thus reducing death rates. Since World War II, western medicine has applied its sophisticated techniques to underdeveloped countries. Medical missionaries, using relatively inexpensive insecticides, antibiotics, innoculations, and vaccinations applied to masses of people, have reduced the death rate drastically, leaving the birth rate, always large, either unchanged or somewhat increased as a result of improvements in health and longevity. This has greatly increased populations in the poverty-stricken countries of Asia, the Near East, Africa, and Latin America, which now contain 69 per cent of the world's adults and, through marked decreases in infant mortality, 80 per cent of its children.

In most of the underdeveloped countries the death rate has dropped with record speed. Thus, for example, on the island of Mauritius in the Indian Ocean, within an eight year period after the war, the life expectancy increased from 31 to 51 years, a gain that took Sweden 130 years to achieve. In Taiwan, within two decades, the life expectancy increased from 43 to 63 years. This 20-year gain in life expectancy took 80 years to bring about in the white population of the United States. These figures are typical of what has happened in most underdeveloped countries. In many of the very poor countries the population is increasing at the rate of over 3 per cent each year, which will double it in 23 years. The world population as a whole is increasing at 2 per cent each year, which will double it in about 35 years. The oncoming generation of poverty-stricken, economically unproductive young people will increase the birth rate further as they come of age. And this oncoming generation in many areas is now hungrier and more illiterate than its parents, and has fewer job opportunities. This is bad news in countries with rising expectations now containing over two-thirds of the world's people, such as China, India, Pakistan, the United Arab Republic, and various Latin American countries where the average per capita income is less than $100 per year ($2,800 in the U.S.). It is very bad news for us in the richer countries because of the jealousies, hatred, and revolutionary ardor our opulence induces.

Nothing like this population explosion has ever happened before. It took over a million years for the world's population to reach its first billion, around 1830. It took only 100 years more to reach its second billion in 1930. It reached its third billion 30 years later in 1960. At present growth rate of 2 per cent, it will reach its fourth billion in 1975, its fifth billion in 1985, and its seventh billion around the turn of the century—and on it goes.

Since population growth depends only on the diffence between births and deaths, there are only two solutions to the social disease of overpopulation. One is to increase death rates and the other is to decrease birth rates. So far we have manipulated death control by decreasing death rates and so increasing the population. No one I know advocates reversing this process, although a nuclear war would certainly do it, and such a war is made increasingly likely by the runaway populations. The alternative solution is birth control and family limitation planned on a rational basis.

### What Can Be Done?

There have been marked advances in the technology of fertility control in the form of the contraceptive pills, intrauterine devices (IUDs), and other procedures. IUDs have been used extensively in some of the underdeveloped countries, but the all-important motivations to have small families are usually lacking in the very poor countries. Agricultural countries depend upon many sons for farming; the need for large families declines with industrialization. It also declines with reduction in death rates, and Roger Revelle has argued that decreases in infant mortality can reduce the need for large families to insure mature sons, so that paradoxically the cause of the population growth may react to retard it.

Better education and desire for upward social mobility are powerful motivations for smaller families, since educational opportunities and advancement can be made available by poor parents for one or two children but not for five or six, and most educated women prefer to have jobs and careers instead of repeated pregnancies and a host of children. It is a fact that in countries in which education and economic levels rise, the number of childen per family declines. However, the growth rates in industrially underdeveloped countries show little sign of being brought under control so far by voluntary family planning, even where this is socially acceptable, and governments may find it necessary to use tax incentives for small families instead of for large families, as they often do, and tax penalties for large ones to stem the flood of births. Moreover, I expect that increasing numbers of governments may come to pay individuals for permitting themselves to be sterilized, as is done now in India at government expense. In addition it has been suggested that marriage licenses could be very expensive; a child tax could be levied and all illegitimate pregnancies could, by law, be terminated. These drastic and highly undesirable measures will be necessary if voluntary control fails.

## Concern for Mankind

If other methods fail, our crowded planet with its population growth rate and increasing international tensions may resort to nuclear war, which would indeed solve population problems for all of us. In such a war there can be no winner no matter who fires the first shot. Many of those who might survive blast, fire, disease, starvation, and social collapse would acquire an added burden of lethal and deleterious mutations causing cumulative genetic damage and deaths in the generations that follow. Over 99 per cent of all mutations are lethal or harmful and all are inherited. All of our human genetic material, the DNA of all the people in the world, adds up to less than a pound. It is appalling to consider the arrogance and stupidity of any one generation which, for ephemeral political differences, as judged over the time span of generations, is prepared to wreck this irreplaceable genetic material that has taken three billion years of evolution to produce and that makes us human beings.

These various crises and problems have come about from the very rapid advances of science and technology operating in a framework of rigid social institutions, beliefs, myths, and prejudices that are ill-adapted to meeting change, and it is in changes in our beliefs and values that our hope must lie.

Brock Chisholm has pointed out that concern for the welfare of the human race is not within the tradition into which any of us was born and has no conscience value. It must be learned intellectually against the pressures of many competing loyalties. Most of us are entirely creatures of accident; the accidents of time, place, class, and family. All of which are very poor reasons for believing in anything, and yet it is from these loyalties that a child acquires his most intense beliefs at a very early period. Today, children of the world are still being taught that utterly false doctrine which makes the welfare of part of the human race more important than that

of the whole. Every prejudice and orthodoxy which limits freedom
of thought and enhances prescribed and unchanging attitudes is an
obstacle to developing better human relations and peace in the
world. Chisholm concludes that the most pressing problem of education would appear to be the liberation of our children from many
of our own limiting loyalties, and I might add this may be one of
the brighter sides of the current student rebellions.

Toynbee has said, concerning revision of our concepts of national sovereignty: "We have either to break with it or destroy
ourselves. If we now decide that we must jettison the institution of
national sovereignty, we need not fear that we shall lose ourselves
in a political vacuum."

We have to learn to live in a world governed by enforcible
supranational law against war. This demands some form of world
government, under which the sovereignty of nations with respect
to their war-making potential is subordinated, similarly to that of
our individual states in relation to our federal government, or of
the Swiss cantons in relation to the government of Switzerland.
This means control of war by a world federation. It involves the
disarmament of nation states, except for lightly armed internal
police. It requires enforceable laws against war supported by an
armed international police force powerful enough to prevent war.
Unless men everywhere can bring themselves to this, history may
record—if there should be any history after a third world war—
that man's million-year-old neocortex had turned out to be a
rapidly evolving phylogenetic tumor capable of inventing terrible
weapons of destruction, but incapable of controlling their use.

# Chapter Three

# Human Brains, Behavior and Language

It is a paradox that the brain, man's most distinctive organ, is so inadequately understood in evolutionary terms. We do know that relative to other structures it evolved very rapidly, and that it reached its modern size forty to eighty thousand years ago. We also know that the evolution of the human brain consisted of additions to, rather than remodeling and expansion of, pre-existing parts of a simpler mammalian brain. It must be assumed that this dramatic piece of hominid evolution was an adaptation to the Pleistocene environment in which it occurred. But it is problematical that a dependence on toolmaking, language and complex social organization adequately accounts for this truly phenomenal organ of man.

A far more basic adaptation may have been involved in the evolution of the human brain. Rather than viewing the human brain as necessary for the existence of technology, agriculture, and civilization—really incidental developments occurring long after the brain had attained its modern size—we must assume that this unusual brain was necessary during man's uniquely long growth and maturation period. Certainly the human brain is an organ capable of incredible feats of learning during a time in the life span when survival chiefly depends on that ability. Thus the brain is complete at birth and matures more rapidly than any other organ system. Having essentially served its survival function, perhaps already by the end of the first few years after birth, it nevertheless lingers on at huge metabolic cost to its adult host. And this is not even to mention the expense measured in terms of neuroses and psychoses, the pathologies to which such an elaborate mechanism is prone.

It is fascinating to speculate how much of man's complex culture, his religions, philosophies, art, social arrangements, his evident compulsive need to elaborate on anything and everything, is ultimately simply the machinations of a giant computer. A computer since early childhood relieved of its original function, yet never turned off. Voracious for input, and too often motivating the organism upon which it is dependant, yet which it rules, to frivolous if not damaging behavior.

# THE HUMANNESS OF MAN

*Isaac Asimov*

Isaac Asimov, author and essayist, is a professor of biochemistry at the Boston University School of Medicine. His book *The Human Brain: Its Capacities and Functions* is an exhaustive treatment of the topics discussed in this article.

Men have in the past sometimes tended to set up a firm and impassable wall separating the behavior of man from that of all creatures other than man and to label the wall "reason." Creatures other than man we might suppose to be governed by instincts or by an inborn nature that dictates their actions at every step—actions which it is beyond their power to modify.

Man, on the other hand, according to this view, has certain attributes that no animal has. He has the capacity to remember the past in great detail, to foresee possible futures in almost equal detail, to imagine alternatives, to weigh and judge in the light of past experience, to deduce consequences from premises—and to base his behavior upon all of this by an act of "free will." In short, he has the power of reason; he has a "rational mind," something, it is often felt, not possessed by any other creature. That man also has instincts, blind drives, and, at least in part, an "animal nature" is not to be denied; but the rational mind is supposed to be capable of rising above this.

Yet the division between "rational man" and "irrational brute" cannot really be maintained. It is true that as one progresses along the scale of living species in the direction of simpler and less intricately organized nervous systems, innate behavior plays a more and more important role, and the ability to modify behavior in the light of experience (to "learn," that is) becomes less important. The difference in this respect between man and other animals, however, is not that between "yes" and "no" but, rather, that between "more" and "less."

Does the fact that behavior can be modified even in simple animals wipe out the distinction between man and other creatures? Of course it doesn't. That the gap (only man can compose a symphony or deduce a mathematical theorem) exists is obvious and incontrovertible. The only question is whether the gap exists by virtue of man's exclusive possession of reason. What, after all, is reason?

In the case of simple organisms, it seems quite clear that learning, in the sense of the development of behavior not innate, takes place through conditioning, and we are not trapped into believing that anything resembling human reason is involved. In mammals, with more complicated nervous systems than are possessed by any creatures outside the class and with, therefore, the possibility of more complex behavior patterns, matters are less clear-cut. We begin to recognize in mammalian behavior a similarity to our own and consequently may begin to be tempted to explain their activity by using the word "reason." A cat trapped in an enclosure from which an exit is possible if a lever is pushed or a latch is pulled will behave in a manner so like our own under similar circumstances as to convince us that it is disturbed on being enclosed and anxious to be free. And when it finds the exit we may say to ourselves, "Ah, she's figured it out."

But has she? Or is this an overestimate of the cat's mental power? Apparently the latter. A trapped cat makes random moves, pushing, jumping, squeezing, climbing, pacing restlessly. Eventually, it will make some move that will by accident offer a way out. The second time, after a shorter interval of trial and error, the cat will do the same. After enough trials, it will push the lever and escape at once. The simplest explanation is that is has conditioned itself to push the lever by associating this, finally, with escape. However, there would seem to be also a matter of memory involved; a dim process that makes the cat discover the exit more quickly (usually) the second time than the first.

Animal memory has been tested by experiment. A raccoon can be relied on to remember for up to half a minute; this interval increases as animals with a more complex nervous system are chosen. A monkey may sometimes remember for a full day.

We might conclude, though, that superior memory does not alone mark the difference between man and other animals, since even in man, who certainly has the best memory in the realm of life, trial-and-error behavior is common. The average man, having dropped a dime in the bedroom, is very likely to look for it randomly, now here now there. If he then finds it, that is no tribute to his reasoning powers. Nevertheless, let us not downgrade memory. After all, a man does not have to indulge in trial-and-error only, even in searching for a dropped dime. He may look only in the direction in which he heard the dime strike. He may look in his trousers-cuff because he knows that in many cases a falling dime may end up there and defy all attempts to locate it on the floor.

A man can, in short, simplify the problem somewhat by a process of reasoning based on memory. In doing so, however (to jump back to the other side of the fence again), it is possible that the trial-and-error method does not truly disappear but is etherealized —is transferred from action to thought. A man doesn't actually look everywhere for a lost dime. He visualizes the position and looks everywhere mentally, eliminating what his experience tells him are unlikely places (the ceiling, a distant room) and shortening the actual search by that much.

In moving up the scale of animal behavior, we find that modification of behavior goes through the stages of (1) conditioning by circumstance, (2) conditioning after trial-and-error, and (3) conditioning after an etherealized trial-and-error. If it seems fair to call this third and most elaborate form of modification "reason," it next remains to decide whether only human beings make use of it.

Monkeys and apes remember accurately enough and long enough to make it seem unlikely that they can be thoroughly bereft of such etherealization, and indeed they are not. Chimpanzees reaching for bananas will stack boxes or use a short stick to get at a large stick, and do so in such a way as to make it clear that reason is at work.

At what point in the animal kingdom trial-and-error is etherealized to a sufficient degree to warrant the accolade of "reason" is uncertain. Not enough animals have been tested thoroughly. If the chimpanzee can reason, what about the other apes? What about the elephant or the dolphin.

One thing is sure. Reason alone does not explain the gulf that lies between man and other animals.

But is it enough to compare man and animals on the basis of so relatively simple an act as finding an escape route or a lost object? Can we generalize from finding a dime to reading a book? Some psychologists have rather believed that we could. The behaviorists, of whom the American psychologist John Broadus Watson was most prominent, tended to view all learning in the light of conditioned reflexes.

The conditioned reflex differs from the ordinary reflex in that the cerebrum is involved. If the cerebrum is involved, then it is reasonable to suppose that as the mass and complexity of the cerebrum increase—and they have increased to the greatest extent in man—so will the complexity and intricacy of the conditioned reflexes increase. Speaking and reading are complex conditioned responses, as are typing or whittling or any of a myriad other mechanical skills; and man is capable of all this not because he has something lower animals do not have, but because he has what they all have—only far more of it.

One might insist that the highest attributes of the human mind—logical deduction and even scientific or artistic creativity—can be brought down to hit-and-miss and conditioning. If we imagine that this is what happens in the human brain, we must also expect that there would exist in the brain large areas that do not directly receive sensation or govern response, but are devoted to associations, associations, and more associations. This is exactly so.

Thus, the region about the auditory area in the temporal lobe is the *auditory association area*. There particular sounds are associated with physical phenomena in the light of past experience. There is also a *visual association area* in the occipital lobe surrounding the actual visual area and a *somesthetic association area* behind the somesthetic area.

The overall association area is sometimes called the *gnostic area*. The overall associations are fed into the area lying immediately in front, the *ideomotor area,* which translates them into an appropriate response. This information is shunted into the *pre-motor area* (lying just before the motor area in the frontal lobe), which coordinates the muscular activity necessary to produce the desired response, this activity being finally brought about by the motor area.

When all the association areas, the sensory areas, and the motor areas are taken into account, there still remains one area of the cerebrum that has no specific and easily definable or measurable function. This is the area of the frontal lobe that lies before the motor and premotor areas and is therefore called the *prefrontal lobe.* Its lack of obvious function is such that it is sometimes called the "silent area." Tumors have made it necessary to remove large areas of the prefrontal lobe without particularly significant effect on the individual, and yet surely it is not a useless mass of nerve tissue.

There might be a tendency, rather, to consider it, of all sections of the brain, the most significant. In general, the evolutionary trend in the development of the human nervous system has been the piling of complication upon complication at the forward end of the nerve cord. In the early hominids, even after the brain had achieved full human size, the frontal lobes continued development. Neanderthal man had a brain as large as our own, but the frontal lobe of the brain of true man gained at the expense of the occipital lobe, so if the total weight is the same, the distribution of weight is not. It is easy to assume then that the prefrontal lobes, far from being unused, are a kind of extra storage volume for associations, and the very epitome of the brain.

Even granted that the behaviorist stand is correct in principle and that all human behavior, however complex, can be brought down to a mechanical pattern of nerve cells (and hormones), the further question arises as to whether it is useful to allow matters to rest there.

Clearly we have much farther to go than the distance the pat phrase "trial-and-error" can carry us. Briefly, as a change progresses, there can come a point (sometimes quite a sharp one) where our view of it must change, where a difference in degree suddenly becomes the equivalent of a difference in kind. This is a "phase change." When the process of etherealized trial-and-error becomes as complicated as it is in the human mind, it may well be no longer useful to attempt to interpret mental activity in behaviorist terms. As to what form of interpretation *is* most useful, that is not yet settled.

The concept of the phase change can be used to answer the question of what fixes the gulf between man and all other creatures. Since it is not reason alone, it must be something more. A phase change must take place not at the moment when reason is introduced but at some time when reason passes a certain point of intensity. The point is, one might reasonably suppose, that at which reason becomes complex enough to allow abstraction; when it allows the establishment of symbols to stand for concepts, which in turn stand for collections of things or actions or qualities.

Once it is possible to conceive an abstraction and represent it by a sound, communication becomes possible at a level of complexity and meaningfulness far beyond that possible otherwise. As the motor areas of the brain develop to the point where a speech center exists, enough different sounds can be made, easily and surely, to supply each of a vast number of concepts with individual sounds. And there is enough room for memory units in a brain of such complexity to keep all the necessary associations of sound and concept firmly in mind.

It is speech, then, rather than reason alone that is the phase change, and that fixes the gulf between man and nonman. The existence of speech means that the gathering of experience and the drawing of conclusions is no longer a function of the individual alone. Experience is shared and the tribe becomes wiser and more knowledgeable than any individual in it. Moreover, experience unites the tribe throughout time as well as throughout space. Each generation need no longer start from scratch, as must all other creatures. Human parents can pass on their experience and wisdom to their children, not only by demonstration but by verbalized, conceptual explanation. Not only facts and techniques, but also thought and deductions can be passed on.

More and more it is becoming fashionable to look upon the brain as though it were, in some ways, an immensely complicated computer made up of extremely small switches, the neurons. And in one respect at least, that involving the question of memory, biochemists are coming to look to structures finer than the neuron, and to penetrate even to the molecular level.

Memory is the key that makes possible the phase change. It is only because human beings can remember so much and so well that it has been possible to develop the intricate code of symbols we call speech. The memory capacity of even an ordinary human mind is fabulous. Consider how many faces we can recognize, how many names call up some past incident, how many words we can spell and define, and how much minutiae we know we have met with before. Estimates are that in a lifetime, a brain can store 1,000,000,000,000,000 (a million billion) "bits" of information.

In computers, a "memory" can be set up by making suitable changes in the magnetic properties of a tape, changes that are re-tained until called into use. Is there an analogous situation in the brain? Suspicion is currently falling upon *ribonucleic acid* (usu-ally abbreviated RNA) in which the nerve cell, surprisingly enough, is richer than almost any other type of cell in the body. I say sur-prisingly because RNA is involved in the synthesis of protein and is therefore usually found in those tissues producing large quanti-ties of protein either because they are actively growing or because they are producing copious quantities of protein-rich secretions. The nerve cell falls into neither classification, so the abundance of RNA within it serves as legitimate ground for speculation.

The possible number of different arrangements of subunits within an RNA molecule is astronomically immense—much, much larger than the mere "million billion" I mentioned above. It has been suggested that every "bit" of information entering the ner-vous system for the first time introduces a change in an RNA mole-cule contained in certain neurons reserved for the purpose. The changed RNA molecule produces a type of protein not produced hitherto. When further "bits" of information enter the nervous system, they can presumably be matched to the RNA/protein com-binations already present. If the match succeeds, we "remember."

This is, as yet, only the most primitive beginning of an attempt to analyze the highest functions of the human mind at the mole-cular level, and to carry it further represents the greatest possible challenge to the mind.

It seems logical, somehow, to suppose that an entity that under-stands must be more complex than the object being understood. Where the limit of understanding will be, or whether it exists at all, we cannot well predict, for we cannot measure as yet the com-plexity of either the mind or the universe outside the mind.

However, even without making measurements, we can say as an axiom that a thing is equal to itself, and that therefore the human mind, in attempting to understand the workings of the human mind, faces us with a situation in which the entity that must understand and the object to be understood are of equal com-plexity.

Does this mean we can never truly grasp the working of the human mind? I cannot tell. But even if we cannot, it may still be

possible to grasp just enough of its workings to be able to con-
stuct computers that approach the human mind in complexity and
subtlety, even though we fall short of full understanding.

If we could do even so much, we might learn enough to prevent
those disorders of the mind, those irrationalities and passions, that
have hitherto perpetually frustrated the best and noblest efforts of
mankind. If we could but reduce the phenomena of imagination,
intuition, and creativity to analysis by physical and chemical laws,
we might be able to arrange to have the effects of genius on steady
tap, so to speak, rather than be forced to wait for niggardly chance
to supply the human race with geniuses at long intervals only.

Man would then, by his own exertions, become more than man,
and what might not be accomplished thereafter? It is quite certain,
I am sure, that none of us will live to see the far-distant time when
this might come to pass. And yet, the mere thought that such a day
might some day come is a profoundly satisfying one.


# THE EVOLUTION OF MAN: WHAT WENT WRONG?

*Arthur Koestler*

Arthur Koestler, writer, is the author of *The Ghost in the Machine,
Darkness at Noon,* and many other works dealing with the problems
of twentieth-century man.


If one looks with a cold eye at the mess man has made of his
history, it is difficult to avoid the conclusion that he is afflicted by
some built-in mental disorder which drives him towards self-
destruction. We know that among social animals fighting is a ritual
which stops short of serious injury. The prey that the predator kills
always belongs to a different species. Murder *within* the species,
on an individual or collective scale, is a phenomenon unknown in
the whole animal kingdom, except for man and a few varieties of
ants and rats.

Evidently something must have gone wrong at some point in
the evolution of *Homo sapiens.* But when we ask what it is that
has gone wrong, we usually get the dusty answer that all evil

From *Current*, Vol 96 (June 1968), pp. 61–4. Reprinted by permission of A. D.
Peters & Company.

stems from the selfish, greedy, aggressive tendencies in human nature. That is the explanation that has been offered to us for the past 3,000 years by Hebrew prophets, Indian sages, Christian moralists and contemporary psychoanalysts; but, speaking in all humility. I find this answer unconvincing and unsupported by the historical record.

What the record indicates is that in the major disasters in our history, individual aggressiveness for selfish motives played an almost negligible part compared to unselfish loyalty and devotion to tribe, nation, religion or political ideology. Tribal wars, national wars, civil wars, religious wars, world wars are waged in the purported interest of the community, not of the individual, to decide issues that are far removed from the personal self-interest of the combatants. No doubt the lust for rape and plunder provided delightful incentives for a minority, but for the great majority the primary motive was fanatical loyalty, to the point of self-sacrifice, to king and country, leader or group.

In other words, the main trouble with man appears to be, not that he is an excessively aggressive creature, but an excessively loyal and devoted creature. He seems to have a stronger biological need than any other species to *belong,* to attach himself to a person, a group or idea, to transcend the claustrophobic confines of his self. He cannot live alone and he cannot leave alone.

One possible reason for this tendency may be the protracted helplessness and dependence of the human infant. Another reason may be increased dependence on solidarity and cooperation of our primate ancestors when they took from the forest to the plains and turned into carnivorous hunters of prey bigger and faster than themselves. Primate societies living in the wild are also held together by strong bonds, and groups of the same primate species living in different localities may also develop different traditions and customs. But the cohesive bonds within primate families do not grow into neurotic attachments, the cohesive forces within primate groups do not attain the intensity and fervor of tribal feeling, and the differences between primate groups of the same species do not lead to violent conflicts. Only in *Homo sapiens* did the cohesive forces within the group develop into fanatical loyalty to tribe, totem and its later symbolic equivalents; and only in our species did the repellent forces between groups develop into intraspecific warfare.

What I am trying to suggest is that the aggressive, self-assertive tendencies in the emotional life of the human individual are less dangerous to the species than his self-transcending or integrative tendencies. Most civilizations throughout our history have been quite successful in taming individual aggressiveness and teaching the young how to sublimate their self-assertive impulses. But we have tragically failed to achieve a similar sublimation . . . of the self-transcending emotions.

## The Role of "Blind Devotion"

The number of victims of individual crimes committed in any period of history is insignificant compared to the masses cheerfully sacrificed *ad majorem gloriam,* in blind devotion to the true religion, dynasty or political system. When we speak of "blind devotion" we implicitly recognize the uncritical nature of the self-transcending urge in forming attachments to a person, group, race, flag or system of beliefs. . . .

Thus during the most of human history, the self-transcending urges of the individual could only express themselves through devotion to a narrowly defined group, with which he identified himself to the hostile exclusion of other groups; as a result, the disruptive forces have always dominated the forces of cohesion in our species as a whole. The main peril of self-transcending devotion is that it frequently acts as a vehicle for a vicarious, unselfish kind of aggression. We enter into an identificatory rapport with the hero on the movie screen, and as a result hate the perfidious villain; our anger is a vicarious emotion experienced on behalf of another person who does not even really exist, and yet we produce all the physical symptoms of a true emotion. Similarly, the emotion displayed by a crowd of demonstrators is an unselfish type of emotion derived from the identification of the individual with the group.

When alone, man is inclined to act in his own interest, regardless of others; when identified with a group, the situation is reversed. The egotism of the group feeds on the altruism of its members.

Human history is pockmarked with the scars of this infernal dialectic. As to its origins, some clues are perhaps provided by the biological factors previously mentioned—the long infantile dependence and strong social interdependence characteristic of our species. There is also the peculiar ability of the human brain to sustain belief-systems, rooted in emotion, which are incompatible and in frequent conflict with its reasoning faculties. The result is the split-minded, quasi-schizophrenic mentality, which seems to be inherent in man's condition and is reflected in his absurd and tortured history.

Let me mention briefly two further factors which seem to be

equally basic to the human predicament. The first is the emergence of language as an exclusively human blessing and curse. Language promotes communication and understanding within the group; but it also accentuates the differences in tradition and beliefs between groups and erects separative barriers between tribes, nations, regions, social classes. According to Margaret Mead, among the two million Aborigines in New Guinea, 750 different languages are spoken in 750 villages, which are at permanent war with one another.

## The Role of Ideology

Even more dangerous, however, than the divisive effect of different vocabularies is the power of language to crystallize the implicit habits and ways of life of different communities into explicit doctrines and moral imperatives. If the citizens of Lilliput had not been blessed with language, they could not have fought a war on the question of which end to break the egg because they would not have been able to transform a habit into an ideology.

Equal in importance to the discovery of language and of the use of tools is man's discovery of death. But we should rather say: the discovery of death by the intellect and its rejection by instinct. Instinct takes existence for granted and cannot conceive of nonexistence. The refusal to accept death as a natural and final phenomenon became a dominant motive in all human cultures, and a paradigm of the split mind. It populated the atmosphere with invisible presences, most of them malevolent or at least capricious and unpredictable, who had to be propitiated and appeased at a heavy price.

The institution of human sacrifice is a phenomenon curiously neglected by anthropologists, although it is found in every part of the world at the dawn of civilization, and even at the height of pre-Columbian cultures. It is epitomized in one of the early chapters of Genesis, where Abraham prepares to cut the throat of his son out of sheer love of God. The ubiquity of human sacrifice is one of the earliest manifestations of the paranoid trend in the human psyche. The forms changed, but the trend persisted throughout the holy massacres of history, culminating in the genocidal enterprises of our time. Even the promise of eternal life was offered only to a minority of mankind, at the price of eternal torment for the vast majority. Paradise was an exclusive country club, but the gates of Hell were open to all.

There is of course a reverse side of the medal. Devotion is not always misguided, language produced the treasures in our libraries, the discovery of death is the foundation on which pyramids and cathedrals were built. However, we are now concerned not with the glory of man but his predicament, and today that is the more urgent subject; it has achieved an urgency as never before. History is accelerating at an unprecedented rate, like molecules of a liquid coming to the boil.

The contemporary equivalent of the Writing on the Wall are the diagrammatic charts of the exponential curves representing the various explosions that surround us: population explosion, knowledge explosion, communications explosion, and the explosion of explosive power. We may have seen the curves in learned magazines, but none of us has seen a curve representing progress in theoretical and applied ethics. The reason is presumably that there is no progress to report since the days when Buddha sat under the banyan tree, waiting for his oxcart.

In contrast to the exponential curve, which shows at first a slow, then an ever steeper rise until it seems to rocket into the sky, the missing ethical curve would show a blurred, wavy line with inconclusive ups and downs, and would never get off the ground. This contrast provides us with a simple overall view of our history; it reflects the consequences of the split mind.

## Where Nature Erred

Evolution proceeds by trial and error, so we ought not to be surprised if it turned out that there is some construction fault in the circuitry that we carry inside our skulls, which would explain the unholy mess we have made of our history. The ultimate cause may be the exceptionally rapid growth of the hominid brain in the course of the last half-million years—a phenomenon which seems to be unique in evolutionary history.

The brain explosion in the second half of the Pleistocene seems also to have followed the exponential curve which has become so familiar to us—and there may be more than a superfical analogy here, as both curves reflect the phenomenon of the acceleration of history on different levels.

But explosions rarely produce harmonious results, and the evidence seems to indicate that in our case the result is insufficient coordination between the phylogenetically old areas of the brain and the new, specifically human areas of the neocortex, which were superimposed on it with such unseemly haste.

A distinguished neurophysiologist, Prof. Paul MacLean, has

coined the term "schizophysiology" for this disorderly state of affairs in our central nervous system. While our intellectual functions are carried on in the newest and most highly developed part of the brain, he says, our affective behavior continues to be dominated by a relatively crude and primitive system, by archaic structures in the brain whose fundamental pattern has undergone but little change in the whole course of evolution from mouse to man.

The consequences of this built-in schizophysiology range from so-called normal behavior, where emotional bias distorts our reasoning only within tolerable limits, through neurotic and psychotic disorder in the individual, to the collectively held beliefs in irrational causes to which we are emotionally committed in blind devotion and militant enthusiasm.

The question is, as Bertrand Russell once said, how to persuade humanity to acquiesce in its own survival. The thermonuclear reaction, once invented, cannot be disinvented, and the Pandora boxes of biological warfare are just waiting to be opened. One cannot play Russian roulette for long.

The biological evolution of man seems to have come to a standstill, at least since Cro-Magnon days; since we cannot in the foreseeable future expect a change in human nature to arise by a spontaneous mutation, our only hope seems to be to discover techniques which supplant biological evolution and provide a cure for our collective ailments. Recent advances in the sciences of life seem to indicate that once man decides to take his fate into his own hands, that possibility will be within his reach.

# DOLPHINS AND THE MIND OF MAN

*W. Tschernezky*

W. Tschernezky is a member of the technical staff of the zoology department at Queen Mary College, University of London.

As long ago as 1870 Alfred Russell Wallace pointed out that the brain of a savage is very little inferior in biological terms to that of a philosopher and quite disproportionate to his requirements.

From *New Scientist*, Vol. 39 (Aug. 22, 1968), pp. 377–80. This article was first published in *New Scientist*, the weekly news magazine of science and technology, 128 Long Acre, London W. C. 1. © IPC Magazines Ltd.

The appearance of the prehuman and human mind is usually recognized by the following anatomical and social features: binocular
vision; the vertical position of the body and skull; the ability to
manipulate freely hands which are not supporting the body; a decrease in size of the jaws; complicated vocal communications and
articulate speech in the case of Man; an intricate social structure;
and the use and making of tools.

The most important external stimuli accounting for human evolution which are usually suggested are the appearance of mountain
ridges, the replacement of forests by open grasslands, and some ac-
companying climatic changes.

If these suggestions about environmental stimuli are correct,
then the mammals completely lacking these morphological qualities, and evolving in simple and constant surroundings, would be
expected to possess a very underdeveloped brain and intelligence.
But there is no doubt that the cetaceans—the family of fish-like
mammals—possess large complicated brains and high intelligence.
According to Pierre Grasse, the common porpoise, weighing 70 kg
has a brain weighing 555 g—roughly 1½ times as large as that of
a chimpanzee of the same weight. A dolphin weighing 150 kg has a
brain weighing 1000 g—about twice as large as the brain of a
gorilla of the same weight.

A. Alpers and J. C. Lilly have both reported many experiments
that demonstrate the very high mental abilities of dolphins. So between them and the high primates there exists a mysterious parallelism in the development of the brain and its functions, in spite of
the widest possible difference between their environments, origins
and the structure of the rest of their bodies. Clearly, the brains and
mental abilities of animals can evolve independently of their surroundings and the structures of their own sense organs and the organs which carry out their various functions.

The independence of behavior and physical structure was
richly illustrated by Charles Darwin when he discussed how, in
evolution, habits often changed before the structures had altered
to suit them. To the examples he gave in The Origin of Species can
be added other instances: the monkey Macaca irus which swims
regularly and eats crabs; the carnivorous giant panda Auluropoda
melanoleuca which feeds as an herbivorous animal; the grey fox
Urocyon which has taken to climbing trees; the tree kangaroo
Dendrolagus which has also assumed an arboreal mode of life in
spite of its feet having lost a grasping hind-limb digit; the bat
Noctilio leporinus which has acquired the habit of preying on
fishes.

H. Harlow, too, has stressed that chimpanzees in experimental conditions are able to solve problems on a level of complexity never met with in the natural environment. So the phenomenon of brain size disproportionate to an animal's requirements, which Wallace mentioned for savage *Homo sapiens*, can be observed to some degree and in various forms in many branches of the animal kingdom as well.

Because the functions of the central nervous system, expressed in mental activity directing the rational adaptive actions of an individual, are qualitatively different from the functions of all other biological systems, it is reasonable to expect that its evolution must also have proceeded in qualitatively different ways. For instance, the increase of body size or of some single organ has appeared in some instances to be the cause of extinction of a species, because natural section exterminates the over-developed forms as well as the underdeveloped ones. But the increase of brain size, the complication of its structure, and the extension of its functions can never decrease the adaptive ability and vitality of an animal. If the usual mode of natural selection could be called *two way selection,* then the second one could be qualified as *one way selection* and seems to be the basic reason for the accumulation of surplus mental abilities. And this surplus could have been (and, indeed, still is) the most universal form of *preadaptation* to the various changes in surroundings. It has operated in the simplest form when a primeval environment has been invaded by Man with his agriculture, domestic and imported wild animals, buildings and so on.

Also the surplus intelligence and resulting exploratory behavior permits the animal to penetrate actively into quite new environments. Rational behavior secures a profitable but "unnatural" mode of life, to which the structure of the organism has not necessarily been completely adapted. Now, if the evolution of the central nervous system can proceed remarkably independently of the environment, then the evolution of behavior must have some form of directing influence on the morphological evolution of the subordinate systems of organs. Darwin in his theory of sexual selection, described in *The Descent of Man,* limited the directing influence of habit to courtship behavior only. But numerous and diverse examples of noncorrespondence between form and function, show that habit changed before structure, and that it can give direction also to other forms of morphological evolution, first of all to the evolution of the effector organs, which carry out the animal's various functions in response to nervous stimuli.

Coloration, structures and movements, very similar to those resulting from sexual selection, could be associated with behavior having nothing to do with mating. An example is the warning coloration and movements of harmless snakes imitating the warning display of the venomous rattlesnake or cobra. Here the forgotten words of Darwin from *The Origin of Species* are particularly appropriate: "in either case it would be easy for natural selection to adapt the structure of the animal to its changed habits, or exclusively to one of its several habits." The directing influence of locomotor habit is especially clearly seen in cases when *similar* animal shapes and structures are developed through a *similar* mode of exploiting *different* environments; and when different structures appear in the same surroundings.

For example, a similar reduction of the size of the shell appeared among the snail family, the gastropods, both in the sea and on land as an evolutionary adaptation to a similar new *habit*—an increase of mobility and penetrating ability. "Streamlining" also appeared in a variety of environments; the similar elongated "snake-like" body, with reduced or absent limbs developed in typically terrestrial burrowing amphibians and reptiles; but also in the typically parasitic and aquatic, divergent, jawless class of fishes called cyclostomes, more advanced fishes and even to some extent among dinosaurs and ancient whales. The whale family and the bat family developed a similar ability for echo-sounding navigation in quite different environments. The principle of evolution directed by habit explains also why radical adaptive radiation, leading to the appearance of very different forms, can occur in the same unchanged environment.

According to E. B. Worthington, fishes of the genus *Haplochromys* inhabiting Lake Victoria, produced during the Pleistocene period species with small hair-like teeth, feeding on plants and small animals, mollusk-eaters with large flat teeth for squashing the shells, and fish-eating predators with long jaws and large teeth.

If the environmental factors were really so important in producing the adaptive radiation of mammals, then the whale family, the cetaceans, evolved in oceans would be represented by one or only few very similar "most adapted" forms. In reality, the similarity among whales is superficial and relates mainly to a similar locomotor habit; looking at them more closely you see that they are built in different ways according to different feeding habits: filtrating balene whales, fish-hunting dolphins, active mammal-eaters, killer whales, great squid-eaters, the sperm whales, the blind dolphin of the river Ganges, and the paradoxical sea unicorn.

According to the view I am putting forward here, the morphological divergence in uniform environment started from psychological deviation. For example, predatory *Haplochromys* appeared because the more aggressive part of the population embarked on a more efficient mode of feeding and not because competition with weaker forms "forced" the stronger to eat them. Also the broad mouth and throat, powerful jaws and teeth of killer whales evolved in generations of dolphins which had *actively* chosen to prey on warm-blooded sea animals, not because they were *forced* to adopt this most active mode of life by conditions in their environment to which they became adapted or because of competition with less aggressive members of early toothed whales.

The directing power of behavior was also mentioned by Darwin in *The Descent of Man* when he wrote about some crustaceans, flies and moths: ". . . the males and females of some animals differ in structures related to the different habits of life, and not at all, or only indirectly, to the reproductive functions." After Darwin, J. M. Baldwin in 1896, A. N. Severtsov in 1931 and many others discussed the influence of mode of life on morphological evolution; but this idea was not applied to the most suggestive case—the evolution of Man.

If the evolution of the structures of the human body has really been so important a directing factor in the progress of the pre-human and human mind as is often asserted, then similar bodily structures in modern animals should have had a similar progressive influence on their intelligence. Since, in most cases, they have not increased the mental abilities of modern animals, there is no reason to suggest that they acted as powerful brain stimulators in the one exceptional case of the evolution of Man's ancestors. The dolphin shows that the brain can be strongly developed without stereoscopic sight. In the lemurs, the lowest of the primates, the development of binocular vision does not create an appreciable increase of intelligence. The human-like stereoscopic vision appeared in the first man-like apes long before the brain of even the early hominoids of the human family. The ability to leap on long hind legs does not make *Indri* an especially intelligent lemur; walking is reflected to a certain extent by the structure of the gibbon's skull but has no progressive influence on the evolution of its brain. The nearly human bipedalism of the hominoid australopithecines was associated with nearly ape-like brains. Among modern primates the most successful manipulators with thumbs opposed to fingers—allegedly, the most important development leading to the use of tools—are the macaques and baboons, quadripedal forms in which supporting and locomotor functions of the fore limbs are fully preserved. The baboons also possess powerful jaws; the mandrill, for example, is a very poor illustration of dependence of manipulating ability on bipedalism and of its connection with a finer structure of the face, resulting from more advanced feeding habits.

The most skillful designer and manipulator among the mammals, is the beaver, but its intelligence, as in the case of the monkeys mentioned above, is much lower than that of the apes. The woodpecker finch *Camarhyncus pallidus* uses a cactus thorn or a twig to catch insects. This skill resembles very much the use by chimpanzees of branches for catching termites, but the mental abilities of the two tool-users are very far from being comparable. Nor is there any direct dependence of the complexity of an animal's social organization upon the degree of its mental abilities, a fact which can be readily observed among modern primates and carnivores.

These simple examples show how easy it is to assemble facts contradicting the widely understood conception of human evolution. And it looks as if the above-mentioned factors in Man's evolution have been overestimated and that which follows—underestimated.

The common ability to use complicated vocal signals which belongs to both forest dwellers—the apes—and the ocean dwellers—dolphins—is the characteristic which best accords with the mysterious parallelism of their highly developed brains and mental abilities. On this ground there is every reason to suggest that vocal signalization, prelanguage and language were factors incomparably more involved in the progessive evolution of prehuman and human brain and mind than were binocular vision, manipulating hands, bipedalism and the other classical developments.

The influence of behavior on the physical development of Man could be illustrated in the most illuminative way in terms of the so-called "principle of fixation of phases" expounded by the Soviet biologist, A. N. Severtsov. This principle states that the most profitable temporary position of an organ during its most intensive function becomes, in the process of evolution, transformed into a permanent structure. Following this approach, the appearance of binocular vision may be explained as the transformation of the most efficient position of eyeballs and associated muscles from a temporary into a permanent one. The emerging of the manipulating hand can be explained in a similar way: at the beginning, the advancing brain of an early human ancestor used a generalized palm which was most effective when the thumb was opposed to the fingers for grasping objects. According to Baldwin's ideas, mutations coincided with adaptive modifications, and the necessary phases would be gradually fixed by selection directed by habit.

The human *bipedalism* and vertical position of the skull must also have originated in the same way from temporary positions. The instep of the foot most probably originated from temporary arch-like bending of the joints between the bones of the foot. The permanent result of this evolutionary step is mechanically the most satisfactory position to resist the body weight of a prehuman when standing on its hind limbs.

After such changes the acquired habits of the human ancestor were supported by a more efficient effector system. The appearance of a strong and coordinated physical basis for a behavior pattern ensured its further progress in the same direction. In this way, the brain, changing the structures of organs in the necessary direction, so to speak, created the instruments for its own further perfection.

Ancient primates used sound signalization in various ways. Also different organs were most used as resonators. As a result, the howler monkey, *Alouata,* developed a special cavity in the larynx that makes a most powerful and perfect mechanism for producing a roar. In gibbons and particulary the soamang *Hylobates sydactilus*, laryngeal sacks serve as resonators; the proboscis monkey, *Nasalis larvatus*, has a long, soft proboscis hanging in the flat, long base of its nose which is connected with producing vocal signals. In Man the high back of the nose contributes in large degree to the clearness of articulate speech, and serves as a resonating device. If the tendency in man-like apes was to use sound basically for the production of loud cries, and only partly for signals with different meanings, then early Man used his voice more for the production of complicated articulated signals.

It is quite logical to suggest that the perfection of the sound signalization was very gradual and that the development of prelanguage started long before the ancestor of Man started to be a regular toolmaker. From this point of view it is of particular interest that the recently discovered *Oreopithecus* combined a large brain, short fine face and—already abandoning ape-like features—a high bony back to his nose. It is quite probable that these progessive features are correlated with each other, and that the high back of the nose indicated a good resonating ability and a degree of perfection in making sound signals.

If this argument is valid it looks as if vocal signalization, prelanguage and language were the most perfect assisting factors created by the brain for its own perfection.

As Darwin mentioned in *The Descent of Man* in respect of sexual selection, the selection directed by behavior presupposes that the intelligence of an organism has reached a level where its behavior has become an important factor in the individual's survival. This means that evolution of plants and lower animals, where rational behavior is absent or consists of standardized instinctive actions, must proceed in a less perfect way than the evolution of higher and rationally acting animals. There must, in short, take place an evolution of evolution itself.

The selection directed by mind and habit over many generations should be most strongly expressed among the most intelligent animals—whence the exclusively rapid and radical evolution of Man.

# HOW BABIES LEARN TO TALK

*Eric H. Lenneberg*

Eric H. Lenneberg, a professor of psychology and neurobiology at Cornell University, has been a research associate in the Department of Psychology of The Children's Hospital Medical Center, Boston. He is the author of *Biological Foundations of Language*.

The sky is getting lighter; I can see it behind the window shades. I hear some rocking sounds from the nursery. David is awake. Did he just make a noise that woke me up? Or was it the alarm clock, giving its warning click just before it rings? No, it's not even six o'clock yet; another thirty-five minutes of rest. But burying my head in the pillow does not bring back sleep. I hear David babbling, "Mabba, gagga, dadach . . ." or something like that. His sounds are richer than the alphabet can reproduce. Writing them down strips them of their qualities of pleasure, curiosity, self-sufficiency. What

From *Parents Magazine*, Summer 1964, pp. 66+. Reprinted by permission.

I hear are not the sounds of English. No adult could have made those cooing, intonation-laden sounds, alive with breath, clumsy in their execution, shot through with shrieks of pleasure.

He is thirty-two weeks old. If I weren't his father but had to guess at his age from these sounds, I would have said not younger than twenty-nine weeks and not older than thirty-five. To make such guesses is now part of my job.

David does not sound different from the way his older sister sounded at the same age; nor different from hundreds of other well babies whose voices and cries, laughter and little grunts I have listened to at the Children's Hospital Medical Center of Boston, and the baby sounds recorded by my colleagues in Japan, New Guinea and Brazil.

It was the regularity with which the various types of noises appear in a child's development which intrigued me years ago and eventually led me into an area of research as fascinating as the unraveling of the history of man himself, and as fraught with suspense as any thriller.

The first question to be answered by my investigations at Children's Hospital was whether my original observations were valid. Do healthy children go through the same noise-making stages at a given age?

Mothers constitute the most ancient corps of researches of human development. Long before Dr. Gesell had published learned books on the sequence of developmental events in the healthy child, mothers knew what to expect of their babies at given ages. But strangely enough, neither mothers nor the world's experts on child development paid much attention to the regularity of noises babies make as they grow up. Yet these very noises, together with the baby's ability to attend to the spoken word, seemed to me to be the most important factor in the evolution of modern man. So I began making tape recordings of sounds of children ranging in age from seven days to ten years. The material grew by leaps and bounds, and a sizable library of tape recordings was established containing samples of the sounds of well children, of children with various diseases, of mentally retarded children and of children born deaf.

Over the years many interesting and important discoveries were made. For instance, when I examined the development of sounds and the onset of speech in normal, healthy children I found that there are regular sequences of changes and that the development of sounds and speech is usually (but not always) accompanied by definite achievements in bodily movements. By the time a child can pull himself to a standing position he makes babbling sounds that resemble syllables of the grown-up language; by the time he can stand alone and is good at creeping he has a couple of words he can use consistently. After he is quite good at walking he has a speaking vocabulary of some twenty words and he understands four times as many. By two years his coordination and strength are good enough to enable him to walk stairs, one foot at a time, and at the same time he begins to make phrases out of the words he knows. From this time on, language develops much more rapidly and dozens of new words are learned every week. At three he can carry on a good conversation and it becomes a more common problem to get him to be quiet than to talk.

The simultaneous development of language skills and bodily movements made me wonder what the relationship between the two might be. Could one be the cause of the other? I looked through my records of normal children and compared them with children with various abnormalities. There was one little fellow, whom I shall call Fred, who had been diagnosed as a mongoloid—a form of mental retardation caused by an abnormality within every cell of the body. The records indicated that he was late in sitting (twelve months), late in standing (twenty months) and late in walking (thirty months). His sounds and speech development were also late. By twenty months he did not have a single word but was babbling with intent and conviction, sounding like a child who could say something but the words were all foreign. By twenty-eight months Fred could say Mama and Daddy, but his speech did not begin to develop properly until after he could run around efficiently, negotiate curves without falling and, in short, be comfortable on his feet. By this time he was four and a half. But now many new words were acquired every month and he was making fairly sudden but good progress. By seven his language was as good as that of an average four-year-old and by eleven he hardly ever made a mistake. The only difference between his language and that of other children was that he spoke a little faster and sloppier, which made him somewhat hard to understand. His parents and a speech therapist were unable to cure him of this habit.

Fred's story interested me very much. I noticed that his language learning fell into the same pattern as that of normal children, except that everything took much longer; he was a retarded child.

Subsequently I studied about one hundred retarded children and found that most of them begin language after they have learned to walk and, generally, that the same relationship holds for this group as for other children. In most individuals, language develops no faster and no slower than walking, running, hand coordination and other bodily movements. However, not all retarded advanced to the exceptionally high level Fred did. In many instances, both coordination and speech were slower to begin with and never devoloped beyond a certain stage.

This observation suggested that both the development of language and the development of coordination might be related to a common, more fundamental process, that of growth and maturation. In children where the general rate of development is slowed down, the correspondence between language and coordination still remains the same as in normal children. A retarded child may not start walking until after his second birthday; nor will his vocabulary expand until he is quite competent on his feet.

However, the correspondence between walking and the onset of speech is sometimes disarranged. One of my little friends, Gordon, was a perfectly healthy specimen, bright as a button, whose command of English at two years was as good as any three-year-old's but he had barely begun to take his first steps. This happens every now and then and should give no cause for alarm. There are children whose fundamental maturational process is normal in rate, but for one reason or another their muscles take longer than usual to gather strength and, thus, their walking may be slow in coming while their speech develops satisfactorily. Walking will usually develop in due course, and a pediatrician can readily explain the situation to the worried mother.

Eddie's case, also rare, illustrates some of the variations in developmental patterns. Eddie, in contrast to Gordon, could sit at six months and toddle happily through the apartment by the time he was one year old. There was never any question about his health or intelligence. At the age of two, however, it became apparent that he was slow in speaking. In fact, he was still not using words. However, it was obvious that he could understand speech as well as any other child the same age. The parents were, understandably, worried about this and consulted a pediatrician who ordered a number of tests to be made. Nothing abnormal was found except what the parents already knew—he was slow in speaking. The doctor wisely advised patience, certain that the child was not retarded; this had been demonstrated by the tests. The next year proved the physician correct. Eddie began to talk by the time he was three. At first he was very difficult to understand and the parents once more asked their doctor whether Eddie ought to have speech therapy.

This is a controversial question. Some authorities would have advised Eddie's parents to engage a speech correctionist, but their physician knew of a child who had been sent for speech lessons at the age of three and who had become very shy and self-conscious about his substandard speech habits during the course of the treatment. This same child's parents had continually corrected him at home—an undesirable practice. Eddie, on the other hand, received no special help even though his intelligibility was far from perfect. Nevertheless, in my periodic examinations of this child, I noticed slow but constant improvement. By second grade he had overcome his difficulties, apparently with no other help than the powers of natural development within him.

Eddie's case shows us that it is possible, though not common, that walking and coordination, in general, develop at the usual time, whereas language acquisition, alone, lags behind. In most instances this is not a sign of general retardation but of a slowly developing link in the long chain of events that must come together to produce good speech. Here again, nature usually runs its prescribed course and language will come about when the child is maturationally ready for it. I have mentioned the stories of Gordon and Eddie to show that language and coordination are actually not dependent on each other but, instead, that they both depend on a common third factor, namely, an internal process of maturation.

What is actually meant by maturation? Just what is it that must mature? The answer to this is not very difficult to guess: the brain. The brain changes considerably between birth and puberty, when it reaches full maturity. First, there is an impressive change in size and weight. From its initial three hundred and fifty grams, the brain grows to thirteen or fourteen hundred grams, and this growth is far from a simple expansion in size. The internal structure of the brain changes at the same time. Nerve cells move away from one another and come to be less crowded. This makes it possible for processes to be extended from each cell to many other cells. Thus internal connections that are necessary for behavior, such as language, may become established. In addition to anatomical changes, the chemical composition of the brain is also altered. Substances are laid down that existed only in tiny amounts at birth, while other elements are gradually eliminated. It has also been discovered, with the help of modern electronic instruments, that the way the brain functions undergoes considerable modification during infancy and childhood.

Eighty per cent of all of the maturational changes take place during the first two years of life. This is the time of the most rapid development of the brain; during the next two years another

10 per cent of the brain's mature values are attained. After four years of age the rate of brain maturation slows down to a snail's pace and full maturation is not reached until the early teens. Between the ages of twelve and fourteen the development comes to a standstill and almost no further changes take place.

Now let us relate the development of language to the maturational history. The infant's brain appears to be unable to grasp and produce language until it reaches a certain state of maturation, at approximately eighteen to twenty months of age. By about thirty months of age the most perfect period for language formation begins, as the brain reaches an ideal state for learning this skill. This state lasts to about the age of eleven to fourteen years. Throughout this time period, the physical maturity of the brain is about 85 to 95 per cent complete.

Among the most astonishing findings of my investigations at Children's Hospital has been the discovery that the acquisition of a child's first language requires that the brain be almost but not quite "finished," so to speak. Once the brain reaches full maturity in the early teens its ways are set, so that it can no longer become organized for language.

This discovery was made by a careful study of the language disturbances resulting from brain injuries. There is a certain area in the brain which, when injured, interferes with the use of language. An adult person may lose forever the faculty of speech through relatively minor damage to one of the language areas. But a similar injury to a child would result in only temporary language disorder. Within a year or less a child will regain language no matter where his brain injury is located, provided it affects but one side of his brain.

From this type of observation we may conclude that originally, during childhood, many areas in the brain have the capacity to serve language. If one part is destroyed, there are other parts that can carry on with the job. As a person gets older and the brain reaches maturity and settles down to its permanent way of functioning, there is also a process going on inside the brain which we may call specialization. Certain parts specialize for one function, other parts for another. No longer can areas of the brain adapt themselves to functions for which they are not specialized.

Thus, language comes to be localized in specific regions of the brain, and once these regions are destroyed, the brain cannot reorganize itself the way it once did during the formative years, when language is acquired for the first time or reacquired after an injury has destroyed the original language site. Once this brain organization has come about, it may be put to other uses than the acquisition of the first language. For instance, we can learn foreign languages and this facility remains available long after the development of the brain has reached completion.

Language can only come about during a certain phase of brain maturation. But, of course, maturation alone does not cause the child to speak, nor does it solely determine how well he will speak —what words he will learn and use, what kind of typical sentence structure and idea arrangement he will develop, what accent he will hear and take as his own. Maturation also does not determine what role verbal communication will play in the child's emotional and psychological development—how he will use words to interpret and influence his environment.

All these are traits which are first fostered or impeded by the significant influence in a young child's life—principally his parents. All other things being equal, the young child who hears good speech—words well spoken and chosen from a well-stocked vocabulary—will have a head start on the development of such traits.

The converse is also true; it stands to reason that if a young child never hears a word, he cannot know it. And poor speech patterns, as occur in children from deprived backgrounds, have a severely limiting effect on their early intellectual development.

Above and beyond the start of speech, then, which comes about in the due process of maturation, patterns of speech and thoughts are first learned by the child from those who speak to him. What does this imply for most of us parents? First, it means not to worry about start of speech. This accomplishment will occur when the child is ready. For instance, what does it mean if a child is not talking by the age of two and a half? In most cases it means that he will be speaking by the time he is three and a half. Delayed speech does not usually herald mental retardation, though some forms of mental retardation may be accompanied by speech problems. Most types of mental retardation, however, manifest themselves before the age of three and there are always many other signs that indicate retardation long before the speech problems are discovered.

Growing up consists of a number of roughly simultaneous processes. Sometimes one is a little slower coming than another. Because we are usually much more aware of progress in language acquisition than progress in, say, the child's ability to hold and use a pencil, we don't realize that partial lags are quite common among the total panorama of skills. When the cause of such lags is a subtle lack of balance in maturational processes—and most lags are—

there is no reason to worry. The child will soon catch up spontaneously.

Growth and maturation are not likely to come to a sudden stop. Special training may, in some cases, do more harm than good because a minor and temporary deviation is treated as if it were a major problem. Children begin to think of themselves as different and parents erroneously consider their children to be abnormal. Once we understand that maturation plays an important role—in fact, sets the pace of language development—it becomes clear that the wait-and-see attitude is often the best. If a minor speech problem, such as poor articulation, persists to the age of seven or eight, there is still enough time to deal with it by means of special corrective measures.

On the other hand, if a child has not yet even begun to use words and simple phrases by his third birthday, he ought to be examined by a pediatrician. The doctor will make sure that the child is in good health. It is very important to rule out the presence of some general disease which might be delaying the development of language, and which could be treated if discovered in time.

Though, in general, we should not worry over common lags and bumps in a child's speech—word repetition, mispronunciations, and so on—we should keep in mind that the way we speak, the words we use, the reasons for which we speak, the emotional tone of our communications, expressing love, anger, approval, disapproval, and so on, influence the way in which our children will put speech and verbal concepts to intellectual and emotional use.

Are there guides to follow, then, things to do or not to do? As in most aspects of our relationship with our children, a loving honesty is the best policy. The practice of respecting speech—of saying what we mean—is important in helping to teach a child to trust verbal communication and to use it honestly and accurately.

Research into language learning and its physical causes is still in its beginning, but the insights gained so far have given us valuable clues about language training and rehabilitation. Meanwhile, parents are granted admission to watch, free of charge, the world's greatest spectacle: the acquisition of the most ancient and most complicated human skill by the least experienced and youngest members in the society of man.

# Chapter Four

# Variation in Human Morphology and Behavior

Cultures around the world vary in the degree to which they allow human, biologically based, differences to express themselves. Each society has standards of accepted behavior which may or may not permit expression of the full range of potential behavior of which its members are capable. This is not to imply that individuals are biologically highly specified; it is merely to point out that human organisms are highly variable, and that, in fact, we do not all march to the same drummer. Anthropologists attempt to see an individual as a whole organism, avoiding "body-soul" kinds of distinctions. A person's behavior is obviously not determined wholly by his biology, but certain predispositions undoubtedly exist and can be measured. The extent to which these predispositions will express themselves depends of course on the social and physical environment in which the individual must operate. The fact is that no two people are alike and that any culture is a leveling device which makes it *appear* that individuals are really quite similar. Those persons who are indisputably different are too easily regarded as pathological on the basis of qualitative, value-motivated rationalizations rather than statistical or functional reasoning.

## HOW YOUR CHILDREN GROW

*Wilton M. Krogman, as told to Anne Selby*

Wilton M. Krogman, a professor in the Division of Graduate Medicine, University of Pennsylvania, is a physical anthropologist specializing in the growth and development of children.

He was seven years old. He stood straight and still in the narrow doorway leading into my office. His eyes were big and bright, with just a little look of fear in them. He didn't flinch when his mother said to him, "Come along, maybe the doctor can tell us what to do about you." But he blushed when she added, "He's the runt of his class, and we want to know if there is something you can do to make him grow."

I beckoned to the boy, and he came to me. I perched him on my desk, this well-built, nice-looking youngster, and I caught an ankle in my hand. I nodded to him like the fifty-eight-year-old professor I am, and slowly his look of fear was replaced by one of curiosity. With mock seriousness I studied his foot and pinched the toe of his shoe. He filled that shoe, all right, and it was big for his age.

"Do you have a dog?" I asked. He shook his head. "Do you like dogs?" He jerked his head "yes" and grinned. I told about a puppy I'd seen at a friend's house the night before. "He's going to be a big dog," I said, "because he's got big paws. And you know what? When you grow up, you're going to be a fairly big man—because your feet are fairly big for your size right now. And one thing's for sure, boys and puppies grow up to their feet."

His mother looked at me, aghast, and opened her mouth to speak. I held up my hand and quickly said, "We're going to take some measurements of your fine son and talk with you and his father. You'll find that what I've told him is true." I didn't tell her then—although you may be sure I told her privately later—that calling her son a runt was more harmful and insulting than she could know.

---

From *The Saturday Evening Post*, July 14, 1962, pp. 50–53. Reprinted by permission of the authors.

## Sons Taller Than Fathers

In the past twelve years I have kept detailed records of nearly 4,000 children, and there are some things I know about how your child is going to grow. For example, your normal, healthy son will be an inch or more taller than you, his father. And, mother, the same is true of your daughter. Your children will mature sexually earlier than you did. Why? Because American youngsters are not only growing taller, they are growing up faster.

Nevertheless the height to which your child grows is determined by his or her inherited capacity—and there is no medicine, no "shot," no drug of any kind that will spur growth beyond the limits nature has set for the individual.

There is a crude rule of thumb you can use to forecast your child's height at eighteen or nineteen. Simply take the child's measurement at age of two, double it and you will be within an inch or so of final height. Some years ago a group of scientists tested this rule with 100 boys—ninety-nine of them at maturity were within a half inch of the forecast.

## Miss America Not Average

But why all this preoccupation with height? The answer is simple—Americans make a cult of size. We're in love with an ideal—men should be tall and muscular, and women should be petite and well-rounded. But the measurements of this year's Miss America—35-24-35—are certainly not average dimensions, for the truth is that all women aren't beauty queens any more than all men are built like college halfbacks. Actually some of us are tall, some short, some fat and some skinny.

Isn't it only natural that our children are going to be the same? But I have found that this is a tremendously difficult thing for parents to accept.

It isn't hard to understand why parents who come to me are mostly worried about boys who appear too short for their age, or girls who seem too big. But there have been times when I have been asked about boys who apparently have grown too much, too fast. In these cases it is often helpful to refer to the newspapers' sports pages, where there are stories about the so-called giants of basketball who stand six-eight, six-ten and taller. Most of these players are many inches taller than their fathers. Why? Because of the natural variability of our species. In every generation there have been such rare examples of extreme tallness. But the "why" of those cases is not the major question about growth. The real question is: Is our race getting bigger, and is there any limit to man's growth pattern?

I can't answer with scientific exactness. But we have learned from evolution that all species seem to have a size boundary. And so it is with man. There is no question that man's curve of tallness is increasing—about an inch per generation. But I believe man's boundary is about six feet. That gives us about two inches to go. Of course, we shall continue to produce our giant athletes who seem to go into the stratosphere. They are not freaks. I have measured some of these boys. Almost without exception I have found them to be well-developed, well-proportioned in every regard. They are far bigger than the average, but they are within the range of the normal. And it has been only recently that we have understood what the pattern of the normal is.

Fifteen years ago the Graduate School of Medicine of the University of Pennsylvania, where I am a professor of physical anthropology, decided it was time that we studied the growth pattern of the normal child in the Greater Philadelphia area. For too long and in too many quarters we had come to think of growth as interesting only in terms of the ill, the abnormal, the freaks and the obese. Yet how can we know about the unusual when we have no standard for the usual? In other words, how much could we tell about the effect of illness on growth if we didn't study the healthy, the normal youngster on the road to maturation?

### New Concepts of Growing

Those were some of the questions we wanted to answer. We scientists at Penn weren't alone in seeking answers. In California, in the Midwest, in New England and in other sections of the country fine work has been, and is being, done. And as a result I think we have learned new concepts—and a new understanding of the whole business of growing.

At the Child Growth Research Center—sponsored by the University of Pennsylvania and Children's Hospital in Philadelphia and aided in part by a United States Public Health Service grant—we have taken 50,000 X-rays of children at various ages. With the cooperation of the Board of Education and the Catholic Archdiocese of Philadelphia, we have gone into our city's schools and traced the growth pattern of about 1,000 youngsters—boys and girls, white and Negro—from the age of six until they hit their teens. By thus studying a large group of youngsters, we can better understand how each child will grow.

In our packed cabinets of case histories—as well as in our hearts —are the stories, sometimes sad, sometimes heartening, always human, of children and their parents' concern for their growth.

Children are individuals. And their size is their own—inherited from their parents and their parents' parents. One mother in California completely ignored this when she wrote me about her son. He was short, she said, just as she was. She didn't want him to be anything less than a six-footer. She had tried bone meal, extra vitamins and stretching exercises throughout his adolescence—all in hope of making him taller. And all had failed. Her question to me was whether my experience indicated she should consult a surgeon about an operation to double the length of his thigh bones.

There is, of course, no such operation. But you can gather some measure of her anguish from the fact that she would even consider such a procedure. And think too of the torment her son must have known.

Would it reassure her, I wondered, to know the story of my experience with a father who was also concerned about his son's seeming lack of size? He knew that, generally speaking, boys are going to be an inch taller than their tallest parent because of better diet, better medical care and a better life. That wasn't good enough for him.

As he talked to me, I estimated his height—five-foot-three, maybe four. The father, following my eyes, realized what I was doing. He scanned my frame, which is six-foot-five. Interrupting himself, he suddenly said, "You've got to understand something. I was always small. You don't know what it is to be small, the runt at school, in college and at work. Did you ever think what it would be like to have to look up every time you met anyone over fourteen years old? Well, I know about that, and I don't want it for my boy."

## Father Thinks Too Big

There was nothing wrong with his son's growth pattern. The problem in that family was the father's attitude. His son was a fine youngster and well put together. We could foretell that he would be a couple of inches taller than his father at maturity. But the father was trying to achieve through his son a life he had wanted for himself and never had—that of a tall, robust man, maybe the star tackle on his college football team. He had to understand that he had a new—and big—job in helping his son grow up. One thing he certainly had to do was stop talking about size as though it were the only requirement for happiness and success.

For example, I am what the books call an unusually tall man. But that never helped me pass an examination in college and, just as you do, I know that the achievement of a happy life requires more than height in any man.

In the various studies that have been made, we have learned that there have been some changes in our children's growth pattern since 1900. We know that a boy born in 1950 was the same length at birth as a boy born in 1900. But three-year-old boys measured during the 1950's were two inches taller than those of the early 1900's, and fifteen-year-old boys were four inches taller. Youngsters today, however, slow down in late adolescence— and finally, at full growth, end up about an inch taller. Better environment contributes to this speed-up.

But basically I am not concerned with how tall a boy or girl is— say, on the child's tenth birthday. What I work with is the biological age. Let me illustrate.

A ten-year-old boy was brought to our growth center. He measured a bare four feet—short for his age. His parents were concerned. We X-rayed one of his hands and a knee. There was a time when we X-rayed eleven parts of the skeleton to determine biological age, the scientific term for the level of development. But we now know that the hand, with its fifty telltale points of bone growth, and the knee are the best gauges of bone growth. Our plates on this particular ten-year-old showed us that he had the hand and knee of an eight-year-old. His parents wanted to know if this meant he was dwarfed. Of course it didn't, it simply meant that their fretting about his size had been needless. Instead of having eight or less years of growth left, as some of his bigger ten-year-old classmates had, this youngster had about ten. He'd catch up and probably pass some of the larger boys because of his inherited height potential and a longer biological growth period.

I think birthdays are great and should be celebrated with cakes and candles and presents. But they don't mean much in terms of a child's growth. Just because Johnny had his tenth birthday on November 18, 1961, doesn't mean that his bones are ten on that day, or that his growth is the equivalent of ten full years.

Heredity is the great master in the field of growth. But environment certainly plays a role. The well-fed, the well-cared-for, on the average, will have a better chance to achieve their full-growth potential than those who lack the proper physical and mental environment. However, though a poor environment may prevent a child's reaching his full-growth potential, a proper environment can do nothing to increase that potential—nor can drugs. There are short children by inheritance. There are also children who are short because something has interfered with their growth. If I find from the X-rays of a child's hand and knee—and from other linear measurements—that there are disturbances in the bone development, I have a real clue that his shortness is due to something other than his heredity. A health history of the child is compiled. If this child has been chronically or severely ill during the first three years of life, the chances are that illness has stultified growth of the long bones.

Sometimes we come across the problems of nutrition. In either case we refer the youngster to a pediatrician or another medical specialist. As a growth researcher I can tell if bone development is abnormal, but it is the medical men who take over at that point to discover why. Only a qualified medical clinician can prescribe the medication that will enable a child to reach his potential if illness or some glandular deficiency has seriously retarded his growth.

## Cutting Texans Down to Size

One of the best features of working in a big city is the variety of people who live in it. And that variety is important in our studies at the growth center. For example, a youngster whose grandparents came from southern Europe may not have inherited the same physical size as a boy whose forebears came from one of the Scandinavian countries. This racial inheritance is the key factor in why men and women seem to be taller in certain parts of the country.

That issue—sectional differences in size—is frequently raised to me by a home-town booster. Have you met the man from Texas who's sure that the men in the Lone Star State are bigger than any others in the world? I have. And I tell him that I know of no climatic factors or regional dietetic balances that might make a difference in size. I speak to him as a physical anthropologist.

When I look at a map of our country, I see the cities and the states; but I also see something more. I see the areas of concentration of the Swedes and Norwegians, the Danes and those from northwest Germany. Where they have settled, you can expect the men to be tall. And their grandsons and great-grandsons are the tall men of the West. On an average the men of the North Central states—from Ohio west to the Dakotas—are slightly shorter than those in the Northeast, the band stretching from Pennsylvania to

Maine. And where is our man from Texas? A little shorter than the Far Westerner, but taller than the man from the Northeast. And, oh yes, you can put the men of the Southern states with Texans. Differences in average size in various areas of the country are due mainly to the fact that people from the Old World tended to settle with their own kind in the New World.

### Daughters With Big Feet

And so we try to learn as much as we can—not just about home life and parents, but also the ethnic background. But I've found in Philadelphia—and I'm sure it's true all over the country—that talking about ethnic background won't be much consolation to mothers with a certain type of problem. What they are worried about is the size of daughter's feet.

One mother recently told me that she was actually ashamed of her daughter's feet. "She's only thirteen," this mother said, "and already my shoes are too small for her." The legendary basis for her concern is part of our folklore. Remember Twinkletoes? Our ideal for women is petite. It's the ugly stepsister who has feet too big for Cinderella's slipper.

The only word for mothers in such a situation is "relax." Our daughters are getting bigger and along with that go bigger feet. There have always been enough big men to go around, and there always will be. And besides, there are few men indeed who won't take a second look at the stately Junoesque woman.

But in all probability most thirteen-year-old daughters won't develop into Junos. And that isn't what concerns them anyway. What most of them are bothered about is that they're so much taller than the boys they played with last year. What parent hasn't heard this cry about the boy down the street: "But he's such a child! I don't want anything to do with him!"

It's not hard to understand what the girl means. She's young, she's romantic, she has the picture—the man must be tall, taller than she. And because the girl thinks that way, the thirteen-year-old boy down the street has a future. He's not only going to catch up to the girl, he'll probably pass her in height by the time they're both sixteen. And by then he may well be the man she most wants on the other end of the telephone.

Nature sets no metronome by which every child must grow, in the same way, day by day. There is an "average" rate of growth, but 16 per cent of our normal youngsters will reach their full height and weight sooner than the average; and 16 per cent will reach it later.

## Bone Age Is The Clue

I like to think of youngsters as traveling on a broad highway of growth—a highway wide and long enough for each to follow his own way. Let's watch three boys on this road. See how Fred, Jim and Bob grew during a six-year period:

| Height | Fred | Jim | Bob |
|---|---|---|---|
| At age 9 | 49 in. | 54 in. | 56 in. |
| At age 10 | 51 | 56 | 58 |
| At age 11 | 53 | 58 | 60 |
| At age 12 | 55 | 60 | 64 |
| At age 13 | 57 | 65 | 67 |
| At age 14 | 60 | 69 | 69 |

These ages, however, are in terms of birthdays. They are not the real clue to how tall these boys are going to be at maturity. The telltale eye of the X-ray machine is the real tip-off. So when we X-rayed Fred's hand and knee, we found that his bone age was more than a year less than his chronological age. Significance? He'll be growing for a year past his supposed point of maturity at about the age of eighteen.

Bob is a different story. When he cut the cake for his fourteenth birthday, his bone age was already past fifteen. So we know that he'll probably stop growing around seventeen. The figures show that he stretched most between his birthday ages of eleven and twelve, then he slowed down. What about Jim? He's a tie—his chronological age and his bone age are just about the same. Our studies showed that he'll be the tallest of the three.

## Genes Dictate Heights

None of us grows in a straight, even line. We stretch, we fill out. And when your son is stretching, his best friend may be filling out. Vice versa too. But if you're one who likes rules of thumb to make predictions, here's an interesting idea that's supported by the statistics. In the years after birth, head and neck double in size from birth to maturity; the trunk triples, the arm length increases by four and the legs by five.

If you ask me why children grow as they do, I could say that their growth is a function of time linking with structural or configurational changes. What that means is, I really don't know. But we do know that each of us has genes for height and shortness. If your father was tall and your mother short, you'll carry genes for each; but it's the inheritance from the taller parent that predominates. That doesn't mean that very tall men will always have very tall children. We humans carry a mixture of contrasting genes for being tall, for being short, for being light—and dark—of complexion. The results of a child's mixture cannot be predicted with certainty. But obviously the chances are that taller parents will have taller children.

No scientist wants to see any child neglected on the road to maturity. But to the healthy normal youngsters whom I have seen, I say, "You will grow—in your own way." And to their parents I put my plea, "Don't judge your son or daughter harshly simply because he does not fit into what you think is a proper growth pattern."

Thoreau, in *Walden,* had one thought I like to remember: "If a man does not keep pace with his companions, perhaps it is because he hears a different drummer. Let him step to the music which he hears, however measured or far away."

So should it be with our children. Let them grow, each in his own way, in his own sweet time.

## ANATOMY IS NOT DESTINY

Sex, according to Freud, is a biological drive clamoring for gratification from the moment of birth. In normal human beings, its imperatives can be throttled by the rules of morality, but they can never realy be denied. In the current issue of *Trans-Action* magazine, sociologists William Simon, 38, and John Henry Gagnon, 37, argue heretically that Freud was mistaken: the sex drive is not strong but weak, and can be easily resisted. Moreover, sex forms no integral part of man's inherited endowment; sexual behavior is something he must learn.

Where Freud went wrong, the authors contend, was in interpreting the sexuality of children with grown-up eyes. "It is dangerous to assume," they write, "that because some childhood behavior appears sexual to adults, it must be sexual." Parents who catch a young child playing with his genital organs will instinctively define the act as masturbation; to the child, the experience may well be a nonsexual experience of bodily discovery. Nonetheless, the child is taught, directly or indirectly, that certain activities are sexual in nature as soon as he is considered mature enough to absorb the lesson.

## The Beast Within

Gagnon and Simon argue that Freud's error has been compounded by a tendency to confuse the adult obsession with sex, which is powerful, and sex education, which is incessant, with the sex drive—which is neither. "The whole imagery of sexuality as 'the beast within' was true because society defined it as true," says Simon.

In the authors' view, a much stronger case can be built on the premise that sexual expression is primarily a social phenomenon. Far from asserting a primordial urge, it varies from culture to culture and from individual to individual. In Polynesia, what the West calls foreplay is epilogue, not prologue, to coitus. Gagnon notes that for some writers—among them Lawrence, Hemingway and Mailer—sex is as much a political as a procreative process; Lawrence's *Lady Chatterley's Lover* struck a calculated blow against the morality of the time. To prostitutes, it is only a livelihood, and frequently no more erotic than punching a clock. Some clerical celibates abstain for life without showing any adverse physical or psychological effects.

## A Few Universals

Gagnon and Simon developed their Victorian-sounding conclusions amid the welter of sexual data still accumulating at the Kinsey Institute, where they worked together for three years. Gagnon is now with the sociology department at the Stony Brook, L.I., campus of the State University of New York; Simon is program director in sociology and anthropology at Chicago's Institute for Juvenile Research. Both writers found that Freud's views on sex are not only misbegotten but unrealistic and sadly out of date. One of the reasons that his theories still command popular respect "is that in a word fraught with instability and change, one wants to be able to hold onto a few universals. Freud tried to define an inner core of constants in man." Among them he placed the sex drive, and in a period of rapid change, it can be comforting to know that some things do not change at all. "But a man's anatomy doesn't become his destiny," Gagnon says. "Man is primarily a social being, unlike the animals, and his destiny is determined socially, not biologically or instinctually."

# BODY IMAGE—MALE AND FEMALE

*Richard M. Kurtz*

Richard M. Kurtz is a professor of clinical psychology at Washington University.

The human body has been an object of study ever since the time of Hippocrates. Many investigators, for example, have suggested that there are connections between a person's body shape and his temperament and behavior. Thus people who tend to be fat were supposed to be phlegmatic; middle-girthed, muscular mesomorphs were supposed to be inclined toward extroversion, and to make up the majority of criminals.

But what impression do we get of our own bodies, and how does this affect our self-images, our feelings of worth and virility, our happiness and our behavior? In spite of the psychological importance of the answers to such questions, very few people have ever done research in this area.

Now it seems reasonable to postulate that a person is concerned, often absorbed, with these impressions and attitudes about the appearance of his body. It also seems reasonable that he would judge these impressions along three major dimensions:

—First, *value*. Is his body, as he ses it, a "good" or "bad" kind of body? How good or bad?

—Second, *potency*. Would he consider it strong or weak, and how strong or weak?

—Third, *activity*. Does he look upon himself, and his body build, as essentially as active or passive kind of body, and how active or passive?

These questions were put to my subjects—89 men and 80 women, all young, white college students, and most of them middle-class. Using a seven-point scale, they were asked to rate themselves on 30 different body concepts, such as "size of my arms," and "color of my hair." The results were broken down according to sex, according to the general size of the subject (large, medium, small),

From *Trans-Action* Magazine, Vol. 6 (Dec. 1968), pp. 25–7. Copyright © December, 1968, by *Trans-Action* Inc., New Brunswick, New Jersey.

according to the subject's general build (leptomorph—thin and narrow; mesomorph—medium muscular; eurymorph—wide and squat).

From my findings it seems plain that people—especially women —do have general, global attitudes toward their body builds, and that they do have opinions about whether their bodies are good or bad, strong or weak, active or passive.

As is evident to almost everybody, men and women are built differently, and are aware of the difference—although there is some overlap, especially these days. Women especially are aware of their distinguishing characteristics, and in considerably greater detail than men.

A person's attitudes and expectations about his body are, as a matter of fact, closely related to his sex. Our society seems far more conscious and more admiring of the female form than of the male. Judging by advertisements, for instance, it must be impossible to sell cars, Coca-cola, yens, and blood tonic unless a girl in a bathing suit goes along.

A great awareness about one's bodily appearance is obviously more acceptable in women than men—a finding supported by common observation. It is part of being a woman in our society to try to "be attractive"—to focus attention on the parts of the body that are well-proportioned and sexually stimulating, and to try to play down attention on those that are not. Men are not supposed to take such an obvious and active interest in their bodily appearances.

## Women Like Their Bodies More Than Men Do

It seems logical, then, to hypothesize that a woman has a more clearly differentiated body concept than a man—that women draw finer distinctions between the qualities of parts of their fingers than men do about theirs. This hypothesis turned out to be true. Consistent with this, women tend to value their bodies more than men do; they tend to show more approval of what their full-length mirrors tell them.

This finding clearly contradicts the psychoanalytic theory that women have a lower evaluation of their bodies than men because of "penis envy." The women in this study, whatever their secret and suppressed feelings might be, and whatever the findings of other cultures, indicated that they had a higher evaluation of their bodies.

On the other hand, since muscular strength, aggression, and dominance are considered desirable, masculine characteristics, men should rate their bodies higher in potency than women do—and this was confirmed.

Among men the large mesomorphs—being not fat or thin, and inclined toward muscle—liked their own bodies better than all other male types did. They also thought themselves the most active. This fits in with our conventional idea of the he-man. But this picture, especially for potency, was not consistent down the line. Thus, large mesomorphs and small mesomorphs thought their bodies more potent than did any of the varieties thin men (leptomorphs). But so did the large and medium euryomorphs, the squat men—more so, in fact, than the medium mesomorphs did! These findings are tentative, and seem a little confused. But what they may indicate is that men not only associate potency with physical strength, but also with sheer bulk—reflected by a similar association, or confusion, in the English language, in which "stout" can be used to mean either fat or strong, but always means bulky.

Among women, the large, thin leptomorphs liked their bodies more than all other types liked theirs. The eurymorphs—usually broad-hipped, big-breasted—generally saw their bodies as more potent. Again, whether this self-evaluation came from an association of bulk with strength, or whether "potency" was considered symbolic of sexual or reproductive capacity in women, must be left for a future study. But however potent the fat women were, the thin women considered themselves most desirable, an opinion generally shared in our nation.

Several investigators have shown that college and non-college men and women tend to look down upon the thin and the stout in favor of the mesomorphs, to attribute more undesirable personality attributes to people with extreme body builds. In people's stereotypes, the skinny are usually pinched and mean, and the fat are usually gluttonous, unattractive, and insensitive. Do leptomorphs and eurymorphs themselves consider their body builds less desirable? The men do; but the women, as noted, do not.

Investigators seem to agree that the eurymorph—being broad and usually overweight—is basically more passive, calm, and lethargic. His opposite number—the thin, narrow leptomorph—is often characterized as active, excitable, and tense, with a faster reaction time. Logically, I expected the leptomorphs to judge themselves as more active than the eurymorphs. But this, strangely enough, was not true—for either sex.

Now, in American society it is apparent that height is related to how people feel about their bodies. Consider the demand of small men for shoes that will increase their height. In our culture, height in men, among other physical characteristics, is associated with dominance, self-confidence, and leadership. Many women admire tall men because they can look up to them. Shortness of stature is seen by most people as a liability for a man. And a large body size is seen by many as reflecting an image of dominance and strength. People of large body size are therefore assumed to be more powerful than small people.

## Build and Size Differ in Relevance

Generally, this hypothesis checked out. But there were distinct and significant sexual variations. Tall, thin men put the lowest values on their bodies; tall, thin females the highest. And, as previously mentioned, though the large, male mesomorphs had the greatest belief in the potency of their type of body build, with women it was the large, fat eurymorphs who did. In other words, body build and body size do not have parallel relevance for men and women.

Instead of discussing all the results of this study, however, I would rather discuss what it missed—to indicate future directions for possible research.

No straightforward attitude measure can begin to reveal the complexity and richness of the feelings—conscious and unconscious—that people have about their bodies. One sure way to lose the personal and individual is to analyze central tendencies between groups, as has been done in this study. This may be experimentally necessary—but we should understand what we are losing. Perhaps we can restore some of this richness through depth interviews, or projective techniques.

And what of a person's attitudes and fantasies about the inside of his body, and its products? How does this affect his overall view of what he, and his body, are?

It is also clear that the body dimensions used in this study are not the last word in precision. Might not the actual amount of fat, and its distribution, have more meaning for a person's attitude toward his body than simply the designation of "leptomorph" or "eurymorph?" Further, white college students 18 to 23 years old are obviously not a representative population. In this group there was little significant difference in the findings because of the age spread—but middle-aged and poor people almost certainly regard their bodies differently. The middle-aged—especially women—might well have shown greatest dissatisfaction with their appearances, and lower ratings on potency and activity.

Perhaps to some extent we all live in the past. Do middle-aged people tend to see themselves as straighter, thinner, and less gray—as they were in earlier days and in old photographs? Paul Schilder has speculated that the rapid physical changes during puberty and adolescence may result in a body-concept lag, with the changing body outstripping the mind's grasp of it. Puberty usually does disturb a teenager's attitudes and impressions. Anna Freud has reported that many adolescents develop a sharp increase in puritanical and ascetic attitudes toward their bodies—perhaps indicating a lack of acceptance of the changes, and perhaps also indicating a lower evaluation of their bodies. But this was not explored in my study.

And what of race? Do Negroes have the same attitudes toward their bodies as whites have? Do many really think that black is beautiful, or have they—as Erik Erikson believes—internalized white standards to the extent of downgrading their own distinctive bodily traits? (A recent survey found that whites often consider Negroes "bad," "potent," and "passive.")

To what extent do a person's body attitudes affect—or become associated with—his other concepts about himself? Does the large, male mesomorph, the physical cock-of-the-walk, also tend to regard himself as superior in intellect, athletics, creative ability—to consider himself Abraham Maslow's all-round superior being?

This study, unfortunately, has not been able to answer these questions. It *has* demonstrated that people do have total body impressions that have important consequences. It has shown that, for the population tested, there are meaningful and often complex relationships between these attitudes and sex, body size, and body build. And perhaps it has also demonstrated that down this path of discovery—relating how people see their bodies with how they see themselves—may lie some rich field of understanding not yet explored.

For Further Reading

Paul Schilder, *The Image and Appearance* (New York: International University Press, 1950) contains many of the early psychoanalytic speculations about disturbances in body attitude and body perspectives.

Ernest Kretschmer, *Physique and Character* (2d ed.; London: Kegan Paul, 1936) presents the classical statement of the belief in constitutional ties between body form and personability. While largely discredited as a scientific theory, this book contains an excellent historical review of this area.

Seymore Wapner and Heinz Werner, etc., *The Body Percept* (New York: Random House, 1965) is a comprehensive selection of nontechnical articles dealing primarily with the perceptual aspects of the body attitude area.

# OUR PINT-SIZE ANCESTORS

*Vladimir Vlastovsky*

Vladimir Vlastovsky is a biologist specializing in child development at the Institute for Child and Adolescent Hygiene of the USSR Academy of Science.

Scientists in the economically advanced countries have been struck by the fact that children for the past one hundred years have been growing and developing faster and are taller when they reach adulthood.

Doctors in many countries are working to determine whether this accelerated growth is actually harmful for the health of young people or not. There are many educationists and psychiatrists who now feel that a reappraisal and indeed a sweeping revision is called for with regard to our present ideas about the physical and psychological development of children, as well as the age when sex education should begin. The rapid growth of children is also having widespread repercussions in unexpected domains like the size of school desks and other furniture, sizes of junior models of clothes for boys and girls, etc.

Reproduced from the February, 1966 edition of the *UNESCO Courier*.

In the past 30 or 40 years it has been found that the average height of newborn babies has increased by almost half an inch (one centimeter) and weight at birth has also shown a slight rise. Newborn babies now double their weight one month earlier than in the past.

Compared to children of the second half of the nineteenth and the turn of the present century the height-to-weight ratio of today's youngsters has increased much more rapidly. The differences are particularly noticeable at the age of puberty.

Further information reveals that the average height of . . . 13-year-old boys has increased by almost one inch (2 centimeters) in a decade and their weight by nearly three and a half pounds (1½ kilos). Amongst boys in the 14 to 16 year age group the rate of increase is even greater.

Figures on 15-year-old boys studying in Soviet vocational schools and boys of the same age who worked in Russian industry in 1822 reveal that today's youth are on average seven and a half inches (19.5 cms) taller and thirty-five pounds (16 kilos) heavier than their counterparts of 150 years ago. A less marked increase has also been noted amongst girls.

Comparing the growth rate of children living in towns and rural areas in various parts of the world it has been found that children in large cities grow and develop faster than youngsters in small towns, and small town children in turn develop faster than those in rural areas. In some countries a difference has been observed in the development rate of city children belonging to different social groups.

One consequence of the increase in height and weight of youngsters has been an acceleration of the advent of puberty. A century ago European girls attained puberty on average at the age of 16 or 17. Now it is usually 13 or 14. Similar findings have been made for boys.

Other indications of accelerated development in children today are the earlier cutting of teeth and the ossification of different parts of the skeleton, including the cartilages at the end of the long bones —an important factor determining body growth.

This accelerated growth also means that children now stop growing at an earlier age. In the past, growth continued until the age of 18 or 20; today most youngsters are fully grown at 17 or 18, and girls at 16. This does not prevent them, however, from growing to be taller than their parents.

Investigations carried out in the Soviet Union show that for the past 60 years young people have been maturing at least two years sooner than before, so that a 15-year-old boy of today is as mature physically and sexually as a 17-year-old youth was at the start of the century.

Research in many countries, such as France, Italy, Poland, Czechoslovakia, Great Britain and the United States, indicates that young people are now six to eight inches (15–20 cms) taller on average when they reach the age of puberty than those who lived a hundred years ago. The average height of adults, during this same period, has risen by three to four inches (7–10 cms).

Many theories have been advanced in an attempt to explain this quickened growth, among them the effects of extra sunshine, improved diet, prenatal care and even the stepped up pace of city living. In my opinion the chief cause is probably genetic in nature. In 1924 a Soviet scientist, Victor Bunak, in analysing changes in the height of young men of military age from several European countries suggested that height and growth were not only influenced by economic and dietary factors but also by the genetic changes resulting from the intermarriage of different populations.

There can be no doubt however that the material conditions of life strongly determine the growth rate and are instrumental in favoring or retarding the genetically predetermined potential for growth.

As to the psychological acceleration noted in modern youth, all research conducted in this domain points to the fact that the children of our times are intellectually more developed than those of 50 or 100 years ago. But scientists do not always agree in their assessments of children's capacity for work or their ability to think critically.

Some scientists consider that physical and intellectual development in children proceed simultaneously and in harmony, while others maintain that the intellectual growth lags behind physical growth.

The question naturally arises as to whether such accelerated growth has a negative effect on the health of the growing generation. The widely-held theory that an early development of the body leads inevitably to premature old age and a shortened life span has never been confirmed. To the contrary, it appears that today's women, aside from reaching sexual maturity earlier, retain the capacity for childbearing three to five years longer.

Furthermore, some problems of eyesight characteristic of old age develop five to eight years later now than was the case a hundred years ago.

Nevertheless, some scientists remain apprehensive about the

effect of this accelerated growth on health. They cite cases of spine deformations, a tendency toward asthenia (weakness and fatigue), an increase in the number of children suffering from rheumatism at an early age and numerous cases of hypertension (high blood pressure). So far these apprehensions are insufficient for any final conclusions but they merit the attention of biologists and doctors.

Educators ask: Is this early development good or bad; should we be pleased by it, ignore it, or try to slow it down? There is still no exact answer.

Did this acceleration really start in the 1830's, or is it rather a process that has been taking place since the beginning of mankind and which is gradually gaining momentum?

It appears that the changes in man's growth have their ups and downs—or so some anthropologists and medical researchers feel. In the areas where archeological and paleo-anthropological research have been able to trace successive populations over millenia, scientists note that the size of men underwent much slower —and more variable—modifications.

There have also been variations in the age of puberty among European women. It apparently was the same from ancient times until the fifteenth century. The women of Southern Europe reached puberty at 14, those of Northern Europe at 15. Then it became increasingly late until, by the end of the eighteenth century, it was reached at 17 or 18. But since the 1830's the trend has been reversed sharply.

Where does the overall acceleration tendency stand today? Since it is slowing in some countries and social groups, one can assume that in the economically advanced regions it will come to a halt in the next 20 to 25 years. In the developing countries, on the other hand, the next few decades of improving economic and cultural standards will be accompanied by an acceleration in the growth rate.

Will we then see a period of relative stability, or will there be a decrease in growth and development? At present, it is difficult to judge.

# Chapter Five

# Inferences About Man From the Non-Human Primates

Some investigators believe that the study of behavior of nonhuman primates will provide insight on the nature of modern man. They reason that since *Homo sapiens* shares an ancestry with monkeys and apes he must also share some of their behavior, or at least the predispositions for certain kinds of behavior, even though in the sociocultural context of human societies these basic primate patterns may be variously disguised. This same line of reasoning has appealed to novelists, playwrights and even psychologists who quite predictably ascribe some of humanity's worst behavior to "the ape within."

While most anthropologists have not just joined that chorus, very respected members of their ranks have advocated the study of free-ranging nonhuman primates as a possible source of information on the general nature of our now extinct hominid (i.e., on the line of man) ancestors. While these anthropologists harbor no beliefs that modern man had monkey or ape ancestors *per se,* they do believe that man was the most recently evolved primate and that the other primates do in varying degree resemble some of those ancestors of man. They base this belief on the fossil record which indicates that monkey-like forms do pre-date hominid forms. They also think that human evolution has been unusually rapid compared to that of other members of the order Primates, so that some early hominids from the Oligocence or Miocene are actually more like today's apes and monkeys than like modern man. Since fossil hominids are scarce, and since bones and a few artifacts, even when they are found, provide inadequate evidence of behavior, we must make do with information from the living primates and become expert at extrapolating backwards. Admittedly that is shaky business, and most anthropologists have been quite cautious in their speculations on the origins of various human traits.

# ETHOLOGY: THAT ANIMAL THAT IS MAN

What is man? To this age-old question, the social sciences are now proposing some extraordinarily complicated new answers. First and foremost, man is an animal—but he is neither the end product of evolution nor much more than a mediocre biological success. The body he inhabits is primitive, at least 50,000 years out of date. Basically, he is one of the world's most aggressive beasts, who, the scientists say, fundamentally enjoys torturing and killing other animals, including his fellow man in the sport known as war.

He considers himself more or less monogamous. But, according to the new scientific theory, he is not really, and he was never intended to be. His hormones urge him to copulate with his sisters and daughters, just as all other mammals generally do. But his cortex tells him to barter his females to strangers for political advantage, and he listens. He would like to murder his father, but this natural impulse is cunningly suppressed: one day he will be the old man. He feels as strong an affinity for his buddy as for his wife—or even his mother, once he has been weaned. But, says the expert, the rage and the lust in him are perpetually rampant. Everything he possesses, everything he is, he owes to the intellectual control that stays the trigger finger.

## Flesh and Bone

Such a sober, even cynical analysis of man does not fit well with his image of himself as a civilized and cultured being. Yet within the past decade, this rough vision of man as a relative of the primates one step removed from the jungle has been put forward by a number of behavioral scientists working in such fields as genetics, neurophysiology and primatology. Says anthropologist Robin Fox of Rutgers, whose specialty is the sexual conduct of man the animal: "We are only beginning to understand the implications of extending to behavior the same kind of analysis that has proved

Reprinted from *Time*, the Weekly Newsmagazine, Jan. 17, 1969, pp. 42–3. Copyright Time Inc., 1969.

successful with flesh and bone."

The subject of man as an animal is older than Darwin. But to Darwin's insights into man's evolution, the new approach is adding radical new dimensions. It rejects the view that biology has nothing to do with behavior, and proposes the hypothesis that culture itself has a biological basis. "What we are saying," says Fox, "is that it is highly probable that the species is predisposed to behave in certain ways and that these ways are probably more numerous and specific than has been thought."

One obvious way to learn about these predispositions is to study the behavior of man's nearest neighbors, the monkeys and great apes—and to study them not just in the zoo or laboratory but in their natural habitat. In studying the baboon, for example, Berkeley anthropologist Sherwood L. Washburn and his Harvard disciple, Irven DeVore, are concerned mainly with what this primate can reveal about man. The baboon's hierarchical society, commanded by dominant males, suggests the fundamental pattern to which man's ancestors may have subscribed, long before marriage was invented. So far no primate study has turned up a societal unit that duplicates the human family.

Monogamy, in fact, turns out to be biologically "unnatural." As Fox puts it, "Man is by nature promiscuous, but works hard in the opposite direction." How then did the family structure evolve? The answer, suggest the ethologists, has a great deal to do with the uncertain history of the development of man's only major biological specialization—his brain. From a scratch start with the simians, this marvelous cultural device grew threefold in man in one million years—an evolutionary rate of unprecedented rapidity. Asks Fox: "Did the growth of the brain lead to the capacity for greater social complexity, or vice versa?"

One widely accepted speculation is that the pressures of survival put a heavy premium on the dawning intelligence of man. The first toolmaker gained an enormous survival advantage over his fellows —and may have asserted it by cornering the local supply of women. This male dominance operated to drive less intellectual males to the periphery of the troop, or tribe: it also served to transmit the toolmaker's genes to the next generation.

Gene Pool

Had early man been naturally monogamous, evolution might not have favored intelligence and the dramatic expansion of the brain. "If every male had been allowed the opportunity to contribute equally to the gene pool," writes Fox, "then we might have been forever stuck as *Homo stupidus*." He and others, notably

Washburn and British ethologist Michael Chance, have devised theories for explaining how the banished, peripheral males might eventually win their spurs.

They had to be both patient and abstemious—qualities that, on examination, involve considerable intelligence. Chance has called this process "equilibration"—defined by Fox as "the ability to control and to time responses, to understand the consequences of one's actions." The foolish peripheral male obeyed only his hormones, invaded the dominant male's harem and was either killed or ostracized. The clever male restrained this impulse and intelligently awaited a fruitful opportunity to topple, replace or succeed the Sultan.

From this conjecture flows a host of fascinating theories. On the ability to inhibit the sex drive, all of civilization may be based. Says Fox: "Control over sex and aggression: feelings about status and personal well-being; group loyalty; conscience and guilt; sensitivity to incestuous impulses; identification with and rebellion against the older generation; possessiveness over females and sexual jealousy; the desire for variety in sex life—all these are part and parcel of the evolution of the brain."

The new investigation of man's animal nature is rather humbling in its impact, but it also goes a long way, in the ethologists' view, to explain why he acts as he does. Canada's Lionel Tiger—who appropriately met Fox at the London Zoo and now works with him at Rutgers—has a theory to explain why men dominate politics. He argues that men are biologically more political than women, in the sense that they have a greater ability for what psychologists call "bonding" or the ability to forge lasting relationships. He suggests that there is an attraction of man for man that is of the same order of intensity as sex but that exists for political rather than reproductive purposes.

Animal studies can also be used to criticize existing social institutions. In all the lower primates, the education process is informal. Washburn has shown, for instance, that primate curiosity —which in man would be called basic research—comes into play when the animal is well-fed and secure; only then is he in the mood to gratify this intellectual need. Similarly, the juvenile ape, observing grownup behavior, mimes it in his games. For this pleasurable educational system, modern man has substituted the discipline of the classroom and the material rewards of grades, both of which, in Washburn's view, offend man's basic biological nature.

## Murder and War

Probably the most controversial studies of man and animal—

notably by Konrad Lorenz—have to do with the biology of aggression and its implication for modern society. Evolution indicates that the aggressive instinct tended to preserve order within a tribal structure. But most human aggregates have gone beyond the tribe. And perhaps as an inevitable result, aggression no longer keeps but strains the peace. In man's simpler and less crowded past, aggression was both useful and effective; in man's present, it can lead to such thoroughly unanimal behavior as murder and war.

This is partly because the human animal straddles the past and the present. "It is not only our bodies that are primitive, but also our customs," Washburn writes. "They are not adapted to the crowded, technical world dominated by a fantastic acceleration of scientific knowledge. There is a fundamental difficulty in the fact that contemporary human groups are led by primates whose evolutionary history dictates a strong desire to dominate. Attempts to build personal or international relations on the wishful basis that people will not be aggressive is as futile as it would be to try to build the institution of banking with no auditing on the basis that all employees will be honest."

As the proponents of the new theory themselves admit, it is still only theory. They are not working with fossil teeth and jaws but with habits and customs that naturally left no physical trace. All that they have guessed about man's biological history remains to be proved. But the guesses carry many implications. Perhaps the most significant is that civilization's splendid institutions owe a part of their balance to the wily jungle primate still surviving beneath man's cultural veneer. He is really a part of the design. His contribution, only just beginning to be perceived, can be ignored only at the risk of civilization itself.

# THE NAKED-APE CRISIS

*H. F. Ellis*

H. F. Ellis is a professional writer whose topics range from science to football. A regular contributor to *Punch,* his writing appears occasionally in American periodicals.

This is a last-ditch attempt to differentiate myself from a ten-spined stickleback. The thing began when naturalists grew tired

From *The New Yorker* Magazine, March 23, 1968, pp. 129–31. Reprinted by permission; © 1968 *The New Yorker Magazine,* Inc.

of shooting and stuffing the creatures they loved, or pinning them in rows in glass cases, and began peering at them instead in the wild state. Fabre spied on beetles. Eliot Howard spent a lifetime watching warblers through binoculars and came up with his theory of bird territory. Julian Huxley observed crested grebes as they had never been observed before. Konrad Lorenz kept a close eye on jackdaws, geese, and dogs. Niko Tinbergen enlisted in a herring-gull colony. Soon there was scarcely a bird, an ape, a gazelle, a dragonfly whose bowings and scrapings, preening, threats, empurplings, and sac-swellings were not being observed somewhere by somebody. Amid the welter of head-noddings and twig-fiddlings thus brought to light, it was natural that certain resemblances between animal and human behavior should be noted. When a gull pulls furiously at grass because (so they say) it is frustrated by two antagonistic drives, its affinity with a man who lights a cigarette while trying to decide between Scotch and bourbon is fairly clear.

It had not at this stage been suggested that because Horace Walpole decorated Strawberry Hill with colorful Gothic bric-a-brac he was practically indistinguishable from a bowerbird. The differences between man and beast were at first apparent even to the animal-behavior observers, or ethologists, who were at pains to remind their readers that animals were not human. "Let us have none of this anthropomorphism!" they cried, carefully putting quotation marks around any tiresomely humanoid words like "affection," "cruel," or "happy" that had crept unawares into their texts. As recently as 1953, Tinbergen was writing, "It is scarcely necessary to stress the differences in type of organisation between human societies and those of gulls."

It is highly necessary now. Scarcely had these ethologists finished shaking their fingers at sentimentalists who spoke of animals as though they were men when they themselves set to work to prove that men were animals. Zoomorphism became rife. Mr. Robert Ardrey has devoted a whole book to it, coming up with the conclusion that the Italian lives in a *noyau* and bases his home life on that of the sportive lemur, whereas the American, at home in a nation, is more of a howling monkey. Mr. Ardrey himself, when engulfed at the time of Pearl Harbor in a wave of patriotic fervor, hardly knew whether he was a chacma baboon or a roebuck. Zoologist Dr. Desmond Morris, whose book about man, *The Naked Ape,* has lately appeared, seems to be in hardly better case. "The book," he has explained to an interviewer, "deals with sex, fighting, feeding, parental care, exploration, and comfort. They're exactly the same chapter headings I used for my thesis on the 10-Spined

Stickleback. I wanted to demonstrate how alike we all are in certain respects."

I shall not read it. Though I prefer to do my fighting and feeding without constantly comparing myself with a stickleback, these sociological generalizations do not especially alarm me. If it is Mr. Ardrey's territorial imperative that urges me and the rest of my troop to defend ourselves, or if I am called upon, as indicated by Dr. Lorenz, to discharge my aggressive drives after the manner of a dabbling duck, I shall not make an issue of it. It is in the particulars of behavior, rather than the general, that I wish to dissociate myself from the animal kingdom.

"It is tempting," writes Dr. Lorenz, "to interpret the greeting smile [in man] as an appeasing ceremony which . . . has evolved by ritualization of redirected threatening. The friendly tooth-baring of very polite Japanese lends support to this theory. It is also supported by the fact that in genuinely emotional intensive greetings between two friends, the smile surprisingly becomes a loud laugh. On considering one's own feelings it seems incongruous that, on meeting a friend after a long separation, the roar of laughter breaks forth unexpectedly from the depths of instinctive strata of our personality. This behaviour of two reunited human beings must inevitably remind an objective behaviour investigator of the triumph ceremony of greylag geese."

I have not had the good fortune to be present when Dr. Lorenz meets an old friend after a long separation, and cannot tell whether I should be objective enough to be reminded of greylag geese. But I am by no means ready, on the available evidence, to have the smiles of my friends written off as redirected threatening. If the good Doctor had made as intensive a study of long-lost friends as he has of geese, I would give him best. But has he? Ethologists do not dream of making assertions, drawing conclusions, evolving theories about baboons or even three-spined sticklebacks without prolonged observation and experiment. They put rats in mazes and make oyster-catchers sit on square eggs. I have not heard of similar work being done on Italians or old friends. I myself once broke into loud laughter on meeting a brother after years of separation. But there was an extraneous factor, which seemed to me to eliminate my instinctive strata. His face, after a lengthy tour in West Africa, had become unexpectedly round and red, and upon this tropical moon he had chosen to perch a small brown trilby hat. Dr. Lorenz had not thought of that. He had better put a small brown hat on a greylag goose and see what sort of triumph ceremony that evokes.

The horse in my paddock inclines its ears toward me when I call but promptly flicks one of them to the north-northeast if some more interesting sound, such as a power mower, starts up. A Mrs. Dinwiddy, to whom I sometimes speak at sherry parties, undeniably listens with at least one ear to what the couple behind us are saying. An ethologist would at once dismiss her as a horse. But she is not. The point I wish to emphasize, before man has been stripped of every vestige of dignity, is that her ears remain stationary throughout. This lack of overt physical response to stimuli is the shining glory of the human race. We must cling to it.

What is urgently wanted is a close study of human behavior designed to demonstrate how unlike ring-tailed lemurs we all are in certain respects. It must be undertaken by a man objective enough to seek out behavioral norms before leaping to conclusions. He will have a job on his hands, though. It is a great deal more difficult to observe our own species, or order, under the proper conditions than it is to watch lemurs or owls. I had just got my wickerwork blind erected in one of London's public parks, waved goodbye to my assistant, and settled down to watch the behavior patterns of urban courting couples when a helmet was pushed through the flap and its owner asked me what I thought I was up to. With crested grebes, if two persons enter a blind and one goes away, the birds are satisfied and resume their occupations. But policemen can count. So valuable time had to be wasted while I tried to explain the urgent need for statistical proof that the human race, ethologically speaking, differs markedly from the rest of the animal kingdom. "For instance, the ruff," I told him, "when ready to mate, turns white, black, purple, chestnut, or buff round the neck, and develops uncouth ear tufts. I expect to show that that is an awkwardness from which Londoners, in normal circumstances, are free."

"Is that so?" he said.

"Yes," I said. "And what's more, the head of the North African fresh-water fish *Tilapia zillii* becomes velvet black at such times, with turquoise spots, while the throat and chest turn blood red. Even if some ethologists may conceivably be reminded—"

"Binoculars, too, I see," the officer said, making a note of it.

"Naturally. You may not be aware that the American sage grouse, by expansion and contraction of the necksacs during courting, produces a sound that can be heard a mile away on a still morning. For comparative purposes, it is essential to be able to carry out long-range observations. After eating eels—"

"Shocking, this is," he said. "Peeping Tom. It's an offense."

I had been about to tell him, as a further instance of the kind of behavior rarely found in human beings, whether courting or not, that the common heron, *Ardea cinerea*, removes gel slime from its plumage by sprinkling its head and shoulders with a kind of powder secreted in a pocket near the base of the tail. But it was clear by this time that he was the sort of man hardly worth distinguishing from an animal. You get these zoomorphic freaks. "For example," I said instead, trying to find a homelier example, "when feeding her young, does your wife regurgitate half-digested fish?"

He turned so extraordinary a color around the neck that a less objective observer might have supposed he was ready to mate. But I have been long enough at the game to recognize aggression when I see it, whether in stickleback or man. We now had an almost perfect setup for a demonstration of the territorial imperative. The blind was my territory, and so long as I was in it I must be the dominant individual.

The policeman, however, had pretty obviously never read Mr. Ardrey, so I took to my heels. This proves, I think, that I am less of a chacma baboon than some other ethologists I could name.

# MAN HAS NO 'KILLER' INSTINCT

*Geoffrey Gorer*

Geoffrey Gorer, a professor of anthropology at Cambridge University, England, is author of *Modern Types,* and many books in social anthropology.

One of the most persistent and widespread beliefs about "human nature" held by men of goodwill in most of the advanced societies in the world is that human beings are "naturally" peaceful and gentle, considerate of their fellow human beings and unwilling to

From *The New York Times Magazine*, Nov. 27, 1966, pp. 47+. © 1966 by the New York Times Company. Reprinted by permission.

hurt or kill them save under the (assumedly) exceptional conditions of war.

This belief in the essential gentleness of "human nature" can only be maintained by a wilful blindness that refuses to recognize the evidence which history, social anthropology, the daily newspapers and television so constantly provide of man's willingness to hurt and kill his fellows, and to take pride and pleasure in so doing.

In recent months we have read detailed accounts and seen gruesome pictures of Ibos and Hausas gleefully slaughtering one another in Nigeria, of massacres of Indonesians and Chinese in Java and other islands of the archipelago, of Chinese youngsters with red armlets self-righteously humiliating their elders, not to mention both sides in Vietnam. If we try to console ourselves by claiming that most of these slaughters and humiliations were the acts of people who were not civilized and not Christian, this consolation should be short-lived. The Boers and white Rhodesians claim Christian justification for the ill-treatment of their fellow citizens with darker skins; the pictures of the school at Grenada, Miss., are surely not forgotten; and no recorded "uncivilized" nation has equaled the systematic humiliation and slaughter practiced by Christian Germany and her allies a bare generation ago.

All known societies make a distinction between murder—the killing of a member of one's own group—and the killing of outsiders. We can understand murder for jealousy or gain or safety, however much we reprobate and punish it; we think it "rational." But when somebody kills without a "rational" motive—nurses in a dormitory, students from a university tower, policemen in a street —we are puzzled, disturbed and fascinated. The murder of eight nurses or three policemen will hold our attention over longer periods and with more intensity than the slaughter of masses of Javanese.

Contemporary psychological science is at a loss to account for people killing one another without a "rational" motive, according to our standards; an implicit hypothesis in all Western thinking, both scientific and popular, is that man has built-in instinct: against killing except under extreme provocation. When people in our own societies kill without a "good reason" we tend to use the term "psychopath"; but this is really a scientific-sounding confession of ignorance and impotence.

Sometimes this pseudo-explanation is applied to killers by other societies but more frequently the Malayan term "running amok" is used. In Malaya, and some other societies, individuals may suddenly start killing strangers, and amok is the Malayan term for this kind of behavior. This is, however, a description, not an explanation.

Some people reject the hypothesis that man is naturally peaceable and instead, invoke the hypothesis of a "killer instinct" as an aspect of man's hereditary endowment. This "instinct" is held to be normally under strong restraint in "civilized societies" but capable of erupting in "psychopathic" individuals and nearer the surface in "savage" societies. Were there evidence for such an "instinct" it would offer a sort of explanation for the joy of killing, for which there is such plentiful evidence; but I will argue that this is an unnecessary hypothesis.

The most important statement, almost without question, about this aspect of human nature made in this century is that contained in the recent book of the ethologist Konrad Lorenz, translated into English under the title, *On Aggression*. He shows that all the carnivores, the mammals which kill other species for their food, have innate inhibitions (instincts, if the term be preferred) against killing members of their own species, with two exceptions—rats and men. The animals with potentially lethal teeth, claws or horns can be automatically stopped from pressing an attack on a fellow member of the species by signs of submission, either flight or some physical analogue to raising the hands or showing the white flag. Once the species-specific signs of submission are made, the attacker automatically halts; he literally cannot kill his defeated rival.

Dr. Lorenz argues that there is an evolutionary connection between the larger carnivores' lethal physical equipment and the innate inhibitions against using this physical equipment on fellow members of the same species. In comparison, man is physically ill-equipped; his teeth and nails are not adapted to killing large animals of other species; and even his strong and clever hands could seldom be used on healthy beasts. It has indeed been argued that very early man, away from the seacoasts, relied on carrion for his protein. Since man is so physically ill-equipped for killing, he did not acquire the built-in inhibitions against killing other men as part of the evolutionary protection of the species, as wolves or tigers did for their co-specifics. And then he invented weapons.

To avoid confusion, it should be emphasized that for all carnivores, including man, killing other species of animals for food is innately of a different nature from killing members of the same species for rivalry or jealousy or pleasure. In animals, there is no connection between hunting and ferocity toward members of their own species; ethology gives no support to the arguments of tender-minded human beings that man would be less ferocious if he abstained from eating meat.

The Latin proverb, *homo homini lupus*—man is a wolf to man —has been taken over by nearly every society which derives customs, laws or language from ancient Rome. This is a libel on the wolf, which is a gentle animal with other wolves. Ethologically more appropriate would be *homo homini Mus rattus*—man is a rat to man—for exceptionally among carnivores, rats do sometimes kill other rats. In his mating and child-rearing patterns, in his vision, and in some other aspects, man resembles birds more than he does other mammals; but in his treatment of his own species there is an uncomfortably close analogy with rats.

Rats live in packs or hordes; and (still following Dr. Lorenz) they do not fight seriously with, much less kill, members of the same pack. But they are quite merciless to members of alien packs; they kill them slowly and painfully and (if one wishes to be anthropomorphic) they seem to get pleasure from so doing. They share our lack of built-in inhibitions against killing members of the same species.

The analogy with human beings is almost total. Human beings also live in packs (in most cases the pack is the society) and the killing of other members of the pack is always forbidden (save, occasionally, under carefully defined rules) and typically subject to very severe sanctions; but this ban and these sanctions do not usually apply to members of other packs. As is well known, very many primitive tribes have only a single word to designate members of the tribe and human beings; they alone are fully human, members of other packs are (so to speak) subhuman, and killing them is not murder. This primitive type of rat-thinking is never far below the surface, even among the civilized and sensitive.

Where human beings differ from rats is in their very varying definitions of who shall be included within the pack. Usually, the pack is the society or tribe, people who speak the same language (typically unique to the tribe) and between whom real or supposititious bonds of kinship can be traced; but there are variants in both directions.

The smallest packs known to me are those described by Dr. and Mrs. Ronald M. Berndt, who studied four contiguous language groups in the Eastern Highlands of New Guinea. Here the people one should not kill are certain specified kinfolk and a few relations of one's wife or wives. Everyone else, irrespective of ancestry or language, was fit prey for the "deadly game" of death, for only by killing can a man earn power and prestige. The dead were eaten and, in the case of women, raped either before or after death.

The only reason why these packs had not exterminated one another before the Australians pacified the area a bare decade ago is that they practiced a policy of preservation of human game. They seldom killed more than they could eat, and left the temporarily weak in peace to breed. The gleeful, guiltless accounts that Dr. and Mrs. Berndt gathered from the participants in these orgies of slaughter, cannibalism and rape read like a nightmare vision of human savagery.

New Guinea also contains one of the relatively few tribes described by anthropologists in which the joy of killing seems to be completely absent. These are the Arapesh, studied by Dr. Margaret Mead and Dr. Reo Fortune. They will be discussed in more detail subsequently.

For most of humanity, the tribe is the unit within which killing is considered murder, and outside which killing may be a proof of manhood and bravery, a pleasure and a duty. Such killing may be done by individuals—head-hunters, scalp-collectors, as part of a vendetta or raid—or by groups; in the latter case the killing is called "warfare." The differences in quality and scope between tribal warfare and modern war between nation-states are so great that it might be useful if different words were used for the two activities.

The nation-state was invented after the Neolithic revolution, less than 10,000 years ago; and this is a very short period in man's evolutionary history. One of the advantages of the nation-state is that it greatly extended the area within which killing would be murder; a number of tribes were brought under the same law and equally protected from mutual slaughter. This amalgamation is not now an easy one, as the sad condition of contemporary Nigeria or Indonesia demonstrates; and it probably was no less difficult in the past. There are no reliable contemporary records of the establishment of the first nation-states, mostly along the great rivers of Asia and North Africa; by the time adequate historical records commence, a dominant group had succeeded in preserving peace among the component tribes. The pack was successfully extended to include and protect most of the inhabitants of a given geographical area, even though slaves and captives were usually excluded.

The nation-state is really the last successful human invention for extending the size of the pack, within which killing is murder. In the past 4,000 years a number of religions have been founded which would include all believers inside the pack; but no religion has commanded worldwide allegiance; and regularly the outcasts, infidels, untouchables, heathen or heretics could all be humiliated or killed with added pleasure and self-righteousness, because they were members of the devil's pack.

The founders of the great world religions, Gautama Buddha, Jesus, Lao-Tzu, Mohammed, all seem to have striven for a worldwide brotherhood of man; but none of them could develop institutions which would include the enemy, the unbeliever, and give him the same protection from anger, hatred and the lust for killing which they decreed within their own congregations.

Within the last century and a half various millennial ideologies —democracy, Socialism, the Communist internationals, the United Nations—have taken over the goal of the traditional religions; the establishment of a worldwide brotherhood of man, a single pack. They have been no more successful than their predecessors in protecting the enemy, the unbeliever, from the horrible results of righteous anger.

In recent centuries, most men of goodwill have at least paid lip service to the ideal of a universal brotherhood with equal protection for all, whatever might be their actual behavior or that of their compatriots. But this century has seen a most sinister recrudescence of rat-pack ideology, in which human status is denied to all persons who do not share one's hypothetical ancestry or visible skin color: Fascism, Nazism, white supremacy, black power all justify hatred and contempt for those outside the pack; and recent history shows how easily, how very easily this justified hatred and contempt develop into humiliation, torture and killing.

The evidence could be endlessly multiplied to demonstrate that man as a species, has no inhibitions against killing his fellow men who do not belong to the same pack, however the pack may be defined, and often gets intense pleasure and a sense of pride from so doing. But to admit this is not the same as positing a "killer instinct" as part of man's hereditary endowment. There is no logical reason for hypothesizing such an instinct, and some arguments, to be advanced shortly, against doing so.

Because men have no innate instinctual inhibitions against hurting and killing other members of their species, this offers some human beings a potential source of intense pleasure, as do incest, homosexuality and other sexual deviations. Man has no built-in inhibitions against these sources of pleasure either; did he possess them, laws would be unnecessary. Whether any of these pleasures will be sought, how frequently, and by whom, depends on the values of a specific society at a given time and the vicissitudes of individual lives.

Because man can and does gain intense pleasure from humiliating, hurting and killing his fellows, the speculative novels of the Marquis de Sade are extremely important documents, whatever their literary qualities. Save in a directly sexual situation (when he relished flagellation) de Sade was an affectionate, humane and very courageous man. In his 13-year-long solitary confinement he looked without flinching into the deepest recesses of his unconscious fantasies and reported, in fictional form, the pleasures to be derived from the unfettered exercise of power over one's fellow men and women.

De Sade linked these pleasures with the pleasures of sex; this was the only metaphor which contemporary science made available to him and it was congenial to his temperament. Even so, there are many episodes in the novels when power is used for its own sake—power to humiliate, hurt or kill—without any overt sexual gratification. De Sade wished to portray "the spasms of man's loathsome heart and fearful passions" because he was convinced that only by acknowledging the truth about human nature, as he saw it, could a safe and just society be built.

Classical psychoanalysis has in good part confirmed de Sade's pessimistic diagnosis of "man's loathsome heart." Freud always maintained the central position in his theory of the Oedipus complex; and the little Oedipus had murder in his heart, the killing of his father—a point which many contemporary psychoanalysts tend to gloss over. According to the findings of the late Melanie Klein and her followers, the inchoate hatred and rages of very young children produce wishes which, when translated into verbal metaphors, parallel the fantasies of de Sade: cannibalism, poisoning, evisceration, castration, murder.

The history of civilized nations in the century and a half since de Sade's death also confirms his pessimistic diagnosis of human behavior. Although he placed no bounds on his imagination, we have been witnesses to far greater horrors than de Sade could dream of; man can be an even more savage monster than he guessed.

It is possible that, had de Sade's diagnosis of human potentialities been taken consistently into account, the fanatics, torturers and murderers would have had less impunity in the indulging of their fearful passions.

There are, however, a few rays of hope, a few societies where men seem to find no pleasure in dominating over, hurting or killing the members of other societies, where all they ask is to be at peace and to be left in peace. These societies are, of course, small, weak, technologically backward, and living in inaccessible country; only so could they survive the power-seeking of their uninhibited neighbors.

Among these gentle societies are the Arapesh of New Guinea, mentioned earlier; the Lepchas of Sikkim in the Himalayas (whom I studied); and, most impressive of all, the pygmies of the Ituri rainforest in the Congo, studied by Colin Turnbull. These small societies (there are several others), living in the most inaccessible deserts and forests and mountains of four continents, have a number of traits in common, besides the fact that they do not dominate over, hurt or kill one another or their neighbors, though they possess the weapons to do so. Many of them, including the pygmies and the Lepchas until a couple of generations ago, rely almost exclusively on hunting for their protein food.

What seem to me the most significant common traits in these peaceful societies are that they all manifest enormous gusto for concrete physical pleasures—eating, drinking, sex, laughter—and that they all make very little distinction between the ideal characters of men and women, particularly that they have no ideal of brave, aggressive masculinity.

Men and women have different primary sexual characteristics—a source of endless merriment as well as more concrete satisfactions—and some different skills and aptitudes. No child, however, grows up with the injuctions, "All real men do . . ."or "No proper woman does . . .," so that there is no confusion of sexual identity: no cases of sexual inversion have been reported among them. The model for the growing child is of concrete performance and frank enjoyment, not of metaphysical symbolic achievements or of ordeals to be surmounted. They do not have heroes or martyrs to emulate or cowards or traitors to despise; their religious life lacks significant personalized gods and devils; a happy hard-working and productive life is within the reach of all.

As far as the history of these small tribes can be reconstructed, they have always chosen to retreat into ever more inaccessible country rather than stand their ground and fight with invaders. There is no reason to suppose that their psychological or physiological potentialities are different from those of their more aggressive neighbors, but their values certainly are; for them peace and the absence of quarreling and jealousy are far more important than a reputation for bravery and virility. And while the tribes are not broken up, it is likely that these values will continue to prevail. When the tribes are broken, individuals, unsupported by the traditional ethics, might easily revert to rat-pack mentality. Save that they have so far survived, these small tribes have not been conspicuously successful in the struggle for existence and terrain against more ruthless neighbors. Nevertheless, they may offer a paradigm of ways to diminish the joy of killing in the uninhibited human race.

By contrast, the cannibals in the New Guinea Highlands have a highly aggressive ideal of masculinity; and so, in general, do all the peoples who prize the martial virtues and self-righteously kill their enemies or their "inferiors." The New Guinea Highlanders frankly enjoy sex, especially if it approximates to rape; but many other martial societies repudiate all sensual pleasure as unworthy of a Real Man. If our gods and heroes are killers— Lords of Hosts, warriors, successful revolutionaries—and if masculinity is demonstrated by the willingness to give and take "punishment," then the joy of killing is always likely to reemerge.

It seems possible that the youth international, which has developed, nearly the whole world over, in the last generation, has inarticulately sensed the necessity to redefine the concepts of "a real man" and "a true woman" if we are not to destroy ourselves completely. The long hair, dandified dress and pleasantly epicene features (which so infuriate their elders) are a physical repudiation of the ideal of aggressive masculinity which has been traditional in all their societies in recent generations, and which is still maintained by the conventional and the neo-Fascists (white supremacists, Empire loyalists, Birchites and the like) in the same societies.

Even idiotic slogans such as "Make love, not war" (as if the two activities had ever been incompatible!) and the use of drugs make the same point. Mankind is safer when men seek pleasure than when they seek the power and the glory.

If the members of the youth international—the beats and the swingers, the *provos* and the *stilyagi*—maintain the same scale of values and the same sex ideals 20 years hence when they themselves are middle-aged and parents, then they may, just possibly, have produced a permanent change in the value systems and sex roles of their societies, which will turn the joy of killing into an unhappy episode of man's historic past, analogous to human sacrifice, which ascribed joy in killing to the gods also.

The attempts to devise a social unit more inclusive than the nation-state, a brotherhood of man, have all been unsuccessful to date. It is just possible that the youth international, with its emphasis on shared sensual pleasure and its repudiation of the ideal of truculent "manliness," may succeed where the grandiose schemes of idealists have always failed. For man has no "killer instinct": he merely lacks inhibitions.

# Chapter Six

# Human Biology as a Consideration in the Study of Prehistory

Anthropologists, as children of their own culture, interpret prehistory in the light of existing cultural values. This distortion of objectivity is most obvious in the overwhelming emphasis placed on the development of technology by anthropologists who are citizens of the world's technologically most developed countries. We can imagine that artifactual evidence of Paleolithic man examined by a modern Bushman would be interpreted in spiritual rather than materialistic terms. Saddled with his tremendous and demanding brain Paleolithic man truly lived by more than bread alone. Perhaps the current wave of disillusionment and discontentment among youth with the promise of escalating technology will produce a generation of scholars who will read the fossil man evidence quite differently than their Depression-bred seniors.

But equally as fallacious as the "technocentrism" of some modern anthropologists is the argument that the divergence of the human ancestor from the monkey and ape stock was due to some *one* paramount factor, like position in a food chain, or a *single* new anatomical capability like throwing or carrying. Technological inventions which appear very suddenly—which are real breakthroughs—do not necessarily have to be responses to a current need. These breakthroughs could bring about tremendously lopsided situations, so that a part of a given technology is greatly advanced relative to another more primitive part. Evolutionary developments, on the other hand, usually occur very slowly, are adaptive (i.e., solve an immediate survival problem), and occur as part of a whole complex of concomitant changes. Thus the analogy between evolutionary and technologically induced change, which we as products of Western European culture are so apt to make, is usually fallacious. Yet such arguments are very popular in the anthropological literature, partly because they make it appear that prehistory and evolution ratify our current faith in "progress," and also because in this way so much can be explained by so little.

# THE ANTHROPOLOGY OF THE CREDIT CARD

*John Lear*

John Lear is Science Editor of the *Saturday Review*.

In the ancient book of Genesis it is written that man first appeared on earth in a garden abloom with trees. He lost the privilege of arboreal leisure because he took fruit from a tree tabooed and ate it. The fruit was the fruit of knowledge. He was punished for trying to learn too much. In other words, the original human experience was an act of carrying.

Modern books on evolution repeat the main line of this story. According to them, the ancestors of men—ancestors also of chimpanzees, gorillas, orangutans, gibbons, and siamangs—were tree dwellers. They swung through the branches on their arms by day, and slept through the night in nests aloft. They lived in bands of ten to thirty, bossed by one or a very few strong males, in segregated neighborhoods of the forest.

As time passed, the climate of the planet changed, shrinking the forests into scattered clusters of trees.

Ages before, these tree-living animals' ancestors, the lung-fish, native to the sea in which all life originated, had been stranded ashore by the tidal wash of violent storms. After the earliest such experience, the lung-fish must have got back to the water by rowing through the mud on their fins. Later, the distance to the sea

From *Saturday Review*, April 4, 1964, pp. 45–7. Copyright 1964 Saturday Review, Inc.

apparently was too great to allow a return; by that time, the fins were strong enough to serve as walking sticks, and so the family of land-living mammals had emerged.

The tree-dwelling mammals faced a somewhat similar turnabout because of the dwindling forest. They could run on their hind feet alone, but could walk only on all fours. Yet they had to spend more and more time in the tall grass as the trees grew scarcer. Naturally the remaining trees were taken over by the strongest, most vigorous climbers. The weaklings had to amble along as best they could by holding themselves as upright as possible on the ground, finding their way by peering across the top of the grass.

That much of the tale has been repeated many times. What has been neglected is the act of carrying and its consequences.

Late in the month of March 1964 two anthropologists, Charles F. Hockett and Robert Ascher of Cornell University, published a review of man's flight from the trees in *Current Anthropology*. Their report was sufficiently entertaining and instructive to win simultaneous printing in *The American Scientist*. As they see it, the initial act of carrying was not a wilful seeking after forbidden wisdom but a simple striving to stay alive.

"We are speaking here of displacements and movements of whole bands, not of individual animals," the two professors stipulate. "There is one thing that surely accompanied any band whenever it moved: the essential geometry of its territoriality. At any halt, no matter how temporary, whether in the trees, under the trees, or in open country, some specific site became, for the nonce, 'home base'—a GHQ, a center, a focus, relative to which each member of the band oriented himself as he moved about. Headquarters was the safest place to be, if for no other reason than the safety of numbers. In a later epoch—though doubtless earlier than will ever be directly attested by archeology—headquarters among our own ancestors came to be crudely fortified, as perhaps by a piled ring of stones; it became the place where things were kept or stored; in due time it became house, village, fort, city. But earliest of all it was *home*."

Here the narrators pause for breath and ask us to accept that sometime in the interim the early animals we are talking about progressed from hominoids to hominids, from the pre-apes to the pre-man.

"This is also the appropriate point for a warning," they say. We must not visualize this transition "as a fierce, intense, tooth-and-nail struggle. That is assuredly wrong. The typical pace of evolution is extremely leisurely."

But it didn't seem leisurely to the pre-men.

"It is no joke to be thrown out of one's ancestral home," anthropologists Hockett and Ascher remind us. "If the next grove is only a few miles away, in sight, then one has something to aim for; but sooner or later movements must have taken place without any such visible target. Treeless country holds discomforts and dangers. There may not be much food, at least not of a familiar sort. There may be little available water, for the trees tend to cluster where the water is more abundant. And there are fleet four-footed predators, as well as herbivorous quadrupeds big and strong enough to be dangerous at close quarters. One cannot avoid these other animals altogether, since their presence often signals the location of water, or of food fit also for hominid consumption. The quest for food must be carried on constantly, no matter how pressing may be the drive to find a new grove of trees in which to settle. It is a wonder that any of the waifs of the Miocene savannah survived at all. Enormous numbers of them must have died out.

"The trick that made survival possible for some of them was the trick of *carrying*."

The pre-apes probably carried twigs and brush to make their nests, and certainly carried infants. But in the trees, they used their hands mostly for climbing. On the ground, bipedal locomotion freed the hands of the pre-men for carrying, and the survival value of carrying helped evolve a physical structure adapted to bipedal locomotion.

The Hockett-Ascher paper presumes that the earliest ground-carrying may have been "a sort of accident.

"Imagine an early hominid—perhaps even a prehominid hominoid—sitting on the ground and pounding something (a nut, say) with a handy stone. A predator approaches. Our hero jumps up and runs away as best he can on two legs—there are no trees nearby into which to escape—but keeps his grasp on the stone for no better reason than that he does not need his hand for anything else. Cornered, he turns, and either strikes out at the predator with the hand that holds the stone, or else throws it. The predator falls or runs off, and whatever in our hero's genes or life experience, or both, has contributed to his behavior stands a chance of being passed on.

"The first carrying of scavenged food back to headquarters (instead of consuming it on the spot) may also have been a sort of accident. A scavenging hominoid is eating the remains of a predator's kill where he has found it, and is surprised by the predator who is coming back to make another meal from the same kill. The hominoid runs off towards headquarters, still holding a piece of meat in his hand. In due time, he or his successors developed the habit of carrying the spoils off without waiting for the predator to turn up."

The earliest carrying was done by single animals within the band's territory. The moving of things as the whole band moved came later. Unshaped defense weapons. Extra food. Water. Water especially—for primates in general have to drink daily.

Small quantities of water could have been cupped in the large leaves of tropical plants. From the leaves it would have been only a short reach to strands of vine, which might have been pulled from the trees and slung over the shoulders or around the waist as a carrying harness. Later, when the hominids were regularly killing small animals, the hides—useless as food—might have replaced the vines in the harness position.

"A hide cannot be eaten," the Hockett-Ascher study observes, "but if one is hungry enough there is some nourishment to be obtained by chewing at it. Almost as early as the first use of hides as harness, it may have been discovered that a hide that has been chewed is more flexible and comfortable to wear than one that has not. This way of processing hides was still widespread only yesterday. It is unlikely that any direct archeological evidence of these posited early clothing developments will ever turn up. But if clothing of sorts is actually that ancient, then it was already available, with only minor modifications, when it was first needed" to protect the slowly migrating human race in its exploration of territory characterized by cold. The invention of clothing is suspected of being older than the domestication of fire. It may even be old enough to explain the relative hairlessness of *Homo sapiens* today.

Anyhow, anthropologists Hockett and Ascher are persuaded that of the four modern functions of clothing—protection, modesty, vanity, and carrying—carrying was "the one of earliest relevance. If one's way of life rests on hand-carrying, and if the number and variety of things to be carried are increasing to the point of awkwardness, then the invention of a device that helps one carry things has the [most] conservative survival value. . . ."

The Hockett-Ascher account stops far short of the present day. But, given clothing as a vehicle of transportation, the logical and curious mind at once jumps from garments to pockets, from pockets to pocketbooks, from trade-by-barter to commerce through media of exchange, from exchange of coin carried in moneybags to exchange of paper money carried in purses and wallets, from paper money to symbolic money in checkbooks, from these symbols to symbols of them in the form of credit cards, and from credit cards to credit card numbers negotiable by telephone. In return for real or fancied convenience in carrying, men have subjected themselves to numbering, failing meanwhile to note that they, once active transferrers of coins and paper money from hand to hand, are now, as numbers, passively being handled and manipulated by computers. Since computers can do only what they are told to do, and since few people know how to tell a computer anything, a new power complex with built-in impersonality is fastening itself on humanity—who knows when for profit, when for curiosity, when for malice.

The anthropological implications of the credit card could raise disconcerting questions about the direction of man's future. For the social side-effects of this carry-all invention are hardly likely to be less than the side effects of the more limited carrying of the past, and the Hockett-Ascher review characterizes the latter as "incalculable."

The first side effect of carrying was, as has already been noted, the encouragement of bipedal walking, which "in turn selected [for survival and reproduction those pre-men who were prepared] both for carrying and for an upright posture that makes bipedal walking mechanically more efficient.

"A less obvious consequence . . . [of] carrying . . . [was] . . . a kind of behavior that has all the outward earmarks of what we call 'memory' and 'foresight': One lugs around a heavy stick or stone despite the absence of any immediate need for it, as though one were remembering past experiences in which having it available was important and were planning for possible future encounters of the same kind. Taking scavenged meat back to headquarters without waiting for the predator to return to his kill also looks like foresight. We do not mean to deny the validity of the terms 'memory' and 'foresight.' The point is that the outward earmarks surely came first. . . .

"A third consequence of carrying and of wandering was a change in dietary balance. The first tools to be carried were defensive weapons. Often enough no doubt, the use of these weapons against a predator, even if successful, would only scare him off. But sometimes the predator would be killed. Why waste the meat?"

Meat is compactly packaged energy as compared with uncultivated plants. The packages were obtainable in large economy sizes, provided an efficient signaling system was available for collective hunting. The invention of carrying had freed the mouth for chattering. The upright posture encouraged by carrying devices had completed migration of the face from the front (the present location of the faces of dogs, cats, and cows, for example) to the ventral side of the head, turned the axis of the oral cavity to a position approximately at right angles to the pharynx and introduced a marked separation of glottis from velum, thus enlarging the confines of the vocal cords. Generations of chattering had increased the nerve network associated with the vocal tract and enriched the representation of that region in the cortex of the brain. A mechanism. was thus ready to take the call system of the pre-apes—in which each call had one explicit and limited meaning but no other —and transform it into a flexible language. The collective hunt for meat fortified the development of language because the hands of the hunters were occupied with weapons, hence unavailable for any complicated semaphor. The eyes of the hunters had to watch both the prey and the other hunters. Communication was necessarily left to the mouth and ears.

After the hunt, there was often more food than could possibly be consumed by the hunters. Sharing the kill with other members of the band must have come about almost automatically. Sharing led to a more complex social organization, which was still further complicated by another consequence of the upright posture that the invention of carrying had encouraged. Here we enter the technology of sex.

The frontal approach for copulation first became anatomically possible because of the upright stance. This position for intercourse is almost exclusively human (recurring only in the pygmy chimpanzee, the porcupine, the hamster, and the two-toed sloth) and probably changed the relative roles of the adult male and of the infant so far as the female of the species was concerned. After the innovation, there was for her a much closer similarity between the reception of an infant and of a lover. Thus the warmth of mother-infant relationships could have been diffused among other interpersonal relationships.

Language and culture, the principal baggage carried by modern humanity, together selected for survival and reproduction those individuals equipped with bigger brains. Bigger brains meant bigger heads. Bigger heads meant more difficult childbirth. One way out of this difficulty was to expel the fetus earlier. Earlier birth extended the period of helpless infancy, which is also the period of greatest plasticity, during which the newcomer absorbs the extra-genetic heritage of his people. Helpless infants need longer and more elaborate care, which made it convenient for mothers to seek the help of adult males in nursery chores. Thus fathers were domesticated. Thus also was established the custom by which society sanctions reservation of a female by a male in advance provision for his sex hunger.

We come at last to the most sophisticated of all forms of carrying: the carrying of symbols inside the head. The pre-apes knew nothing of this. Their leaders always were the physically strongest adult males. Language altered the power structure by bestowing portable wisdom on receptive individuals, whether strong or feeble. As age permitted accumulation of knowledge, older men became repositories of information on which the band could call.

But what is to happen now that unprecedented stores of data are being filed away in the artificial memories of electronic computers? What now that older citizens are being retired from work by robots and consigned to sanataria by impatient offspring? What is to happen to judgment, which actually is more precious today than ever before because of the complex planning that can be done in an instant of time and the rapidity with which the plans can be executed? Men are already numbered, as individuals at their own instigation, for their own convenience. Are the future days of free men being numbered, too, without thought?

# SPECULATIONS ON PREHISTORY

*Lewis Mumford*

Lewis Mumford, social philosopher and critic, historian and writer, is the author of *Technics and Civilization, The City in History, The Myth of the Machine,* and many other books emphasizing the dehumanizing effects of our technological civilization.

Modern man has formed a curiously distorted picture of himself, by interpreting his early history in terms of his present interests in making machines and conquering nature. And then in turn he has justified his present concerns by calling his prehistoric self

From *The American Scholar*, Vol. 36 (Winter 1966–67), pp. 43–53. This article also appeared in *The Myth of the Machine* (New York: Harcourt, Brace, & World, Inc., 1967). Reprinted by permission of the author.

a toolmaking animal, and assuming, as Karl Marx and his followers have consistently done, that the material instruments of production dominated all his other activities. As long as the paleoanthropologist regarded material objects—mainly bones and stones—as the only scientifically admissible evidence of early man's activities, nothing could be done to alter this stereotype.

Recently, in an extensive review of the whole history of man's technical achievements, I have found it necessary as a generalist to challenge this narrow view. There is sound reason to believe that man's brain was from the beginning far more important than his hands, and its size could not be derived solely from his shaping or using of tools; that ritual and language and social organization which left no material traces whatever, although constantly present in every culture, were probably man's most important artifacts from the earliest stages on; and that so far from conquering nature or reshaping his environmental primitive man's first concern was to utilize his overdeveloped, intensely active nervous system, and to give form to a human self, set apart from his original animal self by the fabrication of symbols—the only tools that could be constructed out of the resources provided by his own body: dreams, images and sounds.

It was not possible to go very far in this restatement without perceiving that the overemphasis on tool-using was the result of an unwillingness to consider any evidence other than that based on material finds, along with a decision to exclude much more important activities that have characterized all human groups, in every part of the world, at every known period. Although no one part of our present culture may, without risk of serious error, be taken as a clue to the past, our culture as a whole remains the living witness of all that man has undergone, whether recorded or unrecorded; and the very existence of grammatically complex and highly articulated languages at the onset of civilization five thousand years ago, when tools were still extremely primitive, suggests that the human race may have had even more fundamental needs than getting a living, since it might have continued to do the latter on the same terms as its hominid ancestors.

If this is so, what were these needs? These questions are waiting to be answered, or rather, they must first be asked; and they cannot be asked without a willingness to look freshly at the evidence, and to apply rational speculation, fortified with careful analogies, to the large blank spaces of prehistoric existence, when the character of man, as other than a mere animal, was first formed. So far both anthropologists and historians of technics, with a few exceptions like Edward Tylor, have guarded themselves against speculative error by taking too much for granted, including their own premises; and this has led to greater errors of interpretation than those they have avoided.

The result has been a single-factor explanation of man's original development centered around the stone tool: an oversimplification in method that has now been abandoned elsewhere as inadequate for the general theory of evolution, and for the interpretation of better documented areas of human history.

What has limited scientific investigation, of course, is the fact that as concerns the unrecorded beginnings of man's life—all but the last 1 or 2 per cent of his whole existence—one can for the greater part only speculate. This is a hazardous business, whose difficulties are not lessened by scattered finds of fragmentary bones and artifacts, since without some imaginative insight and analogical interpretation these solid objects tell all too little. Yet to refrain from speculation may be even more stultifying, for it gives to man's later recorded history an appearance of singularity and suddenness, as if a different species had come into existence. In talking about the "agricultural revolution" or the "urban revolution" we forget how many foothills the race had climbed before it reached those peaks. Without going into the special areas I have covered in my study, let me present the case for speculation as a necessary instrument for arriving at adequate knowledge.

Now there are two ways in which the obscurity of man's early development may be partly overcome. The first is commonly used in all the sciences: deducing from the observed facts the unseen or unrecorded context. Thus if one finds a shell fishhook embedded in a dateable site, one may infer, from that bit of evidence alone, not only the existence of water, even if the stream bed or lake has dried up, but likewise the presence of human beings who included fish in their diet, who selected the shell and shaped the hook after a model that could exist only in their own mind, who were ingenious enough to use guts or plant fiber for line, and who were sufficiently patient and skillful to catch fish by this method. Although various other animals, and birds, eat fish, no other species than man uses a hook.

These conclusions would be sound, although every trace of positive evidence, other than the hook, had vanished, along with the fisherman's own bones. If one remembered to allow for the possibility that the fishhook might have been transported from a distance, all these deductions would be firm and unshakeable.

Under similar limitations, with a similar liability to error, anatomists will derive the character of a whole human body from the size and shape of a broken skull and a few teeth—although the ghost of "Piltdown Man" may rise up to slay them, if they overestimate their powers.

Samuel Butler in his *Notebooks* once speculated on "the finding of a lot of old photographs at Herculaneum; and they should turn out to be of no interest." But he forgot that such a singular find would in itself reveal many matters of extraordinary interest, which would cause a revolutionary rewriting of history: they would disclose that the Romans had invented photography; and this in turn would show that they had advanced beyond the Greeks in both chemistry and physics, knew the special chemical properties of the halogen group, probably had lenses and had done optical experiments, and had at their disposal metal, glass or plastics, with smooth surfaces to use as backing for the precipitated image. Such firm knowledge as we have of prehistory rests precisely upon this kind of identification and inference, usually of commonplace, "uninteresting" objects, like potsherds, animal bones or pollen grains.

In the realm of prehistory the generalist has a special office, that of bringing together widely separated fields, prudently fenced in by specialists, into a larger common area, visible only from the air. Only by forfeiting the detail can the overall pattern be seen, although once that pattern is visible new details, unseen even by the most thorough and competent field workers digging through the buried strata, may become visible. The generalists' competence lies not in unearthing new evidence but in putting together authentic fragments that are accidentally, or sometimes arbitrarily, separated, because specialists tend to abide too rigorously by a gentlemen's agreement not to invade each other's territory. While this makes for safety and social harmony, it ignores the fact that the phenomena studied do not hold to the same principles. Such "No Trespassing" laws, if observed by the generalist, would halt his cross-country excursions, and prevent him from performing his own special function—one oddly similar to that of those Polynesian traders and interpreters who have a license to escape tribal taboos and wander freely over a wide area.

Nevertheless there are certain rules of the game that a generalist must keep, when he tries to fit the scattered pieces of evidence together in a more meaningful mosaic. Even when he seems on the verge of completing an emerging pattern, he must not surreptitiously chip a piece to make it fit, as in a jigsaw puzzle, nor yet must he manufacture any of the pieces in order to fill out the design—although he of course may look in unlikely places for them. He must likewise be ready to scrap any piece of evidence, however he may cherish it, as soon as one of his specialist colleagues discovers that it is suspect, or that it does not fit into the particular environment or the particular time sequence under discussion. When not enough parts exist, the generalist must wait until competent authorities find or fabricate them. But if, on the other hand, his design will not hold all the pieces the specialists present to him, then the pattern itself must be abandoned as faulty; and the generalist must begin all over again with a more adequate frame.

Yet even the specialized scholars who are most ready to decry speculation often succumb to it, chiefly by presenting purely speculative conclusions as if they were well-established facts, without allowing alternative hypotheses. Let me take a case sufficiently remote, I trust, to hurt no one's feelings. From the fact that the thigh bones of Peking Man in the Choukoutien caves were found cracked open, various anthropologists jumped to the conclusion that this creature was a cannibal. *Possibly he was.* But all we actually know is that the bones of unidentifiable humanoid creatures were cracked open, under special conditions that caused them to be preserved.

Apart from marks left by blows on the skull, which might have been made in a futile attempt after death to split it open, or even have happened earlier without causing death, we have no evidence to indicate whether these creatures were killed or died a natural death. If we suppose they were killed, we do not know if homicide was the custom of the country, or whether this was a particular case: certainly no statistically valid conclusions can be drawn on the basis of the few specimens discovered on a single site. Nor yet do we know if they were killed by their own kind, by another group, or by some more predatory hominid of a vanished race.

Further, although the skulls indicate that the brains had been extracted through the base, we do not know if the rest of the flesh and marrow was eaten; and finally, even if cannibalism were firmly established, we still do not know if such victims were habitually slain for food, or whether this was done under pressure of starvation—something that has happened occasionally, as with the American pioneers at the Donner Pass, among people to whom cannibalism was abhorrent. Or again, was this extraction of marrow and brain like that of some later peoples, part of a sacrificial, magico-religious ceremony? And finally, was the marrow used as infant's food, or to help start a fire—both attested uses for marrow under primitive conditions?

Coldly appraised, the probability against cannibalism seems about as great as that for it. Few mammals kill their own kind for *food* under any conditions, and the likelihood is that if this perversion had been as common among early men as it was among many later savages, it would have worked against the survival of the groups practicing it, since the human population was extremely sparse and no one would have been safe against his neighbor's hunger. We know, from later evidence, that primitive hunting peoples feel guilty about taking the life of animals they need for food, and even pray the animal for forgiveness or rationalize its death as due to the animal's own wish. Is it sure then that early man felt less sympathetic toward other human beings—except in surging moments of anger?

Even plentiful examples of cannibalism among "contemporary" savages—for long it was rife in Africa and New Guinea—do not establish it as common early practice. Just as primitive man was incapable of our own massive exhibitions of cruelty, torture and extermination, so he may have been quite innocent of manslaughter for food. The assertion that man was always a killer, and a cannibal at that, once he had acquired a taste for flesh, must reckon with these many alternative possibilities. Any flatfooted assumption of man's aboriginal cannibalism rests on no sounder evidence than the contrary hypothesis, and should never have been presented as if it were unquestionable.

Such pitfalls do not rob deduction, scrupulously applied, of its value. All that this argument suggests is that when alternative explanations are equally plausible and may be equally valid, one must leave the question open, and hope some day to find a bit of positive evidence to clinch this or that hypothesis. But if the deduced traits exist in a kindred primate species, as cannibalism does not, and if it also emerges in later human groups, as with close and relatively durable marital attachments, one may with fair safety attribute it also to early man. I propose to adhere to this rule. But the fact that a question worth opening speculatively may have to remain open for an indefinite time is not a sufficient reason for not posing it at all. This holds for practically the entire sphere of human origins.

In short, Leslie White's point is well taken: "Scientists unhesitatingly tackle such problems as the origin of galaxies, stars, planetary systems, and life in general and in its many orders . . .

If the origin of the earth some two billion years ago, or the origin of life untold millions of years ago, can be and is a proper problem for science, why not the origin of culture a mere million years ago?

The second method available for reading into the aboriginal nature of early man has equally serious drawbacks, so much so that many ethnologists during the last generation often dismissed it as unworthy of scientific consideration. This is the method of analogy: finding parallels between known practices and those that seem indicated by ancient artifacts. During the nineteenth century many primitive tribes, which had for long escaped direct encounters with civilized men, still made their living by grubbing and hunting alone, using stone tools and weapons similar to those that Boucher de Perthes had first uncovered in paleolithic remains in 1832. This led many observers to suppose that the traditions of these contemporary primitives could be directly traced back to ancestral stocks, and that differences in cultural development between groups even corresponded to differences in time.

That was a tempting error. The fallacy lay in forgetting that the surviving "primitives," even if they had long ago retreated into a safe niche, had nevertheless continued the process of cultural accumulation, modification and elaboration: they had long ceased to be culturally naked, and had possibly, as Father Wilhelm Schmidt held in the case of religion, sometimes fallen from a higher early cultural level, through giving later fantasies or inventions free play. Between the language and ceremonial of the Australian aborigines and those of Mousterian culture was a spread of perhaps fifty thousand years: long enough to produce many salient differences, even if certain specific traits might nevertheless have persisted.

Yet once the processes of diversification and degeneration are allowed for, the parallels become suggestive and are sometimes highly illuminating. In fact, one cannot make any valid observation about otherwise unidentified stone tools without reference to similar later tools whose use is known. The Pygmies or the Bushmen of Africa, as they were "discovered" by Europeans more than a century ago, hunted much the same kinds of animals, with much the same weapons as paleolithic man had used in other parts of the world, too, more than fifteen thousand years before; and the Bushmen had even earlier practiced the Magdalenian art of cave painting. Apart from the differences in climatic conditions and human stature, these people were far closer to their remote ancestral cultures than they were to contemporary European man. Although

W. J. Sollas went too far in looking upon the Tasmanian, the Bushman and the Eskimo as the lineal survivors of their respective paleolithic ancestors, early, middle and late, their analogous activities give vital clues to earlier cultures.

Using the Eskimo's stone oil lamp, a paleolithic artifact, one can estimate the amount of light available to painters in caves where similar paleolithic lamps were found. From the Eskimos' thorough utilization of their meager natural resources, under climatic conditions similar to those of the Ice Ages, we can gather much information about the kind of economy that made survival possible and even provided a margin for positive cultural development. So, too, the weapons, the masks and costumes and ornaments, the rituals and ceremonies, give hints that illuminate comparable images found in the caves of Spain, France and North Africa. Yet, as André Leroi-Gourhan has insisted in his recent monumental work, *Préhistoire de l'art occidental,* these hints must not be taken as conclusive demonstrations: the fact that the footprints of boys and youths are found in certain paleolithic caves proves only that the young were permitted or encouraged to enter, not that they underwent an initiation rite. Even the arrows and marks of wounds on some ten percent of the cave paintings are not free from ambiguity: if they reveal a magic hunting ceremony, they may also, he points out, symbolize the masculine and feminine principle: the penis spear, thrust into the vulva-wound.

One of the reasons that important clues to man's early development may have been missed is that the scientific tradition in the nineteenth century was — whatever the individual practices of some scientists—rationalist, utilitarian, and definitely skeptical about the value of any set of beliefs that tacitly denied science's own uncriticized assumptions. While magic was admitted as an early practice, perhaps interpretable, in James Frazer's terms, as an attempt to control natural forces that would, in the end, succumb to the scientific method, anything like the larger consciousness of cosmic forces that is associated with religion, was treated as negligible. That early man may have scanned the sky, and have reacted to the presence of the sun and moon, may even have identified the seemingly fixed pole star, as Zelia Nuttall suggested more than half a century ago, seemed as removed from possibility as the fact that he had produced works of art.

Yet from the moment *Homo sapiens,* at least, makes his appearance, we find evidence in his attitude toward death, toward ancestral spirits, toward future existence, toward sun and sky, that betrays a consciousness that forces and beings, distant in space and time, unapproachable if not invisible, may nevertheless play a controlling part in man's life. This was a true intuition, although it may have taken hundreds of thousands of years before its full import and rational proof could be grasped by the human mind which now ranges between invisible particles and equally mysterious retreating galaxies.

There seems a likelihood that the earliest peoples, perhaps even before language was available, had a dim consciousness of the mystery of their own being: a greater incentive of reflection and self-development than any pragmatic attempt to adjust to a narrower environment. Some of this grave religious response is still present in the legends of creation among many surviving tribal cultures, and notably among the American Indians.

Here again we may judiciously make use of our knowledge of contemporary primitives to cast a fresh light on the beliefs and acts of early man. Take the mysterious imprints of human hands made upon the walls of caves as far apart as Africa and Australia. These imprints are all the more puzzling because so many of these hands show one or more finger joints missing. One would have no clue to this symbol were it not for the fact that there are still tribes equally widely separated where the sacrifice of a finger joint is a rite of mourning: a personal sacrifice to emphasize a greater loss.

Is one not justified in concluding that the mutilated hand on the cave wall is probably a secondary symbol of grief, transferred for perpetuation from the short-lived primary symbol of flesh and bone to a stone surface? Such a symbolic hand may, even more sharply than a cairn of stones, count as the earliest public memorial to the dead. But it is also possible that this rite had an even deeper religious significance; for Robert Lowie describes the same mode of sacrifice among the Crow Indians as part of a truly religious retreat undergone in order to achieve communion with Deity.

In all these cases, the rite itself reveals an eminent human susceptibility to strong feeling about matters of ultimate concern, along with a desire to retain and transmit that feeling. This must have cemented family life and group loyalty, and thus have contributed quite as effectively to survival as any improvement in flaking flint tools. Although in many other species the parent will on occasion sacrifice its life to protect its mate or its young, this voluntary *symbolic* sacrifice of a finger joint is a distinctly human trait. Where such feeling is lacking, as so often in the whole routine of our mechanized, impersonal megalopolitan culture, the human ties become so weak that only stringent external regimentation will hold the group together. Witness the classic case of emotional frigidity, and moral depravity in those New York householders who heard a woman's cries for help in the night, and who watched her being murdered without even phoning for the police—as if they were watching a television program.

In short, to overlook these analogies would be as foolish as to be overconfident in our use of them. At a later stage, as Grahame Clark pointed out, it was contemporary mud-and-reed architecture in Mesopotamia that helped Leonard Wooley to interpret the traces of prehistoric architecture in Sumer; while the circular clay disks found on Minoan sites remained misidentified until Stephanos Xanthodides recognized them as the upper disks of potters' wheels, still in use on Crete. The fact that people in Mesopotamia were still, in the present century, using primitive boats made of bundles of reeds, like those of their ancestors five thousand years ago, as J. H. Breasted delightedly pointed out, gives support to the belief that other artifacts and even customs may have remained stationary over periods our own changeful age finds incredible.

Watchfully and delicately employed, then, speculative deduction and analogical interpretation are indispensable for understanding the behavior of other human beings in other ages and cultures. But it is wiser to assume, in any doubtful situation, that *Homo sapiens,* fifty thousand years ago, more closely resembled ourselves than any remoter animal ancestor, such as the small-brained tool-using australopithecines, who present no other indication than chipped pebbles of being on the road to human development.

By now, I trust, it should be plain that the chronic practice of describing man as a tool-using animal conceals some of the very facts that must be exposed and revaluated. Why, for example, if tools were so important to human development, did it take man at least half a million years—or three times that period, if we place the dubious hominids of South Africa in the direct line of descent— to shape anything but the crudest stone tools? Why is it that the lowest existing peoples, who support a hand-to-mouth existence with a few elementary tools and weapons, nevertheless have elaborate ceremonials, a complicated kinship organization, and a finely differentiated language, capable of expressing every aspect of their experience?

Why, further, were high cultures, like those of the Maya, the Aztecs, the Peruvians, still using only the simplest handicraft equipment a few centuries ago, although their monuments were magnificent and ancient roads like that to Machu Picchu were marvels of engineering? How is it that the Maya, who had no machines, were masters of abstruse mathematics and had evolved an extremely intricate method of time reckoning which showed superb powers of abstract thought? Once one dares to ask these questions the whole course of human history, from the earliest times on, appears in a new light, and our present machine-centered technology no longer seems the sole witness to the far-off divine event toward which all creation has moved.

# Chapter Seven

# The Origin
# of Man

It is really rather a disappointment that the "missing link" hasn't turned out to be one fossil—a rosetta stone that would solve the mystery of the relationship of man to the rest of the Primates. Yet hope springs eternal and false messiahs appear quite regularly now. A tooth, a bone, a fragment of one or the other, appears, each undoubtedly representing a now extinct primate, but we are always left with the question, *which* primate? For we are particularly interested in that *one species* which first diverged from the line that went on to the apes and thus eventually gave rise to modern man.

*Homo sapiens* is no hybrid. He is a descendant of but one species which diverged. But—and here is the principal fly in the ointment— it is highly probable that more than one species diverged, all of which became extinct except *H. sapiens*. And to further complicate the problem, after a divergence, the newly established species may gradually change in morphological and other ways, until the remote descendants of the original divergent species have been so remodeled that they have lost many of the features of the ancestor species that founded their line. By the fossil evidence alone it is very difficult to distinguish differences that are due to a divergence from those due to change over time—i.e., those that do not involve a divergence. To clarify the nature of the dilemma, a rather silly analogy might be helpful. Given a time machine and an absence of incest taboos, there would be no genetic reason why you could not successfully mate with your great grandparent. But could you mate with a lineal ancestor of 8,000 generations ago even if no intervening divergence had occurred? Perhaps those hundreds of generations have been sufficient time for the gradual accumulation of enough genetic change that incompatibility would exist between you and your ancient ancestor, even though your relationship were a lineal one.

In the real world, of course, we cannot perform mating compatability tests between the fossil and the living. Thus, we can only guess whether a given bone represents a lineal ancestor or a coexisting hominid that would have been as incompatible to our great-great (800 times) grandmother as a gorilla is to you today.

# UNRAVELING THE AGE OF THE EARTH AND MAN

*E. L. Simons*

E. L. Simons, a professor of paleontology at Yale University, is a specialist in the origin and evolution of the primates. Besides his articles in professional journals he is a regular contributor to *Scientific American* and other popular magazines.

For thousands of years man has asked and tried to answer a dual question—how old is the earth and how long is it since the appearance of primates and the emergence of modern man? The answers have often been as interesting—and far ranging—as the riddle itself. It was not until about thirty years ago, however, that researchers began offering reasonably satisfactory figures. And it is only since the late 1950's that an abundance of precise dates have become available to chronologists who deal with the prehistoric past.

From *Natural History*, Vol. 76 No. 5 (Fall 1967), pp. 52–9. © *Natural History*, 1967.

Previously, of course, there had been no lack of estimates. They occur, for example, in the sacred books of many religions. In India the Brahmins considered earth and time as eternal, while some Hindu chronologies indicate that thirteen million years had passed since their "golden age" began. Manetho, the Egyptian historian, listed dynasties of gods and demigods estimated to have reigned on earth for some thirty-six thousand years—from the first dynasty of the gods to the thirteenth historical dynasty. Hebrew priestly writers provided a chronology dating creation at about 4000 B.C., and they seem to have based their creation story, in part, on earlier Babylonian myths, some of which implied an even greater time since creation.

Among many Christians it was thought that the Bible narrative and its chronology could be taken literally; and in 1654 Archbishop Ussher of Armagh, Ireland, seemed to find no uncertainties in the Bible record when he calculated from biblical genealogies that the earth had been created in 4004 B.C. in fact, one of Ussher's contemporaries determined the precise time—the twenty-third day of October at nine o'clock in the morning. Jewish scholars, however, studying the same Old Testament sources, dated the world's creation as October 7, 3761 B.C.; with this date the Jewish calendar begins.

Many modern theologians have challenged, sometimes ridiculed, such literal interpretation of scriptural sources. More than fifteen hundred years ago, St. Augustine proposed that the six days of creation might signify only a logical rather than real succession, and at present even conservative Christian scholars usually agree that one can interpret the six days of creation as standing for six general periods, or eras, rather than for specific 24-hour periods. Meanwhile, with the growth of scientific knowledge in the eighteenth and nineteenth centuries, it became increasingly clear to scholars that the earth must be much more than a few thousand years old. A number of ingenious procedures of estimating the age of the earth, of life, or of the oceans were attempted. All these, however, involved relative methods—no broadly applicable "absolute" or "chronometric" ways of dating rocks were yet known. In 1715, for instance, when the astronomer Halley proposed the first scientific procedure for determining an approximate age for the earth, he assumed that if on initial condensation the primal oceans were fresh water, one could calculate their age by dividing the total amount of sodium salts already present in the oceans by the average amount that is added to the oceans each year from the rivers of the world. Later scientists elaborated this approach, but produced estimates that were too small. We know now that accurate determination of the amount of sodium that land erosion adds each year is uncertain, that the amount added per annum has fluctuated greatly and was probably unusually high during the Cenozoic Era. We also know that salt is removed in deep-sea sediments and as salt deposits produced by evaporation in large inland bays. If the addition of salt had always proceeded at the present rate of about 400 million tons of salt yearly, then one would have to conclude that the seas are only about 100 million years old; the uncertainties are such that this can be a minimum estimate.

Another early procedure for estimating the earth's age involved measuring the world annual rate of deposition of sediment, which is brought about by the agents of erosion—principally wind and water—and dividing this into the total estimated thickness of sediments. For if geologists can estimate the average rate at which sedimentation occurs, they can then determine how long it has been depositing the measurable thickness of geologic layers.

In 1799 William Smith, an English canal surveyor, announced one of the basic concepts upon which the science of geology depends. He pointed out that each rock formation he had observed contained fossils peculiar to itself, and that the fossils present in each formation "always succeed one another in the same order." Fossils thus became the chief instrument for quickly identifying the relative age and sequence of each rock layer. Since the day of William Smith, geologists have separated the series of rock layers into six main divisions or eras: the Azoic (without life), Archeozoic (beginning life), Proterozoic (early life), Paleozoic (ancient life), Mesozoic (middle life), and Cenozoic (recent life, including development of mammals).

Adding up the total known thickness of rocks deposited during the Cenozoic, Mesozoic, and Paleozoic Eras, Professor James D. Dana of Yale was able, as early as 1876, to calculate that the relative durations of these areas were in the ratio of 1:3:12. But not having an accurate estimate of the average rate of sediment deposition throughout geologic time, he was unable to successfully convert these ratios to numerical values. Morever, parts of the sedimentary sequence, called the "stratigraphic column," were missing.

The divisions between geologic periods come where early geologists observed great unconformities. An unconformity is a gap between two layers of rock, usually caused by a period of widespread erosion during which all the strata that would have filled the gap have been destroyed. One can easily see that when layers of shale, sandstone, and limestone are laid down on one another, like layers in a cake, those on the lowest levels are older than those above them. But sometimes these relatively flat layers become folded in the processes of mountain-building, and the crests of such folds may eventually be eroded away, leaving a series of worn edges upon which new flat-lying layers may be deposited. Consequently, between the old, folded layer and the newer one immediately above it, the time required to build and erode the mountain is represented only by a surface, seen in cross section as merely a discontinuity. Such a surface is an unconformity, and such gaps make the geologic record seem like a book from which pages have been torn at intervals. So far, it has been impossible to discover all these missing pages in existing deposits. And in the early days of geology there was no way of estimating the lapse of time corresponding to these great unconformities other than by noting the relative amount of difference or the extent of evolution between the fossils above and below the gap.

Within these limitations, by measuring the greatest thickness of each rock layer and adding up the results, one finds that during the Paleozoic, Mesozoic, and Cenozoic Eras, a total thickness of about $68^{1}/_{2}$ miles would have accumulated if deposition had continued in one spot for the whole period of time. This estimate does not include the lapses of time during all unconformities; if one allows for them it would probably increase the total height to nearly 100 miles. One estimate of the average rate of sedimentary deposition is about one foot every 880 years, which would indicate that the last three geologic eras have lasted some 440 million years.

Accurate measurement of the older three eras is impossible because of frequent gaps in our knowledge of sedimentary deposition, but it is thought that they probably lasted over three times as long, or about one and a half billion years.

Despite their ingenuity, the sedimentary methods of dating the age of the earth or the oceans were never too accurate. Their inadequacies were carefully analyzed in 1917 in an important review of "Rhythms and the Measurement of Geologic Time," by Joseph Barrell. Among other things, he pointed out that estimates of time lapse from sediments are uncertain because erosional rates have fluctuated in the past, and the thickest sediments usually accumulate in narrow marine troughs that contain little of the total product of nearby continental erosion.

By the nineteenth century, a number of geologists had taken another tack. They were estimating the length of time since the development of earliest life. In 1867 one of the founders of the science of geology, Sir Charles Lyell, conjectured that 240 million years might account for the successional changes in animal and plant species. But a contemporary estimated only 60 million years for the same span (since the Cambrian Period). The smaller figure led Charles Darwin to write that it could hardly account for the total development and evolution of organisms. At about the same time, however, an even younger age for the earth was proposed by the physicist Lord Kelvin. His estimate came from determining the rate of cooling of the planet from a state of completely molten rock to its present composition, with only a molten core. In a series of papers, he decreased his first estimate of 400 million to only 20 million years. Obviously, this latter figure greatly distressed most contemporary geologists and paleontologists—it did not allow enough time for known changes that had taken place, particularly in earth's fauna. Kelvin, however, had not taken into account an extra source of heat—unknown to him—that would keep the earth warm for a much longer period: the heat produced by radioactivity. Moreover, there is growing agreement among investigators that the earth did not originate as a molten body. More likely, the earth, as well as the other planets, was accumulated through the gradual accretion of smaller bodies and subsequently warmed by heat from radioactive decay.

It may be difficult for today's reader to realize the impact of those various estimates—not only upon others but also upon such scientists as Darwin, Lyell, and Kelvin themselves. They were forced to readjust their thinking from the widespread Christian assumption of a 6,000-year-old world to one that could be several tens of millions of years old. When figures reach such an astronomical scale, it does not require a grand readjustment in thinking to conceive of the world's age as 200 million or even several billion years. Morever, grasping the meaning of such vast amounts of time is beyond the capacity of most of us. Probably as a consequence of this challenge, twentieth-century geochronologists appear to have been more interested in the accuracy of their calculations than in their antiquity.

Methods depending on radioactive processes have been by far the most fruitful and accurate for determining the age of the earth. Only a few of the more informative of these methods can be briefly summarized here, nor does space allow much detailing of the many intricate processes and complex considerations by which geochemists and geophysicists now date rocks. Generally speaking, progress in the past five or ten years has made it possible to obtain accurate dates for the formation of many of the main types of rocks.

The origins of geochemical dating go back to 1905, when Bertram Boltwood pointed out the universal presence of lead in uranium-bearing rocks and observed that the ratio between lead and uranium was often more or less uniform for uranium minerals from the same region. He also expressed his belief that this must indicate lead of some kind is the end product of the spontaneous breakdown of the radioactive element uranium. Later he proposed that if lead was a product of this process of decay, the ratio of lead to uranium should be the same for minerals of equal age. Consequently, if in a given sample we learn both the amount of radioactivity-produced lead and the amount of still-unchanged uranium, the age of the rock can be determined by the relative proportions—if we know the rate at which the uranium disintegrates.

It happens that there are several types of lead, each differing slightly in atomic weight. Such varieties of the same element are called isotopes. The isotopes of lead include: (1) primal lead, atomic weight 204—a lead believed originally formed as that element; (2) uranium lead, at. wt. 206—resulting from the breakdown of uranium's predominant isotope (U-238); (3) actinium lead, at. wt. 207—end product of a breakdown sequence beginning with another uranium isotope (U-235); (4) thorium lead, at. wt. 208— from the breakdown of thorium (Th-232). The rate of uranium is so slow that it takes over four and a half billion ($4.51 \times 10^9$) years for half of the atoms in a starting amount of it to disintegrate. This figure is the "half-life" of uranium. It would take even longer, $13.9 \times 10^9$ years, for half of thorium's atoms to "decay."

But a timing method should be accurate. How can science be so sure that the disintegration of uranium and other radioactive elements has continued at the same rate throughout geologic time? Here is how the rocks themselves indicate that the rates of decay have remained unaltered. Dark mica, or biotite, acts as a sort of photographic plate for the alpha particles released during the radioactive breakdown. If a microscopic particle of uranium is trapped in a piece of this mica, examination under polarized light will show small darkened rings around the central particle. Such microscopic rings form the so-called pleochroic halo and are known from rocks of all geologic ages. They are caused by the discharge of alpha particles, and the distance these particles will travel in the mica depends on the energy of atomic transformation. With uranium, the pleocroic halo will consist of eight separate rings. Very accurate measurements have shown that the energy of transformation, and therefore the rate of breakdown, is constant in all samples. In addition, numerous experiments have confirmed that the constant rate cannot be changed by an outside influence such as pressure or temperature. There is no danger of confusing primal lead (204), which might also be present in a radioactive sample, with the products of atomic breakdown, because the leads of different origin differ in atomic weight.

So far, the oldest rocks carefully dated (in North America) by the uranium method are Precambrian ones in the Minnesota River Valley. The Morton and Montevedes granite deposits in this valley contain zircons indicating they were crystallized at least 3,300 million years ago. In some parts of the world, rocks giving ages of the same order of magnitude are intruded into or overlay older rocks. It has not yet been possible to date these older rocks, because they have been seriously altered by more recent events. Possibly they were more immediately derived from the original crust of the earth, but geologists have not yet found a rock that could qualify as part of the earth's original crust.

However, some scientists believe that meteorites that contain lead may have the same age as the earth and the rest of our solar system. If so, then the age of the earth, as indicated by recently calculated uranium-lead ages of meteorites, increases to approximately 4,500 million years. This figure can be considered within the framework provided by other probing for dates. For instance, recent studies based on radioactive potassium indicate that about ten billion years ago such potassium began breaking down into an isotope of calcium. Here may be a clue to the age of our part of the universe.

Work with this potassium illustrates the usefulness for earthly data of radioactive materials other than uranium and thorium. Specifically, accurate determinations can be made on rock containing carbon, potassium, or rubidium. The two last-named, both members of the alkali metals family, are especially significant. In the past seven to nine years improvement in dating geologic events has come through analysis of the radioactive decay of potassium (at. wt. 40) to argon 40, and rubidium (at. wt. 87) to strontium 87.

These two geochronometric methods have widely expanded the dating possibilities because radioactive potassium and rubidium occur in many more rock types than datable uranium and thorium. (And uranium dates can be used as a countercheck on potassium or rubidium dates if two or more analytical methods can be run on the same rock.) Potassium-to-argon dates are particularly useful to paleontology because they may be determined from rocks often found associated with fossils, such as glauconites (greensands), ash falls, and lava flows. The principle underlying determination of potassium/argon and rubidium/strontium ages of rocks is basically the same as that of the uranium/lead and thorium/lead dating methods, but the laboratory procedures for analyzing the very small traces of these isotopes are considerably more complex.

Combining all these various dating methods, reasonably accurate chronology or geologic time scale is now available for the time during which development of plant and animal life can be traced on earth from the Cambrian Period to the present. This is valuable because, although traces of simple life—perhaps residues of single-celled organisms—have been found and dated back to three billion years ago, the Cambrian is the oldest geologic period in which fossil organisms are abundant and can be traced in detail through successive evolutionary stages. From then on, the geologic calendar can be dated with considerable accuracy. The chart shows dating done in 1961 by J. Laurence Kulp, eminent American geochemist, and revisions made by a Geological Society of London symposium in 1964.

Now let us apply the foregoing techniques to a problem of general interest—to dating the main stages of evolution in the order of Primates, climaxed by the arrival of modern man. About six years ago, Dr. Kenneth Oakley, noted anthropologist of the British Museum, outlined an approximate dating of some of these main steps, but so rapid has been the recent advance of knowledge— not only of dates, but of fossil primates as well—that another analysis seems warranted.

Until recently, the earliest known primates were found in deposits of Middle Paleocene age in western North America, but in 1965, what is probably a primate tooth was reported from latest Mesozoic deposits in Montana. This means that documentation of the emergence of this mammalian order should be sought in the faunas contemporary with the last of the dinosaurs. The date of the close of the Mesozoic Era, when those earliest primates existed, is indicated by several geochemical dates. One was obtained from ash falls in Alberta deposits of the latest Cretaceous substage—on the order of 63 to 66 million years ago. A potassium/argon date, calculated by J. F. Evernden and his associates at the University of California, was derived from a basalt rock near Denver, Colorado. The basalt, which lies above shales or mudstones containing mammals typical of the earliest kinds of Paleocene fauna, shows an age in excess of 58 million years. Consequently,

# Comparative Geologic Time Scale

| Era | Period | Epoch | Distinctive Features | Kulp (1961) | Symposium (1964) |
|---|---|---|---|---|---|
| CENOZOIC | Quaternary | Pleistocene | Early man; continental ice sheets | 1 | 1.5-2 |
| | | | | | 7 |
| | Tertiary | Pliocene | Large carnivores | 13 | |
| | | Miocene | First abundant grazing mammals | 25 | 26 |
| | | Oligocene | Large running mammals | 36 | 37- |
| | | Eocene | Many modern types of mammals | | 38 |
| | | | | | 53- |
| | | Paleocene | Diversified hoofed mammals | 58 | 54 |
| MESOZOIC | Cretaceous | Maestrichtian | First primates (?) | 63 | 65 |
| | | Upper | First placental mammals | | |
| | | | First flowering plants; climax of dinosaurs and ammonites, followed by extinction | 110 | |
| | | Lower | | 135 | 136 |
| | Jurassic | Upper | First birds, first mammals; dinosaurs and ammonites abundant | 166 | |
| | | Middle Lower | | 181 | 190- |
| | | | | | 195 |
| | Triassic | Upper | First dinosaurs. Abundant cycads and conifers | 200 | |
| | | Middle Lower | | (230) | 225 |

Millions of Years

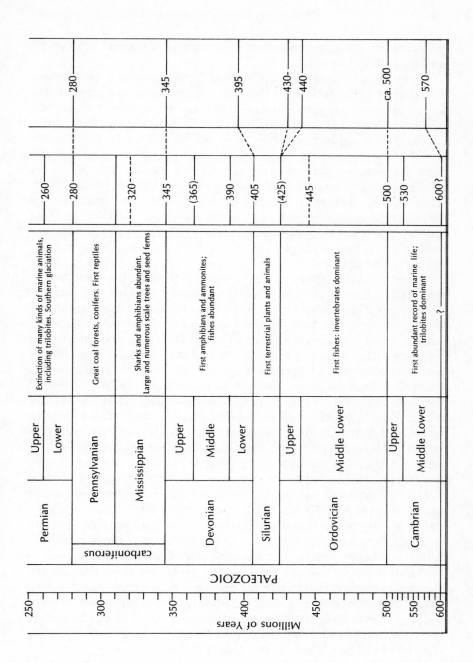

primates apparently came into existence as a group between 60 and 65 million years ago.

The primate fossils so far obtained from rocks laid down many millions of years following that time all resemble the present-day lower primates, or prosimians—including the lemurs, lorises, and tarsiers. These were widespread in the Early Tertiary, particularly in the Northern Hemisphere. They are abundant in the Eocene rocks of western North America and Europe, and are beginning to turn up increasingly in China, in rocks of similar age. Members of the order Primates did not reach South America until the Oligocene Epoch. Although Eocene land mammals are unknown in Africa, it is probable that there were also early primates on that continent, as the ancestors of the Malagasy lemurs of today presumably reached Madagascar early in the Cenozoic Era by way of the African continent.

A second main stage in the evolution of primates was the development from prosimians of the higher primates, or Anthropoidea (apes and monkeys as well as men). Among the many common features of the Anthropoidea that might signal the appearance of this level of primate organization in the fossil record are the characteristic closure of the orbit behind the eye into an eye socket and the reduction of the number of premolar teeth from four to two on each side of each jaw. Both of these features are first observed in fossil "apes" from the Early Oligocene in the Qatrani formation of the Fayum province of Egypt. No geochemically datable rocks have been found in these Egyptian fossil fields, but they are overlain by a volcanic rock that may soon be dated. The animal fauna with which these ancient apes (*Propliopithecus, Aeolopithecus,* and *Aegyptopithecus*) were recovered indicate an earliest Oligocene land mammal age. In North America, Early Oligocene rocks are associated with Chadronian fauna, which Evernden, *et al.,* have dated by the potassium/argon method with ages ranging from 33 to 36 million years. By that time the higher primates had definitely differentiated in Africa, and perhaps elsewhere as well.

At least since Darwin's time, a great problem confronting evolutionists has been: How close are apes and men taxonomically, and when did their ancestry split? Although these questions remain partly unanswered, we can now determine the age of the oldest clear-cut relatives of man, as opposed to apes, from data concerning species of the Mio-Pliocene genus *Ramapithecus*.

This primate, like both modern and primitive man, had small canines and front teeth, a short face, an arched palate, and massive jaws with crowded teeth arranged in a semicircle, rather than in a

U-shaped dental arcade with parallel cheek tooth rows. I have recently placed species of *Ramapithecus* in the taxonomic family of man: Hominidae. The oldest dated members of this genus come from near Fort Ternan, Kenya—from a deposit that the potassium/argon method has shown to be 14 million years old. How much prior to this date the families of man and apes separated is still unknown.

Much more is understood today about the time when modern man's forerunners first began to use stone tools. Paleoanthropologists have usually adopted the definition of man as any hominid that makes stone tools to a set and regular pattern. So defined, the earliest "men" are evidenced by living floors in Bed I of the now-celebrated Olduvai Gorge sequence of Early Pleistocene deposits in Tanzania, East Africa. The deposits of Bed I, in which stone tools first occur, have been dated by the University of California group at 1.75 million years. This figure sums up more than sixty separate potassium/argon analyses. Its accuracy therefore correlates with the accuracy of this dating method.

Admittedly, these oldest dated human cultural sites at Olduvai are not necessarily those of the first actual users of tools. But it can be assumed that tool-using probably did not become general much earlier. If it had, archeologists would presumably be able to document this from sites of tool use and manufacture elsewhere in Africa (apart from East Africa) and in Eurasia as well. Controversy about the toolmakers at Olduvai has been stirred by the unsound taxonomic procedures that have been used to name them. Although the names *Zinjanthropus boisei* and *Homo habilis* have been proposed for them, there is no clear-cut evidence that hominids other than two species of *Australopithecus*—*A. africanus* and *A. robustus*—earlier named in South Africa, existed in Tanzania in Bed I times.

The next important stage in human evolution was signaled by the appearance of large-brained hominids of *Pithecanthropus* type —those with brain volumes of more than 700 cc., as opposed to the earlier *Australopithecus* brain volumes on the order of 400 to 600 cc. The first of these pithecanthropines, from Java, was described in 1892 as *Pithecanthropus erectus*. Investigators usually now consider it to be a species of *Homo*—*H. erectus*. The evolutionary emergence of *H. erectus* appears to be documented also at Olduvai, but is not as precise or certain as we wish because the rock samples from this horizon do not have as suitable a composition for potassium/argon (K/A) dating as do those from Bed I. Drs. Curtis and Evernden have recently rechecked their K/A date from sediments at the top of Bed II Olduvai and have determined an approximate age of 500,000 years. Inasmuch as the Oldowan pithecanthropines were all collected below this horizon, they must be older than half a million years—which correlates reasonably with the recent K/A determination of 0.6 million years on tektites from the Djetis beds of Java, from which the earliest H. erectus come.

For the time period within which the completely modern H. sapiens type of men evolved, another geochronometric method can be used—radiocarbon dating. But because the half-life of radioactive carbon is only about 5,000 years, dates in excess of 40,000 or 50,000 years are inaccurate. Also, the K/A dating method is increasingly inaccurate for dates of less than one million years. Consequently, there is a period during Early and Middle Pleistocene times when dating human remains is difficult and uncertain. During this time, H. erectus populations presumably graded into the Neanderthal type of primitive man, a variety to which most modern taxonomists would give only subspecific status, H. sapiens neanderthalensis. Neanderthalers have been dated as persisting in western Europe for two or three hundred thousand years. They seem to overlap with human fossils that appear to be more like those of modern man, of which the ones from Fontechevade and La Ferassie in France are examples. These most probably represent only the more progressive individuals and not a different race. The more abundant skeletal finds of Stone Age men are about 30,000 to 40,000 years old. Many have been dated accurately by the radiocarbon method and, consequently, the structural and cultural evolution of Late Paleolithic man is well documented and dated. Sufficient to say that within the period in which radiocarbon dating of fossil man is possible, only slight alterations in skeletal anatomy have occurred; as far as the main stages of locomotor adaptation and evolutionary change are concerned, man's ancestors of 40,000 years ago were essentially the same as man is today.

And what may the future reveal about our prehistoric calendar? As more and more fossil-bearing sediments are dated, multiple cross-checks on individual dates will be possible, and this should eventually lead to a nearly absolute chronology for life of the past. Nevertheless, some sediments will probably never be datable, because many lack sufficient concentrations of any of the known unstable isotopes of common elements. Even so, if such rocks contain traces of past organisms, they can be correlated in time with the same organisms in dated rocks.

Some scientists have suggested that when, and if, this geochronological "millennium" arrives there would be great value in rearranging or renaming the divisions of geologic time to correspond with fixed time durations. Thus the Tertiary, which lasted roughly sixty million years, could be divided into six subdivisions of ten million years each. Whatever the course adopted, it is clear that geochemical dating will eventually provide an accurate calendar for placement of fossil species in their proper temporal relationships. Until this is done, science cannot remain satisfied: uncertainties in interpreting the exact course of evolutionary history will remain among almost all groups of organisms.

# MAN'S EARLIEST ANCESTORS

*David R. Pilbeam*

David R. Pilbeam, University Demonstrator in Physical Anthropology at the Duckworth Laboratory of Physical Anthropology, Cambridge University, is the discoverer of several early hominids.

No longer is it a question of whether man has evolved from some prehuman primate but of when and from which primate. Our work on human evolution, like most of the relevant fossils themselves, has been concentrated on the evolution of man during the Pleistocene period, now believed to cover the past three million or so years of geological history. Although there are still doubters, it is widely accepted that we can now trace, often with some certainty, our evolution from such creatures as *Australopithecus* from the South African Early Pleistocene. They were animals standing little more than four feet tall, with ape-sized jaws, teeth and brains. Fossil apes are known from these times too; thus, two million years ago at least, men and apes were already distinct.

Although the pre-Pleistocene hominid story has remained something of a mystery, within the past five years it has become clear that at least one claimant deserves careful consideration: *Ramapithecus*. This is an Indian Late Miocene fossil primate, found in

From *Science Journal*, Vol. 3 (Feb. 1967), pp. 47–54. Reprinted by permission.

the 1930's. It was described then as a hominid—belonging to the same zoological family as does modern man—but was cold-shouldered by the American anthropological establishment. The reinstatement of *Ramapithecus* as an ancestor of the Pleistocene hominids is one of the most important recent developments in palaeoanthropology, for it pushes back the time of differentiation of apes and men to 14 million years ago, and perhaps much further.

Since the work of the eighteenth century Swedish naturalist Linnaeus, every living species of plant and animal has been described by two Latin names. Modern man, for example, is known as *Homo sapiens*. All living men are thought to belong to a single species, and all are therefore regarded as members of *Homo sapiens*. A species is the largest group of organisms that interbreeds under natural conditions, producing offspring fully fertile with others of both their own and preceding generations.

Closely related species, however, are grouped in the same genus. For example, *Canis lupus,* the timber wolf, and *Canis niger,* the red wolf, the different but related species sufficiently similar to be placed in a single genus, *Canis.* The morphological similarities of the two species are due to fundamental genetic similarities.

The unit which evolves is the population, not the individual. The genetic structure of a species changes through time as the relative biological success or failure of each genetic type causes some individuals to leave more offspring, some less, than others. In fact, the species is the important unit of evolution, and before the evolutionary history of a particular group can be studied the fossils must also be divided into species ideally having the same sort of variability within groups and the same sort of gaps between groups as are found within and between modern species.

Related genera are grouped into families, just as related species are grouped into genera. I should point out here that species are thought to be related because they are physically similar, and that they are similar because they evolved from some common ancestor.

The three living great apes—the orangutan, gorilla and chimpanzee known respectively as *Pongo pygmaeus, Gorilla gorilla,* and *Pan satyrus*—are classified in one family, the Pongidae. Hence the term pongid, which can be used to describe any living great ape. Modern and fossil men are classified in another family, the Hominidae (thus the appropriate descriptive team—hominid).

Comprehensive field studies of the great apes, particularly of the chimpanzee, have developed only recently. Already, however, they have revealed the complexities of the social life of these mammals. In certain areas, chimpanzees have developed a simple tool-

using culture. Occasionally they have been seen to band together
for the capture and eating of red colobus monkeys, and they do
share food. The great apes, far from being "brutish" as most nineteenth century naturalists believed, are now known to be intelligent
animals, living in relatively complex groups. Of course, they must
not be treated as models for the early hominids, but it is evident
that complex social behavior is possible with an "ape-sized" brain.

The great apes are certainly man's closest living relatives. To
the classical evidence of dentition, comparative anatomy and
embryology has been added fresh information from such diverse
fields as molecular biology, parasitology and animal behavior. All
strengthen this conclusion. Yet there are many obvious differences
between members of the two families. Is it possible to account for
these differences in evolutionary terms? If so, when did our
ancestors begin to differ from those of the apes?

The living pongids are basically forest dwelling vegetarians,
living in or near the edges of tropical rain forests in Africa (the
gorilla and chimpanzee) and Borneo and Sumatra (the orangutan).
The gorilla eats mostly vegetable food, the chimpanzee and orangutan seem to prefer fruit. Powerfully built creatures, they show
many adaptations to life in or near the trees. The orang is the most
arboreal of the three and spends most of its time eating, sleeping,
playing and relaxing in trees. Newly discovered remains of ancestral gorillas of the Miocene epoch were certainly less bulky and
more arboreal than their present-day descendants. This, the largest
of the living apes, now spends most of its time on the ground. Like
the orang, the chimpanzee nests mostly in the trees but spends
much more time on the ground. Perhaps this is because the local
forest is more open.

Modern man, like his Pleistocene ancestors, is almost entirely
a terrestrial animal. We are erect bipeds and, except as babies, we
do not walk quadrupedally. While most great apes can walk biped-
ally, they rarely do so and on the ground they are predominantly
quadrupeds. Perhaps the most obvious character of distinction
between men and apes is brain size. Human brains are three times
as large as those of chimpanzees and, however one defines the
term, we are certainly more intelligent. Many anthropologists believe that man owes his enormous brain to the habit of tool making,
although it is more likely that an increase in the complexity of his
culture has gone hand in hand with brain expansion.

Human culture must have developed from simpler social traditions, from groupings comparable in complexity with those of
present day chimpanzees. We can recognize the existence of true

culture in the stone artifacts of the archaeological record. However, stone tools obviously represent only a fraction of the learned behavior—language, customs, religions and laws—that make up culture. Stone tool making, to a regular and recognizable pattern, began perhaps two or three million years ago. At that time our ancestors were small brained, like the living apes, but this does not mean that they should be called "apes" or "ape-men." They were primitive hominids. From what we can reconstruct of their behavior, it seems that they were omnivores and hunters like later men, rather than predominantly vegetarians like the living pongids.

Tool making, and before that tool using, has had obvious influences on our anatomy. The jaws and teeth of gorillas differ in many ways from those of men. Most obviously, our teeth are smaller. Gorilla canines are large and projecting. The front lower premolar, because of its contact with the large upper canine, becomes an elongated, rather blade-like tooth. It is described as "sectorial" and with a canine makes an efficient pair of shears for cutting through tough vegetable material such as the bamboos on which gorillas feed. Man, with his modest canines, has no sectorial teeth. Like the posterior premolars, the anterior premolars have two cusps. Our incisors and canines are, in fact, much reduced in size compared with our premolars and molars. Hominid incisors and canines need not be used to dismember prey, nor to break open hard fruits and nuts. Tools can be used in their place. As ancillary teeth and fingers, tools were clearly very important in human evolution. They became not only cutters but diggers, spears and axes. In short, artifacts were used not only as tools, but as weapons too.

The canines of male pongids are larger than those of females; these teeth are important in aggressive behavior both within and between species. In hominids, it is thought, this function of the canines has disappeared. Students of primate behavior such as A. Kortlandt and the late K. R. I. Hall have suggested that this was the original function of tools, as important elements in display and defense in place of large canines. The use of weapons, and the adoption of a bipedal, terrestrial way of life, has wrought profound changes in our behavior and physical makeup. These trends seem to have been well under way in the hominids of the Early Pleistocene. They used and made stone tools, and hunted their food. They were bipeds and their dentition was similar to ours in all features except size.

It has already been stressed that these early men were not "apes." The idea has taken a long time to sink into the collective anthropological consciousness but important recent work on ape behavior has finally dispelled these doubts. Jane Goodall's brilliant field research on chimpanzees in Tanzania has shown us just how complex, in fact, is their behavior. G. B. Schaller has done the same for the gorilla in the Congo. Research into the social structure of the advanced cooperative hunting carnivores such as wolves and Cape hunting dogs, suggests that many of the features in which we differ from nonhuman primates might be due to the evolution of social hunting in the hominid line. Man seems to have evolved from a primate with a social structure similar in complexity to that of the chimpanzee. But he has evolved into something much more than a mere ape, and luckily the course of his evolution is preserved in the fossil record.

In 1856 a Frenchman, Edouard Lartet, described the lower jaw of a fossil ape which had been found in beds of Middle Miocene age at St. Gaudens in south western France. He called this specimen *Dryopithecus fontani*. Others of the same species have since been found in France as well as elsewhere in Europe. During the past 110 years several hundred ape fossils have been discovered in places as diverse as China, India, Russia, Spain and Kenya. All fall between the Oligocene and Pliocene epochs. The rocks from which they come can now be dated radiometrically, and it is doubtful whether many are much older than 30 million or much younger than 10 million years. Altogether, nearly 30 genera and 50 species have been created to accommodate these creatures since Lartet described the first of them. The living and fossil pongids have been placed in separate subfamilies of the Pongidae, the first in the Ponginae, the last in the Dryopithecinae—named after *Dryopithecus*.

An interest in pre-Pleistocene human origins took me in 1963 from Cambridge to the United States, to work with Professor Elwyn Simons at Yale University. Like myself, Simons had been interested for some time in the dryopithecine problem. The larger number of published names for dryopithecines led many palaeontologists to believe that higher primate evolution in the Miocene and Pliocene had been exceedingly complex. Both Simons and I were sceptical of this view and, as more names were published it became increasingly unlikely that they all represented valid species and genera.

Our first task was to study the rather extensive literature on the subject which had appeared since 1856. Soon it became clear that many fossils had been given new names for quite inadequate reasons. The first specimen described from a new species is generally designated the "type"; this is the individual specimen which always carries the new name, as it were, attached to it. Subsequent discoveries should be compared with type specimens and, unless the new finds are sufficiently distinct and different, they should be included in existing species. Individuals within any living species differ one from another—it is even possible to find differences between opposite sides of the same jaw—and unless the variation in the fossils is likely to exceed that range of variation normal for living related species it is unwise to give the new specimen a new name.

Next we turned our attention to dryopithecine "species" from Late Miocene and Early Pliocene deposits in Asia, principally from the Siwalik Hills of northwestern India, but also from China. Almost all the characters which supposedly distinguished these "species" turned out to be entirely trivial—slight differences in the degree of wrinkling on the molar crowns, and in the shape and relative proportions of the various teeth. We found that we could reduce the number of Asian species to four, three of them in the genus *Dryopithecus,* but each distinct from *D. fontani.* The one Siwalik primate that was not *Dryopithecus* was the specimen mentioned at the start of this article: *Ramapithecus.*

This fossil was found in 1932 and described in 1934 by G. E. Lewis of Yale University. He considered it a hominid. Unfortunately few others shared his view. In 1961, Simons had published a new paper on *Ramapithecus,* reexamining the evidence. He concluded that this genus belonged to the Hominidae. Dating placed it in the Late Miocene, perhaps 14 million years ago, and so the antiquity of fossil man (in the broadest sense) was extended back in time by a factor of four or five.

The original *Ramapithecus* specimen consisted of a right maxilla or upper jaw, with two premolars and two molars remaining in it. The canine socket and the root of one incisor, as well as part of the socket of a second, were also preserved. Although the fragment was not very extensive, quite enough was left to demonstrate that this was not merely another ape, another dryopithecine. The small, low crowned molars and premolars, together with the small size of the canine and incisors (inferred from their diminutive root sockets), and greatly foreshortened face, distinguish this hominid from late Miocene pongids. Using the same criteria, Pleistocene hominids such as *Australopithecus* can be distinguished from living apes such as the chimpanzee.

Sorting through the Indian fossil jaws and teeth—the majority of dryopithecines are represented by fragments of this sort—we found that we were able to divide them up into man-like and ape-like forms. A second complete maxilla, first described in 1915 as *Dryopithecus* and misinterpreted since then, joined Lewis's original specimen in *Ramapithecus*. Various isolated upper teeth could also be included. So far, our reidentified hominid specimens were confined, surprisingly, to upper jaw material.

During our survey we found we had also divided the lower jaws into two groups; some ape-like and another man-like. The man-like form had been named, again by Lewis, *Bramapithecus*. Compared with *Dryopithecus*, *Bramapithecus* has relatively square, compact teeth, and a greatly shortened molar tooth row. In *Dryopithecus* the molars are longer and more elongated in shape, and they increase in size from front to back. As in living apes, the jaw is deep, and the whole face projects further forward than is the case in the hominids. This trend is probably associated with feeding habits, with the importance of large teeth for chewing tough vegetable foods, and for carrying and examining objects. In hominids, the use of natural objects as tools and weapons has relieved the teeth of these functions and has helped in reduction of the face. *Bramapithecus* has a shallow lower jaw, and a foreshortened face. It is man-like, so much so that it closely resembles the mandible of a Middle Pleistocene hominid from South Africa originally known as *Telanthropus capensis*, later as *Homo erectus*.

Now we had one hominid genus, *Ramapithecus*, containing only upper jaws, and another, *Bramapithecus*, based entirely on lower jaws. It dawned on us that we were dealing with the two parts of the same form! All the specimens, upper and lower jaws together, went into a single species, *Ramapithecus punjabicus*. The similarities between *R. punjabicus* and the later hominids of the Pleistocene are quite striking. The Pleistocene forms are more completely known and, of course, *Ramapithecus* is known only from jaws and teeth, so the recovery of more complete Miocene material might show that similarities were confined only to the facial region. However, we have to work with the cash in hand, and that is sufficient to tell us that *Ramapithecus* was different from *Dryopithecus* in anatomically, and presumably functionally, important ways. It differs in the same features that distinguish men from apes.

We next turned our attention to the African forms. In the 1920s, E. J. Wayland, Director of the Geological Survey of Uganda, forwarded to the British Museum (Natural History) in London, a series of fossils from Koru in Kenya. The pongids were described by Hopwood in 1933 under the binomen *Proconsul africanus*. Since then, several hundred additional specimens have been recovered from a number of sites in and around the Kavirondo Gulf of Lake Victoria, and also from deposits further north in Uganda. Much later Sir Wilfrid Le Gros Clark and Dr. L. S. B. Leakey diagnosed two more species of the genus, *Proconsul nyanzae* and *P. major*. *P. major* was the largest, as big as a female gorilla. *P. nyanzae* was probably chimpanzee sized and *P. africanus* somewhat smaller.

*Proconsul* has been recovered from sites of mainly Early Miocene date. Recently, rocks from some of these sites have been dated radiometrically to about 20 million years. The earliest Eurasian species of *Dryopithecus* are no older than 16 or 17 million years, and it is quite possible that the *Proconsul* group was broadly ancestral to these later forms.

We concluded that the structural distinctions listed as distinguishing *Proconsul* from the dryopithecines were not in fact particularly important. So the species of *Proconsul* were transferred to the genus *Dryopithecus*. We also thought that *Proconsul* species were ancestral to the chimpanzee and the gorilla. We were not prepared to commit ourselves, however, as to exactly which species was ancestral to which living ape. Many workers had assumed that the chimpanzee and the gorilla have only recently become separated. This view was often linked to theories that the hominids themselves had differentiated only during the Pliocene. But here we recognized ancestral chimpanzees and gorillas, already distinct in the Early Miocene. Also, these forms were relatively unspecialized dentally and skeletally. They had not apparently evolved those great ape locomotor and feeding specializations associated (it is said) with habitual forest dwelling, and with fruit and shoot eating.

The dryopithecine "complex" had thus been reduced to fewer than a dozen species in one genus. Since returning to Cambridge, I have continued multivariate statistical analyses of the dryopithecines. It now appears possible that one of the Asian species of *Dryopithecus (Sivapithecus)*, is ancestral to the orangutan.

In 1962, Leakey described a new fossil primate from a Late Miocene formation at Fort Ternan in Kenya. The find consisted of right and left upper jaws, and an associated lower molar. He called it *Kenyapithecus wickeri*. Examining casts, photographs and the originals, we could find no characters of sufficient difference from *Ramapithecus* to warrant placing it in a new genus. In fact, the two forms were so similar that we were unable to put them even in separate species. The upper canine, which is unknown in the Indian *Ramapithecus,* was small; it was shaped rather like that of a small female *Dryopithecus* but in size was similar to that of man.

Thus in the Late Miocene of India, East Africa, and possibly Europe, too, there lived a primate so similar dentally and facially to Pleistocene man that it was difficult to find characters to distinguish it from *Australopithecus* or *Homo erectus* (a primitive species of *Homo*).

It was said when *Ramapithecus* was first described, and it will undoubtedly be said now, that *Ramapithecus* is not really a hominid, but a man-like ape. Of course, it might be. It might, too, be a hominid-like monkey, or lemur, or horse, or elephant, or whatever you like. I have listed these alternatives in descending order of plausibility, in order to stress that our assignment of *Ramapithecus* to the Hominidae is made because it is the most plausible hypothesis, the best way to account for its physical appearance. We have assumed that the similarities, in almost all known parts, to later hominids were due to the fact that *Ramapithecus punjabicus,* or something very similar, was ancestral to *Australopithecus* and *Homo.* In short, the similarities are homologies, not parallelistic developments. We are proposing the simplest explanation and using the procedure of naming as a way of making evolutionary hypotheses.

More than 30 years ago, a German anthropologist, Paul Alsberg, wrote an essay on the first *Australopithecus* specimen from Taung in Botswana. He argued that the appearance of *Australopithecus* (or indeed of any Pleistocene fossil hominid), with small anterior teeth, reduced canines and a foreshortened face, indicated that it was a tool user. Since then many workers have emphasized that *Australopithecus* must have been continuously dependent on tools for survival. Raymond Dart, the describer of the first *Australopithecus* skull, believes that here was a hunter who used stone and wood implements and made bone tools. It is now fairly well established, that Early Pleistocene man was a tolerably successful hunter.

I have already mentioned that *Ramapithecus* showed the same dental and facial specializations as *Australopithecus.* It is difficult to avoid the conclusion that just as these specifically hominid adaptations were established by the end of the Miocene, 14 million years ago, so too would many specifically hominid behavioral traits be developing at that time. Not only did the separation of men and apes occur further back in time than many believed, but basic hominid features seem to have been established long before the Pleistocene.

As I have mentioned, regular stone tool making began two million or more years ago. Before that, the probable use of implements by hominids is obviously going to be very difficult to establish. One way to attack the problem will be by analysis of faunas associated with the hominids. Do animal bones show signs of bashing or cutting? Is there any evidence of selectivity in the collection of bones which might indicate food preferences? For clarification, these points must await further work, although Leakey has already suggested that some of the associated animal bones at the *Ramapithecus* site in Kenya show evidence of predatory activities.

Björn Kurtén has recently pointed out how deficient Old World Early Pliocene faunas were in the sort of medium-sized, fast-running carnivores that might have been competitors for a hunting hominid. He concludes, ". . . and it would seem that the treeless plain of Pontian [Early Pliocene] times may have held fewer terrors to a fast-moving, quick-witted early hominid than we might be disposed to believe. To an armed band most of the smaller carnivores would be no menace, while the large forms, although invincible as such, could be avoided by decoy and flight."

To the sociability, intelligence, and manipulative abilities of our primate ancestors were added the cooperative hunting activities of the social carnivore, producing a unique and potentially formidable new type of animal—the earliest hominid. The evolution of this new breed was well under way 14 million years ago. There we can, almost, end our story.

Five years ago, Elwyn Simons began field work in the Egyptian Fayum, a region of Eocene and Oligocene sandstones exposed in the desert to the south west of Cairo. The Fayum was once a region of tropical forests and rivers, and in Oligocene times, more than 30 million years ago, the area teemed with all kinds of animals. Among them were primitive apes.

The Fayum had been searched for fossils by American and German expeditions in the early years of this century, and a number of new genera and species of primates were recovered. Only one need concern us here. *Propliopithecus haeckeli.*

*Propliopithecus* has been described as many things in its time: a fossil gibbon, an early great ape, the ancestor of both men and apes, or of men, apes and gibbons. For a number of reasons, *Propliopithecus* is no longer regarded as a gibbon. It has many similarities, though, to fossil and living apes and men but, as one would expect, it is much smaller than either. Its lower jaw—all that is known—measures only about two inches from front to back. However, the morphological features of the teeth, and the shape and proportions of the jaw bone, recall those of the Higher Primates.

The molars and premolars are similar to those of *Dryopithecus* (and these are basically similar, in morphology, to those of later hominids and pongids). The molars are squarish though, and show no size increase from front to back. Also, the front and rear premolars are similar in size; the front premolar is not a sectorial tooth, and this implies that the upper canine was not large. The lower canine was relatively small.

In his field work, Simons not only found further specimens of *Propliopithecus,* but recovered the remains of a creature—later named *Aegyptopithecus zeuxis*—which was a very primitive *dryopithecine.* Yet this is a dryopithecine half as old again as the oldest previously known! The canines were large and the anterior lower premolars were sectorial—the molars were morphologically very similar to those of the earliest *Dryopithecus* from Africa and Europe, and they increased in size from front to back. The upper teeth showed the same sort of similarities to *Dryopithecus* as did the lower. So, here in the Oligocene, perhaps 30 million years ago, we have evidence showing that the great apes had already begun their evolution as a separate lineage. Now, the sort of differences which distinguish *Propliopithecus* and *Aegyptopithecus* are similar to those which distinguish *Ramapithecus,* the hominid, and *Dryopithecus,* the pongid.

Before I actually write that *Propliopithecus* was a hominid, before we commit ourselves to such a small scrap of bone, it is well to remember that the *relative* ages of *Propliopithecus* and *Aegyptopithecus* are still unknown. We do not know whether *Propliopithecus* is older or younger, for adequate field notes that would help in dating were not kept by the early expeditions. We simply cannot say if *Aegyptopithecus* is just a variant of *Propliopithecus,* or if *Propliopithecus* is ancestral to *Aegyptopithecus,* or if the two were contemporaries. If they did live at the same time it is possible that *Propliopithecus* was the earliest known hominid. A few heretics. St. George Mivart was one and Frederic Wood Jones another, believed that men and apes differentiated long ago, perhaps during the Eocene. Recently, W. L. Edwards has outlined the theoretical reasons for accepting an early rather than a late separation of man and ape.

To sum it up: we now know the mid-Tertiary ancestors of the living apes, and we have started to collect information about our own remote ancestors. Yet there is still a long way to go, for we have only the first few links in what must be a complete chain. If we are to reconstruct the ecology and behavior of our evolutionary grandfathers (and granduncles) we need as much fossil material as possible.

We can feel satisfaction in rethinking some of the important aspects of our subject, for a little speculation, even premature speculation, is often preferable to no speculation at all.

For Further Reading

"The Early Relatives of Man," by E. Simons, *Scientific American,*
    Vol. 211 (1964), pp. 51–62.

*Origins of Man,* by J. Buettner-Janusch (London: Wiley, 1966).

*The Origin of Races,* by Carleton Coon (London: Cape, 1963).

# ANCIENT ANCESTOR:
## SKULL OF *AEGYPTOPITHECUS ZEUXIS*

Swinging down from a tree in the lush forest that stood in what is now the Fayum desert region in Egypt, the little creature reached the riverbank and began to drink. Suddenly it was attacked and eaten by a crocodile-like reptile that rose without warning from the water. All that the predator left behind was the victim's head, which sank to the bottom and became embedded in the sand. In New Haven, Conn., last week, some 28 million years after this hypothetical drama, Yale Paleontologist Elwyn Simons displayed the ancient skull and reported that it belonged to the most primitive

Reprinted from *Time,* The Weekly Newsmagazine, Nov. 24, 1967, p. 62. Copyright Time Inc., 1967.

ape ever discovered—the earliest known member of man's family tree.

The skull of the ape, named *Aegyptopithecus zeuxis* (for "linking Egyptian ape"), was found protruding from rock during a 1966 Yale expedition to the Fayum desert. But it was not until the specimen had been returned to Yale and extracted from its rock casement that Simons realized that it was an unusually complete skull of a primate lacking only portions of its top and bottom and four incisor teeth. "Not only is the skull some eight to ten million years older than any other fossils related to man," Simons said, "but it is better preserved than any that are older than 300,000 years."

Scientists established the age of the ancient skull by using the potassium-argon method of dating an overlying lava flow, which is apparently 26 million years old. The location of the skull, 300 ft. below, indicated that it was about 2,000,000 years older. *Aegyptopithecus*, Simons believes, "stands near the very base of the genealogical tree leading to later Great Apes and man. It represents a major stage in the documentation of the forerunners of man."

# EMERGING MAN IN AFRICA

*Ronald Singer*

Ronald Singer, a professor of anatomy at the University of Chicago, is a physical anthropologist with particular interest in human evolution in Africa.

Paleoanthropologists today are methodically uprooting fossil evidence from the African soil and reassembling the evolutionary sequences. Discoveries of the past century have provided a commentary on the origin of the human genus and species, *Homo sapiens*, and many of the so-called missing links have been forged into a likely chain of events.

From *Natural History*, Vol. 71 (Nov. 1962), pp 10–21. © Natural History, 1962.

Mankind was cradled in Africa about one million years ago, some 70 million years after the first primates surged upward in the generalized mammalian genesis that followed the decreasing superiority of Mesozoic reptiles. During that Paleocene period, adverse conditions decimated the giant reptilian genera, and small mammals diversified in geometric progression, either adapting and progressing or becoming extinct along aberrant lines of ecologic experimentation.

During the Lower Oligocene (approximately 40 million years ago), the area that is today called Egypt contained *Parapithecus,* probably the earliest apelike form, as well as *Propliopithecus,* which appears to be a close relative of the ancestral stock of the modern gibbon. Primitive gibbons, long-limbed arboreal apes, are represented in the early Miocene (approximately 25 million years ago) in East Africa by a few genera, of which one advanced form, *Pliopithecus,* spread into Europe and Asia. About 10 million years ago (Pliocene period) it was sufficiently adapted to give rise to the modern gibbons, now confined to Malayan environs.

The Miocene lake bed deposits exposed in the hot, dry gullies on Rusinga Island, near the Kavirondo Gulf of Lake Victoria, have revealed a fairly complete series of fossilized remains of *Proconsul,* an extinct generalized form of ape, of which three widely separated species have been described. They ranged from the size of a small chimpanzee to a large gorilla, and were capable of running and jumping along the ground and along branches. The several dental fragments of the various species of *Dryopithecus* recorded from the Middle and Upper Pliocene deposits of Africa (and India and Europe) reveal considerable variation, so that some resemble the living orang, some the chimpanzee, and others the gorilla, while the cusp pattern of the molars adumbrates those known in the fossil ancestors of *Homo sapiens.* There are many reasons for believing that *Proconsul* or closely allied genera formed an ideal generalized stock that could have given rise to a diversity of evolutionary forms as represented in the Hominidae (extinct and recent forms of man) and the Pongidae (anthropoid apes). In March, 1962, Dr. L. S. B. Leakey announced in the American press the discovery at Fort Ternan in Kenya of specimens stated to be 14 million years old. He claims that this advanced *Proconsul*-like form seems to be midway between the early apes and man. However, these scanty remains at present do no more than confirm the evolutionary potential in a hominid direction of this wide-ranging genus.

The varied and generous African environment provided the lost paradise where the Hominidae separated from the Pongidae, and, during the course of ten million years, radiating forms moved along a number of evolutionary avenues. Many of these avenues led into a cul-de-sac, but some broadened into the human pathway.

The most significant phase in the study of human origins in the first half of the twentieth century was initiated in 1924 when Raymond A. Dart, then the Professor of Anatomy at the University of the Witwatersrand, recognized the importance of a fossil baboon skull brought to him by a student, Miss Josephine Salmons. The skull derived from a quarry being mined at Taung in Bechuanaland, whence shortly after parcels of pink, bone-bearing breccia—calcified sediment or debris cemented in blocks—were dispatched to Dart. Included therein was the endocranial cast or mold of the interior of the skull, as well as parts of the broken skull into which it fitted. He immediately observed with great excitement that the mold was three times the size of a baboon brain and larger than that of any adult chimpanzee. These remains represented the now-famous juvenile *Australopithecus* ("southern ape") *africanus,* which Dart described in 1925 when he indicated the unique presence of hominid characteristics in an otherwise pongid skull. In the face of an effusive series of critical and unbelieving blasts from experts outside Africa, Dart, with his Australian tenacity, persisted in his initial conclusion. Only eleven years later Dart's insight was irrevocably supported by Robert Broom's recovery of the brain cast and skull of *Plesianthropus* (now *Australopithecus*) *transvaalensis,* fondly termed "Mrs. Ples." Subsequent discoveries stimulated research and discussion throughout the anthropological world—some seeking to disprove, others trying to support the descriptions of the many australopithecine fossils found in South Africa.

Thus it was under a cloud that *Australopithecus,* the first of the primitive hominids, was born. Since 1925 skeletal remains of about 100 individuals have been recovered in the Transvaal at Sterkfontein, Kromdraai, Swartkrans, and Makapan Limeworks. Out of this series have crystallized two genera, *Australopithecus* and *Paranthropus* (which some scientists believe should be merged into the former), two species, and four subspecies.

The most spectacular of these Transvaal sites are the caves at Sterkfontein and in the Makapan Valley. In caverns, water-eroded or dissolved out of massive hills of dolomite and travertine, the fossilized remains of hundreds of mammals (antelopes, carnivores, rodents, baboons, australopithecines, and many others) are now found cemented by lime into the floors, which have been disturbed by roof falls and by miners' blasting operations. The success of the

miners has resulted in innumerable headaches for the paleontologist and geologist.

When scientists were first brought to the Makapan Limeworks
caves they found large ramifying blast holes in the side of the hill.
Study and analysis later revealed the likely sequence of events prior
to economic excavations. At some depth below the surface, probably more than a million years ago, a large cavern was formed by
water action on the limestone. Subsequently, through formation
and enlargement of cracks in the roof, a large block of dolomite
crashed to the floor, partly sealing off the lower part of the cavern
and creating another cavern above it. After a further period of
time, water action caused much of the roof to collapse onto the
floor of the upper cavern, so that the "cave" now had a large communication with the exterior. Naturally, while all of this was going
on, percolating water also produced channels deeper down so that
lower caverns, which could later communicate with the upper
ones, were also being created.

When the sediments were being washed into the cave, large
amounts of animal bones were also being deposited on the sloping
floor at various places. The four primary questions that arise are:

Were all the bones, which include a small percentage of australopithecine remains, brought in by different carnivores using the cave
as a lair during a long period of time?

Alternatively, are the fossil remains a midden resulting from
australopithecine occupation?

Did australopithecines alternate with carnivores in occupying
this vast, ramifying cave?

Is this a midden of a more human animal whose victims included
the australopithecines?

Carnivores and rodents have undoubtedly played a part in the
cave story, but as yet it cannot be decisively determined, in the
absence of any lithic industry at the Makapan Limeworks caves,
whether or not the australopithecines occupied them or were only
part of the remains of the predatory activities of carnivores or
some, as yet undiscovered, more advanced hominid form. At
Swartkrans there is suggestion of the latter animal in the few fragmentary remains of *Telanthropus,* which may ultimately prove to
represent a pithecanthropine. Professor Dart has continuously
maintained that the majority of the bony remains were tools of the
australopithecines. However, I am not convinced that any of these
bones were *fashioned,* or manufactured, into tools, although it is
obvious that any sharp or blunt bony object may have been *utilized*
as a tool. In the light of the fact that in South Africa the australo-

pithecine remains have been recovered exclusively from cave deposits, it has been assumed that the ape men were cave dwellers. But if one considers their remains merely as a small part of, and scattered among, the large assemblage of fossilized fauna, then their cave-dwelling nature is purely an assumption, not a conclusion. Actually, the great depth of the caverns, the ape men's lack of knowledge of fire, and the geological evidence of the presence of substantial amounts of subterranean water during the main period of bone deposition work against such an assumption. Furthermore, elsewhere, australopithecine remains have been recovered from open-site deposits, namely Olduvai Gorge, Laetolil, Lake Chad, Jordan Valley, and Java. That such primitive hunters and gatherers of food would have dwelt in caves seems to be an unproved and unlikely behavioral pattern.

One aspect of the possible habits of australopithecines requires comment. At this very early stage of human history it is probable that the man-apes were living either in troops like modern baboons or in family units like modern gorillas. They lived in an environment dominated by giant mammals, such as now-extinct forms of elephant, hyena, wild pig and wart hog, saber-tooth tiger, rhino, lion, baboon—animals that are best avoided in open combat. So far as the man-apes were concerned, despite powerful, large jaws, their canines lacked a "ripping" quality, and gripping hands were the substitutes for claws. Here, then, was the challenge that required astuteness, experience, and the ability to improvise in a difficult situation. Brute strength or speedy legs did not constitute a sufficient defense mechanism, but sharp wits were required as well as the ability to throw stones, wield sticks, and grapple efficiently. The latter may have involved the creation of the idea of teamwork: while one individual held away an animal's savage jaws, another would respond to the call of alarm and move in with a rock, stave, or heavy bone and bludgeon the beast to death. Survival of the relatively defenseless australopithecines may have depended on the development of an efficient communicating system. Consequently, the dangerous environment, interacting with an innate mechanism and ability to adapt rapidly, created the humanizing tendencies. The freed hands and the enlarging brain were the major devices required to open the evolutionary doors to technological skill and social success. The australopithecine remains represent about 100 individuals, which in general were small animals. The *Australopithecus* female, slender and broad-hipped, weighed roughly 60 pounds, the *Paranthropus* probably half as much again. They were essentially bipedal, and had skulls with a combination of characteristics specific to both pongids and hominids. The hominid jaws, teeth, palatal contour, and jawbone are set against a small pongid cranium resting on a projecting, heavy-jowled face. The pelvis and vertebral column are much more like those of a true man than of any ape.

The Transvaal fossils are real "links" and they demonstrate that the anatomical requirements for the erect posture were present before the brain expanded. It would appear that the concomitant attributes of freed upper limbs, such as the manufacture of tools, the development of a technical tradition, and various "superior" sociological adaptations, were advances associated with an enlarging brain. At the Sterkfontein site there are two distinct phases. The earlier contains abundant *Australopithecus* remains (more than 100 specimens) and this extensive deposit has revealed not a trace of stone artifacts or even foreign stone. Overlying this is a more recent breccia with very scanty *Australopithecus* fossils, but here there are complex stone artifacts, which are less sophisticated than the hand ax culture associated with pithecanthropine remains in North Africa (Ternifine and Sidi Abderahman).

The *Australopithecus* remains at Makapan Limeworks are not associated with any stone tools, so that, in general, it can be stated that about 95 per cent of the remains of this genus are clearly not found with stone implements, while about 5 per cent, at only one site, are associated with an early Chelles-Acheul industry. If the australopithecines manufactured stone implements, and there is no way yet of establishing this, then by definition, they were "human," or true men. However, if the australopithecines were not toolmakers, as would seem possible, then there was present at that time a more advanced form whose victims were these ape men and who were the successful competitors for that particular environment. In the evolutionary sense it appears that the presently known australopithecines were "too late" to be the direct ancestors of true man, but they were very close to those ancestors and may constitute an experimental cul-de-sac that radiated from the true hominid ancestral stock.

Geological and faunal evidence available at the South African sites indicates that the earlier Sterkfontein deposit is the oldest (Lower Pleistocene), followed by the Makapan Limeworks, and then the later phase of Sterkfontein. Only *Australopithecus* has been recovered from these sites. This sequence is followed by the deposit at Swartkrans and then that at Kromdraai, and these two sites are typified by the occurrence of *Paranthropus*. The pithecanthropine *Telanthropus,* as well as stone tools, make their appearance at the time of the later deposition at Sterkfontein. It is of consequence to recognize that when *Paranthropus* arrived on the evolutionary scene, toolmaking was already an established industry.

Corroborative evidence of the wide distribution of the ape men in Africa was recently uncovered by Mary Leakey in the vast bone repository in the Olduvai Gorge of Tanganyika, where a systematic fossil hunt has been pursued for about 30 years. This australopithecine skull was dubbed "nutcracker man" by Louis Leakey, because of the large, squarish teeth in the upper jaw, and he referred the material to a new genus, *Zinjanthropus,* but it is highly likely that instead it is another species of *Paranthropus.* On the same level (in Bed I) as "Zinj" were also the remains of many mammals and a large number of stone artifacts. In respect to the latter, the questions once again arise: was "Zinj" the manufacturer or was he the victim of those stone bludgeons, manufactured by a more advanced contemporaneous form? In other words was he the killer or the kill? The latter is suggested by such indirect evidence as: (a) the nature of the associated remains does not differ particularly from the thousands of fossil remains, many similarly grouped, found elsewhere at Olduvai; (b) some of the remains of "Zinj," adult and juvenile, are found scattered in the same area; and (c) a similar scanty distribution of man-ape fragments relative to extensive faunal remains is seen elsewhere, where no stone artifacts have been recovered.

Late in 1960, a large fragment of the lower jaw and two bones (parietals) of a skull of juvenile age (possibly of one individual) were recovered in Bed I, some feet lower than the "Zinj level" and a short distance away. Some teeth, two clavicles, a portion of a foot, six finger bones, and two ribs were also found. Although Dr. Leakey refers to this site as a "pre-*Zinjanthropus* level," it is not clear what the time lapse between the two levels really was. However, it is probable that it was short. A satisfactory reconstruction of the parietal bones is doubtful, and at this early stage of their study it seems that the jaw and cranial bones belonged to a young australopithecine, possibly a species of *Australopithecus.* The juvenile parietal bones are cracked but the fracture is typical of the result of generalized pressure of the tons of soil and rock resting on it rather than the dramatic "murder" first attributed to it in the newspapers. In any event, "murder" is a term applicable only in relation to laws of human society.

The remarkable little australopithecines were not confined only to the Transvaal and Tanganyika. It should be mentioned that as early as 1939 the latter area provided evidence of the presence of

these ape men when some australopithecine-like teeth were discovered by Kohl-Larsen on the Serengeti Plains, not too distant
from Olduvai. In faraway Java an australopithecine jaw was recovered just before the Second World War, and during 1961 remains of man-apes were reported both from Lake Chad in North
Africa and from northern Israel. Thus we are getting a clearer
impression of the widespread nature of the australopithecines,
indicating probable migrations over thousands of years extending
through the terminal Pliocene and early Pleistocene, which resulted
in adaptation to new environments, for better or for worse. We
cannot yet assess when and why man-apes ultimately became
extinct.

What of the earliest recognized true man in Africa? From the
Olduvai Gorge came news in late 1960 of the discovery of "Chellean Man," named because of associations with relatively advanced
implements. He could be considered on the same relative evolutionary footing as *Pithecanthropus* from Java and China, the earliest
toolmakers who knew the use of fire. Chellean Man could be considered as an African variant of the genus, with more massive bony
supraorbital projections and a number of other minor variations.
In North Africa at Ternifine, in Algeria, three human lower jaws
were found with many faunal remains and Chelles-Achel implements. It is considered that these jaws (unhappily placed in a new
genus, *Atlanthropus*) also belong to the African *Pithecanthropus*
complex. The pithecanthropines, with their distinct hominid posture and with only a few ape-like features, constitute essentially a
stage of mankind that is ancestral to the later forms, Neanderthal
Man and modern *Homo sapiens*. Early pithecanthropines probably
overlapped in time and territory with the australopithecines, and
may have survived to less than 400,000 years ago.

Although the term Neanderthal Man should be strictly reserved
for those stocky, cold-adapted men who occupied the continent of
Europe during, at least, the first cold phase of the last glaciation,
about 100,000 years ago, one is tempted to interpret similar morphological types living contemporaneously in Africa and Asia as
racial variants of the Neanderthals. The immediate post-pithecan-
thropine phase is at present represented in Africa by two skulls,
one from Broken Hill in Northern Rhodesia (Rhodesian Man) and
the other 2,000 miles to the south, from Hopefield in South Africa
(Saldanha Man). About thirty years ago the fragmentary remains of
another beetle-browed individual were discovered approximately
1,000 miles north of Broken Hill near the shores of Lake Eyasi on

the Serengeti Plains, not far distant from the Olduvai Gorge. The badly preserved remains were tentatively reconstructed and named *Africanthropus*. Incorrectly placed in a new genus, the *Africanthropus* probably represents a form of *Homo* that is closely related to the Broken Hill and to the Saldanha skulls.

The Broken Hill skull was discovered in the lowest part of what had been a subterranean cave that was blasted open by miners in 1921. As in the case of the Limeworks caves, the skull, fossilized faunal remains, and artifacts accumulated at the bottom of a sloping floor. The skull is massive, with thick, projecting brow ridges, surmounted by a flat, sloping forehead. It is so gross-looking that for many years some scientists preferred to consider it as a pathological anomaly—an acromegalic. However, this doubt was dispelled when, in 1953, the author and a field assistant recovered fragments of a skull at Hopefield, that, when reconstructed, was indisputably akin to Rhodesian Man. The new discovery was named Saldanha Man because of the proximity of Hopefield to the historically known Saldanha Bay. The site is on a farm called "Elandsfontein," and consists of a large eroded area (about 2.5 miles by 1.5 miles in size) in the bushy Sandveld. During the ten years of field work I carried out with teams of students and colleagues, more than 20,000 fossils and about 6,000 stone artifacts have been recovered from the surface of the fossiliferous floors that lie between the 40-foot-high sand dunes of Elandsfontein farm.

This remarkable, fossil-strewn site must be seen to be believed. Almost every foot of the surface between the dunes reveals a recognizable fossilized bone as well as hundreds of minute chips of fragmented bone. From this site more than 35 mammalian genera and many more species have already been diagnosed. These animals represent a mixture of the grassland and bushveld faunas, a situation seen today around the Etosha Pan in South West Africa, where arid conditions have forced these two different types of fauna to congregate around the only constant drinking place in a vast region. The Hopefield fauna, 20 per cent of which are extinct forms, occupied the site during the period extending from the tail end of the Middle Pleistocene to the early part of the Upper Pleistocene of southern Africa—that is, about 200,000 to about 100,000 years ago. The breakdown of the faunal forms, coupled with pollen analysis, leads to a picture of the landscape at that time—open savanna country merging with distant scrub and bushveld, and forested regions scattered toward the mountains on the horizon.

About 15 miles from Hopefield is another fossil site at Langebaanweg. Here, too, commercial interests have unearthed a wealth of fossils—the upper layers overlap the Hopefield period, while the lower, phosphate-bearing strata are yielding fossils of a Lower and Middle Pleistocene epoch: three-toed zebrines, archaic elephants, and short-necked giraffids. Sea invasion of the extensive site (about six square miles) is indicated by the presence of numerous sharks' teeth scattered among some of the mammalian remains. If a hominid should be discovered here, it may well prove to be another "key" form in the intricate evolutionary mosaic.

Thus Saldanha and Rhodesian Man, who, although found 2,000 miles apart, are alike as brother and sister (in the evolutionary sense), represent the African variation of the Neanderthal equivalent of Europe and of Asia. Interestingly, the African and Asian forms are more like each other than either is to the European form. We can picture that distant period as having three major racial variants of mankind on three major continents, which, though separated by distance, came into contact with each other by intercontinental migrations, sharing their cultures and mixing their stocks so as to blend the later, more modern forms of mankind.

Scattered throughout southern Africa are dozens of other sites revealing the fossilized representatives of the subsequent, more modern types, essentially the ancestral stocks of the Bushman, Hottentot, and Negro as physical entities. Many of the skeletal remains display blending of these racial types, now the one accentuated, then another, thereby indicating that about 30,000 or fewer years ago these three racial groups may have been separating from a stock common to all. Thereafter, by drifting apart into different environments, they developed the physical and cultural characteristics that, in the extreme, are widely separated. Recent serological studies of these three living races indicate the remarkable similarity between the Hottentot and Bushman gene frequencies and those of the characteristic genes of the Negroids.

It requires a monograph, not an article, to do justice to the phenomenal wealth of evolutionary material already removed from Africa's soil. An outline of the biological trend in one of the indigenous populations—the Bushmen—was given in *Natural History,* February, 1961, by Professor Tobias. Untouched in the present article is the evolution of their cultures—the stone artifacts, paintings, engravings, or pottery. A glimpse of the tremendous source material available can be given merely by stating that in 1941 more than 2,000 sites displaying cave art or rock engravings had been recorded in South Africa, and since then hundreds of new sites have been noted. Yet despite this mass of information we know very little of the painters of the various styles, of the correlation between cultures in the floors of the caves and the art on their walls, of the composition of the paint itself, and how it has endured untold centuries of rough, rocky walls.

What were the racial affinities between the groups of skeletons recovered in South, East, and North Africa, say, 25 to 50 thousand years ago? When were the crucial periods of contact between Africa, the Middle East, and beyond? In which directions were migrations taking place at certain periods? Who manufactured the beautiful giant hand axes and other stone implements found at Olorgesailie in East Africa and at Stellenbosch in South Africa? These and a dozen more questions face the paleoanthropologist and archeologist of the present and of the future. Africa's rich biological heritage is a challenge to the scientist, and despite all the discoveries already made, it is, relatively speaking, virgin territory for future explorers in both the biological and the earth sciences.

Great discoveries have uncovered the emergence of man in Africa. The synthesis of the knowledge available and the solution to the many mysteries surrounding our ancestral forms await us. It is by no means an idle cliché to repeat the ancient Greek saying, attributed to Aristotle, that Africa is always producing some novelty.

# BONES OF CONTENTION: TWO BENCH MARKS ON THE EVOLUTIONARY PATH REVISITED

The evidence for man's evolution could hardly be more tenuous: a collection of a few hundred fossilized skulls, teeth, jawbones and other fragments. Physical anthropologists, however, have been ingenious at reading this record—perhaps too ingenious, for there are almost as many versions of man's early history as there are anthropologists to propose them. There are only a few facts on which all the scientists have agreed. One is the age of the earliest creature identifiable as a direct ancestor of man: the generally accepted figure for creatures with upright posture and manlike teeth is 1.7 million years. Another is the first appearance of the Hominidae, a family distinct from the apes, whose sole surviving member is modern man: these creatures apparently emerged about 14 million years ago.

Now these two bench marks on the evolutionary path have been revised. Harvard vetebrate paleontologist Bryan Patterson announced that he had discovered the upper part of an elbow on the dry shore of an ancient lake in Kenya, near Kanapoi. Potassium-argon dating (based on radioactive decay rates) of the lava flow that once covered the specimen puts its age at about 2.5 million years—almost a million years older than the previous earliest fossil of a preman. According to Patterson, a detailed computer analysis of the elbow's knobs and hollows showed it to be much more like that of a man than an ape. Patterson speculates that he may have found a fragment of *Australopithecus*, a 5-foot-tall, upright hominid.

Coexistence

No sooner had anthropologists recalibrated their time scales, than the great anthropological field worker Louis Leakey, who has spent 40 years unearthing much of what his colleagues know about man's past from Tanzania's Olduvai Gorge, upset them again. He announced that he had found jawbones, collarbones and other relics whose age had been put at 20 million years by potassium-argon dating done at Berkeley. Leakey says that the fossils, which he named *Kenyapithecus africanus* (because he discovered the creature in Kenya) are the remains of the oldest known member of the Hominidae family. The significance is twofold: first, it apparently pushes the point at which the hominids became distinct from their cousins the apes back from the late to the early Miocene period. Secondly, the discovery fills in an important gap: while the cats, apes and other major vertebrate families were well established by the early Miocene period, the evidence for man's emergence had been missing.

Patterson's and Leakey's discoveries make the puzzle of man's ancestry older, but they do nothing to clarify it. There is disagreement, for example, on which fossil after *Kenyapithecus* represents man's earliest direct ancestor. Leakey nominates "*Homo habilis*," a diminutive, big-brained toolmaking creature whose 1.7-million-year-old remains he discovered at Olduvai. Furthermore, Leakey believes Patterson's elbow is a *Homo habilis* fragment. The other hominid called *Australopithecus*, who most anthropologists consider the first preman, Leakey dismisses as a separate, perhaps later species of hominid. According to Leakey, *Homo habilis* co-existed on the plains and in the groves of Pleistocene Africa with the big-jawed, vegetable-eating *Zinjanthropus* (or "nutcracker man"). Indeed, Leakey maintains there may even been a third hominid at Olduvai.

### Shades

Most anthropologists make no bones about rejecting Leakey's theory. They dismiss hominid No. 3 as "Olduvai George." And they insist that *Homo habilis* certainly does not represent a distinct, separate group but belongs in the evolutionary sequence of *Australopithecus*. Yet even if the anthropologists assemble enough evidence to resolve their differences they may still find themselves in an endless quest. Evolution has been a gradual, subtle process, in which ancestor shades into descendant through generations. "We shall never," warns Leakey, "be able to point to a specific time and a specific creature and say here man began."

# HOMO HABILIS

Holding up a series of plaster casts, British anthropologist Louis S. B. Leakey last week quietly overturned man's previous ideas about his origins.

The casts were of skull fragments taken from the remains of pygmy-like beings three to four feet tall, which the 60-year-old scientist and his wife, Mary, unearthed in the Olduvai Gorge of Tanganyika over the last four years. Leakey named the ceatures *Homo habilis*, Latin for "man having ability." The able men ranged across East Africa for perhaps a million years, between 1 million and 2 million years ago, and Leakey's full revelation of their nature in a National Geographic Society lecture in Washington capped three decades of patient searching (*Newsweek*, May 30). The shape of their heads was very close to that of contemporary man, only

From *Newsweek* Magazine, April 13, 1964, p. 86. Copyright Newsweek, Inc., 1964.

smaller; they walked upright; their hands were capable of precision work, they used tools and built shelters. Leakey said: "We have put back the origin of genus *Homo* at least 1,250,000 years earlier than previously accepted."

Leakey is convinced that *Homo habilis* is on the direct path leading to man. Accordingly, other claimants to that position will have to be pushed aside. The australopithecines, or man-apes, who lived in East Africa at the same time, now appear to represent an evolutionary dead end. Meaning what? The gray-haired scholar summed up "The textbooks have to be completely rewritten—including one of my own now in press."

# BATTLE OF THE BONES: DIFFERING INTERPRETATIONS OF DISCOVERIES MADE BY L. S. B. LEAKEY

Single-handedly, English anthropologist Louis S. B. Leakey has unearthed almost all the new evidence of mankind's genesis in Africa. For 30 years, on hands and knees, the ruddy-faced, white-haired Leakey searched the sun-baked fossil beds of the Olduvai Gorge in Tanzania for the skulls, bones, and tools left by the early anthropoids from whom modern man evolved.

Though his achievements are epochal, Leakey is a loner. Other anthropologists—excited as they are by his discoveries—reject his interpretation of them. And last week at the University of Chicago, Leakey galvanized some of his most eminent colleagues into vigorous disagreement when he asserted that not one or two, but actually three premen coexisted peacefully in Pleistocene Africa, some 500,000 to 700,000 years ago.

As evidence for his view, the 61-year-old Leakey, curator of the Coryndon Memorial Museum at Nairobi, Kenya, exhibited a 500,-000-year-old skull—named LLK for Louis Leakey-Korongo (the Masai word for "little gorge"). LLK, reported Leakey, was discovered at the same level in the Olduvai Gorge fossil beds as the other two other premen unearthed by Leakey: *Homo habilis*, a big-

From *Newsweek* Magazine, April 19, 1965, pp. 57–8. Copyright Newsweek, Inc., 1965.

brained, four-foot-tall carnivore Leakey believes was the oldest manlike forerunner of modern man; and *Zinjanthropus*, a taller, low-browed, possibly vegetarian anthropoid. According to Leakey, LLK and *Zinjanthropus* died out, while *Homo habilis* developed into *Homo sapiens*.

## One Alone?

Most of the scientists at the meeting, sponsored by the Wenner-Gren Foundation for Anthropological Research, drew a simpler picture of man's evolution. John T. Robinson, professor of anthropology at the University of Wisconsin, argued that early man probably had only one cousin—the plant-chewing *Paranthropus* (a group of premen in which most anthropologists put Leakey's *Zinjanthropus*), who proved an evolutionary dead end. Robinson explained away the rest of Leakey's theory by declaring that the *Homo habilis* fossils and the LLK skull belong to transitional creatures linking early man to *Homo erectus*, modern man's immediate ancestor.

There were other objections to Leakey's theory. "I am just asking," said Elwyn L. Simons, professor of paleontology at Yale University, "but could three species of man coexist?" Unlike monkeys, which live peacefully together by occupying separate ecological niches in a forest, others pointed out that men use the whole environment. Pleistocene rumbles over areas, or turfs, would inevitably lead to the elimination of at least one species. As another anthropologist observed: "Strange bedfellows make for broken bones." Despite the extensive criticism, Leakey valiantly, and perhaps stubbornly, stuck to his coexistence theory. Educated during the classical period of anthropology when almost every new fossil was named and assumed to represent a new species, he does not shrink from the prospect of a many-branched evolutionary tree.

The arguments between Leakey and his colleagues go unresolved because of big gaps in man's knowledge of his ancestors. Said Chicago anthropologist Ronald Singer: "There are too few field workers and too many armchair anthropologists." Leakey, of course, excepted.

# Chapter Eight

# The Evidence

# of

# Fossil Man

The theory of evolution was developed independent of any paleontological evidence. The processes of evolution as we now understand them do not require substantiation from the fossil record. Yet it is highly satisfying to document the evolution of a given lineage with a series of fossil ancestors. Our anthropocentrism has ascribed great romance to the quest of the human paleontologist, whose every find is hailed as another link in the chain of human evolution. But is this really so? Probably not, because at present students of fossil man cannot determine whether a given fossil is ancestral to modern man. We do not know how many species of hominids existed or coexisted in the Pleistocene, nor can we explain their morphological differences.

Certainly all men today belong to the same species and therefore are all descendants of one and only one species of hominid. But which one? Some investigators would give all fossil men ever found a place in our family tree. Others would exclude most of them as our direct ancestors. But if the details are unclear, the big picture indicates that although hominids always have varied from one world area to another, the general trend over time was to greater cranial capacity, and reduction of the dentition and the jaw. We also know that the rate of human morphological change was relatively very rapid in the Pleistocene and that this acceleration is *not* correlated with evidence for increasing complexity in the technology. It is doubtful that we will ever find enough fossil evidence to solve these problems. The understanding of our past is still largely based on conjectural, backward projections of evolutionary processes we have discovered operating on modern animals and men.

# THE WORLD OF PREHISTORIC MAN

*Nino Frank*

To think in terms of geography is to think in terms of the universe, someone has said. In our day, when we are ever more oriented to thinking in world terms, the teaching of geography has become a matter of major concern. It is not that scientific study and school teaching are to be confused, nor should we attempt to make every schoolchild into an infant geographer. But geography, treated as a genuine study of the world, can be used more effectively than other subjects as a means of laying the foundations of international understanding.

A glance at the school curricula of most countries, however, shows that the subject of geography is almost invariably cut to the minimum and treated as an adjunct to history. One hour a week is usually all the time allotted to it, and indeed in some schools (North America, Australia and Japan) it is often merely combined with social studies or the study of family and community life.

Yet, great new perspectives are now open to the student of geography through television and films. Aerial photographs taken from helicopters and more recently from artificial satellites have brought "the whole world within reach." Teachers of geography are now better equipped than ever before to bring their subject to life and to broaden the horizons of their pupils.

Let us take only one area of new geographic knowledge, the study of prehistoric times. Now, as never before, it is possible to

Reproduced from the March, 1961 edition of the *UNESCO Courier*, Vol. 14, pp. 14–17.

describe the life of prehistoric men who lived far back in the mists of time. Only a few years ago they were shadowy figures compounded of legend and guess work, but we now know so much about their lives, surroundings and migrations that we are able to form a precise picture of them.

Historians and geographers now have all kinds of research techniques at their disposal which give them reliable evidence on which to base their studies of prehistory. These are made up of a combination of facts about climatic cycles, the evolution of animal species and of man, as well as his cultural development.

Stratigraphy, or the study of soils, pollen analysis and palaeontology are all used to reconstruct a picture of the past. Dating has long been possible through the study of tree rings (dendrology to the specialist) such as the basic research work first carried out with the centuries-old Sequoias of California. Another method of dating is the time-scaling of the gradual retreat of the great Scandinavian ice sheet since the end of the last ice-age. But dating by these means has never been precise enough.

During the last twelve years or so, it has been possible to devise a more accurate method by measuring the radioactivity of certain elements contained in the soil. This method is based on the properties of carbon-14, an isotope of carbon which develops in every living thing when exposed to the effects of cosmic rays and, on its death, enters on a cycle of disintegration.

All that is needed in this process is to discover a site where well-preserved carbon is in evidence (wood charcoal from a hearth, or carbonized bone) and the state of disintegration provides the clue to the precise age of the material. This has made it possible to reconsider the whole subject of prehistory and to revise estimates of the geographical areas inhabited by man in earliest times.

A new branch of geography has only just come into being which estimates and describes the inhabited regions of prehistoric times. Today, 800,000 years and perhaps even a million years after early man first began to grope his way across the globe, science has found a way to reconstitute the geographical world our ancestors knew.

Professor L. R Nougier of the University of Toulouse, and director of the French Institute of Prehistoric Art, has published what appears to be the first survey of *Human Geography in Prehistoric Times*. The book, well-illustrated with maps and drawings, records the achievements of geographers and scientists in many fields, from which the author is able to date, list and describe the peoples and cultures of prehistoric times with more than a hypothetical degree of accuracy.

His method is based on the number, character and location of palaeontological deposits, aerial surveys, the use of radioactivity for dating and other new scientific research methods.

Using this approach, Professor Nougier presents a veritable geographical panorama of life in Western Europe (France, in particular) from Palaeolithic times down to the "Neolithic Revolution." During the period of time he covers, the configuration of the continent remained virtually the same as we know it now.

Professor Nougier takes us back to the first food gatherers who used chipped-stone axes and flake-tools and did not reach the peak of their development until the advent of hunting some forty thousand years ago. In the time of these earliest food gatherers, it is roughly estimated that there were not more than 20,000 inhabitants in the whole of lower Palaeolithic Gaul.

It was a time when the area around what is now Paris was the habitat of rhinoceroses and *Elephas antiquus,* where wild fig and Judas trees grew in abundance. Men used natural caves for shelter, and fed as they could on the meat of sick or wounded game. This was the *ecumene* of the last glacial period before the time of Neanderthal man.

After the food gatherers came the hunters of the carved and painted caves of the Upper Palaeolithic age. They invented a magic art of extraordinary poetic power, only to forget it later for a reason which remains one of the unsolved riddles of prehistory. Their period ranged from 30,000 years to 8,500 years before the first Christian era. During that time the population of the whole of France was not more than 50,000 inhabitants according to Professor Nougier.

The nomadic tendency of early prehistoric men gradually gave way to settlement in fixed and densely populated areas. It was in that way that the prosperity of the valley of the Loing, an important route to the north, came about. Countless palaeontological remains have been found there. The valley leads directly to the Paris region. Although Paris recently celebrated her two-thousandth birthday, there is evidence that settlement of the region dates back centuries before that time. Traces of past cultures have been found in the region, particularly at the confluence of the Seine and the Bievre where there was once a rocky spur, dating back to the mists of antiquity.

Somewhere between ten and twenty thousand years B.C., the first of the new men arrived, bringing with them their marvellous secrets—agriculture, domesticated animals, perhaps even the knowledge of how to construct megalithic monuments. This period —a forerunner of the "Neolithic Revolution"—was first heralded by the gatherers of shell fish and wild berries, and later by men who set out to conquer the mighty forests.

Thus the earliest forest farming civilizations were born, developing their particular round huts and their herds of cattle somewhere about 8,500 B.C., and marking the dawn of the Neolithic age (this occurred much later in the West than in the Middle East and North Africa).

Between 3000 B.C., and 2000 B.C., came the thousand-year era of the Neolithic—the great "Neolithic Explosion" which saw an amazing increase in human population not only in France but in all of the inhabited regions of the globe. From a mere 250,000 the population of the hexagon which was to be occupied by the Gauls in the third millennium, increased in the course of ten centuries to five millions.

This twentyfold increase was made possible by man's changed attitude towards nature, by abandoning his mere parasitic existence for the systematic exploitation of the earth's resources. Professor Nougier estimates that, at this time, the total population of the inhabited world was around 200 millions. Such an amazing increase was not to occur again for at least five or six thousand years, that is, the beginning of the Industrial Revolution.

Geography really began when prehistoric man first asked the question "Where?" Where is such-and-such a river? Where is the large uninhabited cave? Where is the reindeer's plateau? This need of some graphic representation of a place, however rudimentary, was the first step in developing geography.

Of course, primitive man's knowledge of geography was confined to a few rudimentary notions of topography and to an area of a few square miles. This was still the time of wandering peoples with their fabulous tales, and he could not yet know the immensity of the *terra incognita* which his children would inherit.

The earliest signs of geographical interest so far discovered are the petroglyphs, or rock carvings, found both in Brittany and in Scandinavia. They indicate that even men of the Bronze age had been wondering about the particular region in which they lived. Neither the Sumerians nor the Hittites who came later left any evidence of geographical curiosity, but we do know that the Pharaohs of the Middle Kingdom had made a cadastral survey of all the lands and plots of land under their rule.

It was inevitable that having begun by placing things, man sooner or later would wonder just why things were as they were. So it was that having started to explore the earth, men began starting to explain it. In effect, the term "geographical" applies to any fact that answers the double question "Where?" and "Why there?"

All geography from the time of the Ionians and Pythagoreans to that of Henry the Navigator, Mercator and Varenius, swings back and forth between empirical investigation and learning confined to measuring and listing. It is as if man was, and still were, the lord of a manor not yet well known, and in which he remained a stranger.

It was not until the eighteenth century, thanks to contributions made by such other sciences as botany, zoology and geology that the geographer's awareness broadened. Kant first regarded the relationship between man and nature as an essential part of geography. After him came Ritter and Humboldt who proclaimed the principle of the interdependence of all natural phenomena, of which man is merely one.

This planet approach to geography, exemplified by the "human geography" of P. Vidal de La Blache and his followers, involves constant reference to other branches of science. "Geography, as the meeting-place of the physical sciences and the humanities," writes Professor R. Clozier, "calls into play a wide variety of concepts. These can be broken down into facts and if taken singly or in isolation belong to other sciences. But geography puts them back into place in the natural scheme of things."

The question "Why there?" has become paramount. Its influence is particularly apparent in one of the most active fields of geographical research, world monographs, and cross-sectional studies of some isolated factors such as "man and forest," "honey cultures," and the "geography of stock-breeding." One geographer, Josué de Castro, has embarked on a "Geography of Hunger" which a colleague describes as "even more important than a geography of shelter." And what better name to give the detailed research on arid zones now being carried out at UNESCO'S instance than a contribution to the "geography of thirst."

Another study of great importance today is oceanography. It is true that we know less about the seas than we do about the moon. With men of the future ever more in need of extra food supplies, food from the ocean depths (as well as zones no longer arid) will be in great need. But though one result of oceanographic research may provide much needed food for future generations the geographers will be bound to reap the first benefits.

A number of congresses on broad geographical themes were held last year in the Scandinavian countries at Copenhagen, Helsinki, and Stockholm. These meetings, on the initiative of UNESCO and the International Geographical Union, discussed oceanographical, geodesic and geophysical research. Useful results have been achieved. Special mention should be made of the work done by the Commission on Geography Teaching in Schools at the Geographic Union Congress in Stockholm for improving the teaching of this subject as the basis for a new type of humanism.

# WHEN *HOMO ERECTUS* TAMED FIRE, HE TAMED HIMSELF

*John Pfeiffer*

John Pfeiffer, former Science and Medicine Editor of *Newsweek* Magazine, is now a professor of anthropology at Rutgers University. *The Human Brain* and *The Emergence of Man* are two of his books.

Fire has a very special place in human evolution. As the first force of nature to be domesticated, it represented a new kind of biological declaration of independence. Early man was beginning to do what no other species had ever done before, to shape the world according to his own designs instead of merely adjusting to it, and the use of fire became one of his most effective means toward that end. By bringing fire to the places where he lived he created zones of light and warmth in the darkness, halo-spaces within which he could huddle so that the wide wilderness became a little less wild and less lonely. He achieved the freedom to explore new lands with harsh climates, and a way of keeping the night and nighttime prowlers at bay.

Recent research has focused attention on the evolutionary aspects of these developments. In a widely discussed report pre-

From *The New York Times Magazine*, Dec. 11, 1966, pp. 58+. © 1966 by The New York Times Company. Reprinted by permission.

sented in October to the National Academy of Sciences, Curt Richter, a psychologist at the Johns Hopkins Hospital, described work indicating that by changing man's habits the use of fire also changed the structure of his brain and enhanced his ability to learn and communicate. This is only the latest of a number of studies conducted during the past few years which provide fresh information on the role of fire in prehistory. The information comes from new sites, new digging techniques designed to detect clues that would have been missed a generation ago, and observations of living species, including man.

The oldest known hearths have been found at a site discovered by accident six years ago in southern France. Workers dynamiting a road through the valley of the Durance River not far from Marseilles exposed the back chambers of a buried cave and noted old bones among the limestone debis.

Since then investigators under the direction of Eugene Bonifay of the Institute of Human Paleontology in Paris have dug down through cave deposits to a depth of more than 45 feet and uncovered proof of man-made fires—traces of charcoal and ash, fire-cracked stones, and five reddened hearth areas up to a yard in diameter. Preliminary studies of sediments and animal fossils, including the remains of primitive wolves, sabertoothed cats and other extinct species, indicate that the fires which burned in the Durance Valley are about 750,000 years old.

Bonifay has not yet found fossil remains of the creatures who built these fires. But evidence from other sites indicates that they were probably early representatives of *Homo erectus,* the first species generally recognized as true man.

*Homo erectus* was hardly impressive looking. He had heavy brow ridges, a very flat broad nose, a sloping forehead and a massive jaw. On the other hand, his skull housed a respectable brain ranging in size from about 775 to more than 1200 cubic centimeters, which puts it well within the lower limits of twentieth-century man. He stood five feet tall and fully erect, and he used a variety of chopping, cutting and scraping tools as well as fire.

Fossils unearthed in Tanzania's Olduvai Gorge, one of the richest of all prehistoric sites, suggest that individuals like this arose in East Africa about a million years ago, and some time afterward some of them began heading north. Their reasons for migrating are obscure. Food shortages were certainly no problem, for Africa then was everywhere as abundant in animal life as it is today in only the richest game reserves. It was a haphazard sort of process, perhaps a result of the familiar urge to go somewhere else, preferably where no one has been before. Bands of 25 to 50 individuals stayed in one region for several seasons or perhaps for years, moved a few days' journey further along, stayed again, and so on.

Interestingly enough, the coming of the Ice Age probably had a great deal to do with making their migration possible. For one thing, the formation of mile-high glaciers in polar regions affected climates throughout the world, making travel easier. Specifically, it increased rainfall in Africa and created steppes and savannas and lakes in what had been impassable desert, thus opening up routes across the Sahara. Furthermore, growing polar ice-caps locked up enormous quantities of water so that the Mediterranean, among other seas, became considerably shallower and Africa and Europe were connected by natural land bridges at Gibraltar and perhaps from Tunisia to Sicily and the Italian peninsula.

Early man walked from East Africa to southern France, a hike which required perhaps three or four millennia (an average rate of about a mile a year)—and somewhere along the line he began using fire regularly. His primary reason was almost certainly to keep himself warm. He had lived with fire, and died by fire, long before he ever put it to work. In fact, he was born in a time of fire and brimstone, in an era when volcanic upheavals were ripping a giant gash in the earth's crust: the Great African Rift Valley which extends some 4,000 miles from the southern end of Lake Malawi, up through East Africa and Ethiopia, and north as far as the Valley of the Jordan in Israel.

So our ancestors were thoroughly familiar with fire and seem to have taken it largely in stride. Creatures of habit like us, they did not necessarily stay away from catastrophe. We come back again and again to homesteads devastated by floods and volcanoes and earthquakes, and they were no less persistent.

Still no traces of early hearths have been found anywhere in Africa, although investigators have looked carefully; presumably there was no overriding need to make fires in generally mild and subtropical climates. But hearths appear in colder times and colder places, like the Durance Valley site near the glaciers of the Alps.

In other words, early man turned to fire when the pressure was on, and obtained it ready-made from natural sources. (The first sign of fire-making apparatus, an iron pyrites ball with a deep groove produced by repeated striking to create tinder-igniting sparks, comes from a site only about 15,000 years old.) The notion that Prometheus stole fire for man from the heights of Mount Olympus is not as widely believed as it once was. But it has a certain relevance if, as seems likely, volcanoes were a major source of fire in early prehistory. According to Kenneth Oakley of the British Museum of Natural History, other sources were available in less turbulent areas: "Man could also have relied on accidental fires started by lightning in dry brush or grassland or where there were seepages of mineral oil and gas. Occasionally in damp environments coal or shale-oil deposits might be ignited by spontaneous combustion, and during the last century one such fire burned for four years in Dorset."

Hunters camped near fire, which was a natural resource like game and water and shelter, and may sometimes have left other wise favorable areas when fires began petering out. If so, they had to take it with them when they moved away. It had to be kept burning like the Olympic flame, fed and nursed like a newborn infant. Each band may have had a fire-bearer, perhaps one of its older members, who was responsible for carrying and guarding embers in a cup of clay covered with green leaves, and who breathed the embers into flame when the band found a new place to live.

Fire provided more than warmth. It soon became one of the major factors in setting man apart, in widening the gap between him and all other species. For millions of years the precursors of man, ape-like creatures and later ape-men, had been members of the animal kingdom in a sense that we can conceive only dimly— and in a sense that can never be true again. They shared water-holes with other animals and waited their turn during drinking times in dry seasons. They stepped aside unhurried and without looking up as elephants passed, kept their distance from water buffaloes and rhinoceroses, strode unswerving through herds of gazelles, avoided places where lions might be on the prowl.

There were probably even closer associations, such as exist today between baboons and impalas. A common sight on an East African savanna is a troop of baboons feeding together with a herd of impalas in a kind of symbiotic relationship. The large monkeys have fine stereoscopic color vision, while the gazelles have a highly developed sense of smell. Each species is sufficiently alert on its own, but together they are practically invulnerable. It would be almost impossible for a predator to surprise this natural combination, and early members of the family of man may have played a part in similar mutual defense systems.

This idyllic atmosphere, this near-Eden, changed with the increasing emphasis on meat-eating. Most primates live mainly on plant foods, but our ancestors moved into a new ecological niche and began exploiting other animals. At first they concentrated on small game, such as birds and hares and the young of larger species, and confronted lions and other big carnivores only on special occasions. They may have been scavengers and watched hungrily as carnivores ate their fill, and then moved in with vultures and jackals to clean up what remained, So at one stage early man lived in the shadow of more effective killers and had to give way to them when it came to a showdown.

Fire gradually changed all that. Practically from the beginning it must have kept animals as well as the cold at a distance. On icy wilderness nights big cats and other predators, attracted by the smell of meat and the light, stayed outside the protective circle of the fireside. Perhaps man observed that on occasion the animals scrambled even farther away when sparks flew at them out of the flames, and he may have learned to produce the same effect by hurling glowing pieces of wood at their heads. In any case, he eventually began using fire more aggressively, in a shift from defense to offense.

As far as taking the offensive is concerned, the fact that his earliest hearths were located in caves has a special significance. At first he could not select a likely-looking cave and simply move in, because the odds were that it would be occupied by stronger and longer established killers. So more often than not he had to be content with second-best sites, rock shelters and overhangs which provided less effective protection.

With fire, however, he could drive other killers out. Bears and hyenas and many other cave-dwelling animals shared the Durance Valley with early man, but they stayed out of his caves. He became a regular cave-dweller only after he had learned to tame fire.

Further signs of competition have been uncovered at a later site occupied by a more recent form of *Homo erectus,* the famous Peking Man. During the nineteen twenties archeologists began digging in a cave on Dragon's Hill in northeast China about 30 miles from Peking, collecting the fossil remains of hunters who had occupied the site some 400,000 years ago. The deposits were about 160 feet deep, and some of the deepest and oldest layers contained only the bones of large carnivores like the saber-toothed tiger, a giant species of hyena and their prey. The bones of Peking Man predominated in other deep layers, indicating that he occupied the cave exclusively for a time.

The deep layers tell of a struggle for the cave, animal and human occupations alternating fairly regularly. But the pattern changes in higher layers where there are no more alternations and man moved in, once and for all. These also happen to be the layers which contain charcoal fragments, burned bones and other traces of fire. Of course, fire was not the only thing that drove the carnivores away. By this time man was more than just another predator; he had become the most formidable predator on earth. Indeed, he may well have killed off his greatest competitor, the sabertoothed tiger.

The latest testimony to man's prowess as hunter and fire-user illustrates how new excavating techniques provide clues to vanished ways of life. Clark Howell of the University of Chicago has recently completed three seasons of digging in a valley on an arid plateau in north-central Spain, near the village of Torralba. Although the site is about as old as that of Peking Man, it differs in being a temporary camping place for killing rather than a home base. It includes the butchered remains of at least 30 elephants and half a dozen rhinoceroses, which indicate how effective a predator man had become. Not even the big cats went after such game.

The valley site also includes the sort of deposits which are becoming more and more important in modern archeology, relatively undisturbed "living floors" where bones and tools and other objects remain in about the same position as in times long past. Excavating a living floor is one of the most tedious tasks ever conceived in the name of science, since the position of every fragment of bone and stone must be measured—and it may take hours to record the material uncovered in an area about the size of this page.

But the method pays off. At Torralba it has yielded convincing evidence that hunters used fire thousands of centuries ago to stampede their prey. For example, one area contains most of the left side of a large bull elephant, with tusks and bones unbroken and in place—and all preserved in clay-silt deposits, the remains of a fossil swampland. The animal apparently lumbered into the swamp, toppled over on its left side, and sank so deep that only its right side was exposed and accessible to butchery.

This animal may have blundered into the bog. But the fact that many other elephants met the same fate in the same general area argues against an accident and suggests that Torralba hunters played an active role in the bogging operations. Howell has mapped the positions of many bits of charcoal and carbon, and shown that the material is thinly and widely scattered. "Whoever lit these fires was apparently burning grass and brush over large areas and for a definite purpose," the Chicago anthropologist points out. "My guess is that the purpose was to drive elephants along the valley into the swamp."

Fire may also have been used to produce more effective spears. The Australian aborigines charred the tips of their digging sticks lightly, a treatment which hardens the core of the wood and makes the outer part more crumbly and thus easier to sharpen. Man was acquainted with this technique at least 80,000 years ago, as indicated by a yew spear with a fire-hardened point which was found at a site in North Germany, and some investigators feel that equally advanced treatments had been developed as far back as the days of Peking Man.

Cooking is also believed to date back to these times, mainly on the basis of indirect but convincing evidence involving teeth, which are sensitive indicators of evolutionary change. For example, chimpanzees and gorillas have long, sharp canine teeth designed especially for ripping and tearing, shredding tough plant foods, and fighting—while the appearance of small canines among prehuman primates more than ten million years ago indicates that they did not need such massive teeth, since they were already habitual tool users. But molar teeth which serve chiefly for grinding tended to remain large until *Homo erectus* times, when they begin to become smaller, presumably because he was eating softer cooked foods.

Regular cooking may also have helped reshape the contours of the human face, in a kind of chain-reaction process. According to one theory, softer foods put less of a strain on the jaws and jaw muscles, which became smaller along with the molar teeth. This in turn had an effect on the design of the rest of the skull. Massive overhanging brow ridges and other thick bony protuberances had evolved largely as structures to which powerful jaw muscles could be attached, and they were reduced as the muscles dwindled in size. Furthermore the skull itself became thinner, which may have eased the way for an expansion of the cranium to house a bigger brain.

As for the origin of cooking, no one has yet been able to improve on the basic point of Charles Lamb's story about the suckling pig that was done to a turn when a house burned down. There were no houses half a million years ago, but a forest fire could have done the job just as effectively. Or perhaps a careless hunter dropped his share of the day's kill into a blazing fire and relished the meat when it was recovered. Of course, such accidents must have happened many times before man finally made a practice of roasting tough foods.

There were psychological as well as physical changes. Cooking certainly had a great deal to do with promoting more restraint, controlling the tendency to do things on the spur of the moment. Inhibition is as much a mark of evolutionary advance as action itself, and hunters became more human as they learned not to do certain things. For example, with the advent of cookery they tended to spend less time devouring freshly killed game on the spot and more time back at the cave eating with the rest of the band around a hearth. When man domesticated fire, he took an important step toward domesticating himself.

Establishing new patterns of behavior calls for the breaking of old patterns, and perhaps the most significant effect of the use of fire was to change one of the fundamental rhythms of life.

All animals are geared in some way to the same great repeating phenomenon, the regular and predictable movements of the sun. They wake at sunrise and curl up for the night at sunset. But the nature of this dependence goes much deeper than simply making an appropriate response to the light of the sun. Many species tend to go through their normal sleep-waking cycles even when the skies are cloudy and, in the laboratory, even when they are kept in constant-illumination cages.

Such observations point to the existence of an internal timing mechanism, a built-in biological clock which somehow keeps track of the passing seconds and "notifies" the organism when it is time to sleep or waken. It is believed to be a cluster of nerve cells buried deep in the brain, part of the hypothalamus, or "subchamber," which is concerned with temperature regulation and other automatic processes.

The research described recently before the National Academy of Sciences represents an effort to learn more about the basic workings of this clock. Curt Richter's experiments on rats confirmed the general finding that biological clocks work according to strictly determined and precisely regulated schedules. Rats isolated from any clues to the time of day nevertheless awoke and left their nests early in the morning, returned 12 hours later, left again in another 12 hours, and so on. The Johns Hopkins investigator points out that "it was almost as if a switch turned on and off twice a day." He also reports that similar rhythms exist in certain monkeys, and may have existed in man, before the use of fire.

Human evolution is evolution away from rigid and automatic mechanisms, and toward greater and greater flexibility. Over the ages, man became a master at adaptation. Behaviorally this means that he broke away from such things as the 12-hour clockwork cycle of sleeping and waking, a change that would never have occurred without fire. Preserving and feeding the fire required a number of "anti-cycle" activities. Members of the band either had to serve as sentinels and stay awake all night, or else arouse themselves periodically during the night to make sure that everything was in order.

Breaking away from the 12-hour cycle became a matter of life or death, creating exactly the sort of conditions required for evolutionary change. In this case, as always, the process seems almost unfair. Such change was hardest on bands consisting solely of well-adjusted individuals, individuals equipped with first-rate internal clocks that worked as they were designed to work.

Imagine a sentinel sitting at the fireside and looking into the flames and then into the night and back again. His head starts nodding as he fights against the coming of sleep. It is a losing fight, because there is nothing in the night or in the cave to break the monotony, and the sentinel's internal clock is functioning in fine order. He finally dozes off, the fire sputters out, and predators come in for the kill.

This sort of tragedy must have occurred over and over again in early fire-using times; that is, among "conformist" bands. But dozing off tended to be appreciably rarer among bands which happened to include offbeat individuals of the right kind, genetic mutants or "freaks" who happened to have somewhat less effective internal clocks. The use of fire put a premium on a new type of self-control, the ability to stay awake when necessary despite the clock's nagging alarm signals. Anatomically speaking, this is equivalent to a brain with a modified internal clock whose signals are somewhat weakened—and with higher centers large and dominant enough to curb or screen off the demands of the clock.

This type of brain developed very slowly. In the beginning the fortunate mutants were not only few and far between, but they had only a slim margin of superiority over their contemporaries. Perhaps they managed to fight off sleep only an hour or two longer. But it was enough to increase the odds against attack. The extra waking time meant that fires burned an hour or two longer, so that predators left more often to seek more vulnerable game (perhaps to attack bands with less vigilant sentinels), and ultimately that made all the difference. Individuals who could stay awake longer than their fellow men lived longer, had more children and in the long run made up the vast majority of prehistoric populations. Evolution thus favored well-protected bands and weeded out the others.

But notice that the clock is not eliminated or even shut off. "It is submerged rather than absent in man," Richter explains.

"Vestiges... remain in our daily patterns of temperature rise and fall and, to a slightly greater extent perhaps, in persons who are particularly hard to wake up in the morning."

So the clock continues to operate in us, as a reminder of days when our ancestors had no fire and lived as animals among animals. As a matter of fact, it may dominate under special circumstances, such as in mental disease when manic-depressive patients suffer from violent and uncontrollable mood changes which may alternate precisely at 12-hour intervals.

Man created a new kind of day when he introduced fire into his living places, an artificial day which did not depend solely on the movements of the sun. The hours after dark were probably hours of relative leisure. He could use the extra time to think about activities which were becoming more and more complicated (often as a result of the increased use of fire). The elephant hunt at Torralba, for example, required a high degree of organization and planning. Starting brush fires at strategic points along the valley and driving a herd of elephants into the swamp was a large-scale operation, and several bands of hunters must have joined forces to bring it off.

Furthermore, the very existence of such elaborate plans implies the evolution of increasingly sophisticated ways of communicating. Language, the most human form of human behavior, must have taken a tremendous spurt when hunting was on the rise and hearths burned brightly past sunset. There was so much to share: details of past successes in the hunt, tall tales about the big ones that got away, plans for future hunts, rules about hunting territories and the division of kills, and a growing store of myths and legends.

Finally, there is the role of fire in man's earliest religious experiences. Prehistoric hunters carrying torches and lamps penetrated deep into the remotest chambers of caves, covered the walls with paintings and engravings of animals, and met by firelight to practice rituals whose purposes we can only guess at. These underground meetings took place during the last 30,000 years or so. But many investigators are convinced that man engaged in similar activities hundreds of thousands of years before the coming of art, and that he used fire to serve a double purpose—to arouse excitement as well as provide light.

Fire-obsession is observed in primitive peoples and children as well as psychopaths, and it may be of very ancient origin. Oakley emphasizes "the deep subconscious or sensual appeal" of fire, noting that the appeal may be traced back to the earliest days of primate evolution: "The fact that the Philippine tarsier has been named *Tarsius carbonarius* on account of its propensity for picking up hot embers from camp-fire sites suggests to me that man's prehuman ancestors may have been attracted to natural fires and toyed with burning matter." Fire may be a stimulant as potent as drugs in arousing visions and previsions, and as such would have served the purposes of priests and priestesses, the cultural descendants of the fire-bearers of *Homo erectus* times.

The impact of fire use illustrates a chronic, and perhaps the most characteristic, symptom of being human. It all started innocently enough, with what appeared to be a simple need to survive in cold climates and keep predators away. In meeting the need, however, our ancestors found themselves at once the masters and slaves of a force which was to change their living conditions and human nature itself—by creating new problems and new desires, and new ways of arousing and satisfying desires.

The transformation came gradually. But in a basic sense it serves as a slow-motion model for all later and swifter technological advances, including those which involve us today.


# THERE ARE NEANDERTHALS AMONG US


*Carleton S. Coon*


Carleton S. Coon retired recently as a professor of anthropology at the University of Pennsylvania. He is the author of *The Origin of Races* and *The Living Races of Man*.


Neanderthal man, who dropped out of sight about 40,000 years ago, long before the last Ice Age had ended, has lately been turning up in increasing numbers. Anthropologist Ralph Solecki of Columbia University has found three more skeletons of Neanderthal men in Shanidar Cave in Iraqi Kurdistan, making a total of

From *The New York Times Magazine*, March 12, 1961 pp. 32+. © 1961 by The New York Times Company. Reprinted by permission.

six. Like the first three that he discovered there in 1957, these were the bones of people killed by blocks of limestone falling from the ceiling.

Their misfortune was our gain, for six complete or nearly complete human skeletons of a single race and from a single site are a rich haul in the world of those of us who hunt for fossil men, including Neanderthals. The Shanidar skeletons are particularly valuable because they belonged to people who lived where they died and were neither buried nor eaten. The circumstances of their deaths provide evidence of how they lived.

There is a popular misconception about Neanderthal man—that he was a squat, slouching, low-browed, stupid and vicious brute, wooing his women by clubbing them over the head, and eating his parents once they were dead. Anthropologists know better. We know that the collection of individuals called Neanderthals were just as competent hunters, and just as solicitous of their sick and aged, as are the members of any nonagricultural tribe living today, but our information has yet to reach the comic strips and caveman cartoons.

This misconception, the Neanderthal image, began to arise with the discovery of the original Neanderthal specimen over one hundred years ago. Since then the fame of this fossil and of others believed to resemble it has grown until the name Neanderthal is almost as well known as that of Khrushchev, who, had he behaved in an Ice Age cave as he did in the United Nations, might have been ushered out into the soggy snow by a man of his own size and build, clad in skins.

The Neander, whence the name, is a small watercourse flowing through a handsome little valley in the Rhineland country, near Duesseldorf. There a faceless skullcap was unearthed in a gravel pit in 1856, two years before Darwin announced the theory of evolution.

The time could not have been riper for the discovery of a low-browed skull with massive bony ridges shading what was left of its eye sockets. It was called everything from an ape to an idiot, including a Russian soldier left behind in the Napoleonic Wars. Thus was first created the fantasy of the cave-dwelling brute.

This feral image was reinforced in 1911–13 by the French anatomist-paleontologist Marcellin Boule, who described a nearly complete skeleton of a Neanderthal man unearthed in the cave of La Chapelle aux Saints in the Dordogne country.

According to Boule, Mr. Neanderthal was a stunted, barrel-chested creature, who walked with his knees permanently bent, his arms reaching forward, and his head thrust out on a short, slanting neck. His skull was long and low, his forehead almost flat, and his huge eye sockets overhung by a beetling, bony visor of continuous brow ridges. His nose (the bones of which had been broken off) was low and flattened, his jaws protruded in the form of a muzzle, and he had no chin. On broad, stubby feet he shambled about from cave to cave. From such a brute only the most dismal sort of social behavior could be expected.

In 1955, two Professors of anatomy, William Straus of Johns Hopkins and A. J. E. Cave of St. Bartholomew's in London, obtained permission to examine the La Chapelle remains in the Musée de l'Homme, Paris.

They found that the skeleton, which had belonged to a male 40 to 50 years old, was rotten with arthritis. This disease had affected the hinges of La Chapelle's lower jaw, his neck and much of his body. The forward thrust of his head noted by Boule was due in part at least, to a wry neck, and the stunted stature and stooping posture were due to arthritic lesions in his vertebral column. In his youth, La Chapelle had been as tall as the average Frenchman living in the Dordogne today.

Up to the present, archaeologists have found remains of about 100 individuals which can be called Neanderthals. These were excavated at sites in Europe and Asia—and at one site in Northern Africa. The specimens range in completeness from a whole skeleton to a single tooth. They all lived during the first half of the last glaciation, from about seventy-five to forty thousand years ago.

The European Neanderthals were stocky, heavy people, with long trunks, deep chests, and short arms and legs. Their forearms and shins were particularly short, as are those of several peoples living in the Arctic today, from Lapland to Greenland, and of the Canoe Indians of Tierra del Fuego.

These Canoe Indians—specifically the Alakalufs of the Chilean fjords—can tolerate more cold than Europeans because they have a basal metabolism 150 per cent higher than that of white men of the same height and weight. Until less than fifty years ago, some of the Alakalufs were still going about in the sleet and snow of their chilly environment with little or no clothing. The body build of these Indians is similar to that of the European Neanderthals, who may have been cold-adapted in the same way.

The heads of the European Neanderthals were also peculiarly shaped, for their skulls were long, wide and low, looking somewhat drooping or melted down over the ears, like a Dali soft watch. Yet the brains inside were as large as, or larger than, those of most Europeans of today.

Their faces were long, and drawn forward in the center line; their noses were large and salient; their jaws, deep and protruding. La Chapelle, Boule's type specimen, did indeed lack a chin, but La Ferrassie No. 1, who was La Chapelle's neighbor by virtue of having been buried in the next cave, had a bit of chin, more salient than those of some individual human beings living today.

The Asiatic Neanderthals differed from the European Neanderthals in that they were usually taller and sparer, and their braincases were higher and more modern in shape, without the Dali touch. Their faces also had more forehead and more prominent chins.

Modern European man seems not to have been descended from the European Neanderthals, but he could have been descended, at least in part, from a population resembling the Asiatic Neanderthals, if not from the very Asiatic Neanderthals that we know. On this question as on many others scientific opinion is divided.

All of the Neanderthals, Eastern and Western, made the same kinds of flint tools and hunted with the same kinds of weapons— apparently mostly spears—killing the largest species of game available to them. Rhinoceroses, wild oxen, reindeer, wild boars, even mammoths, they were willing to tackle.

It would be wonderful if we could set down a detailed account of the daily lives of Neanderthal men and women, of how they conducted their family affairs, of who married whom and who fed whom what parts of different animals, of how parents reared their children, of how active adults managed to care for their feeble parents, and of many other cultural details.

Such a narrative would tell us how many families lived together in a cave or group of neighboring caves, whether or not the families left the caves for seasonal hunting grounds in the summer, how the men were organized in hunting, and to what extent a band of hunters made war on neighboring bands.

These details we can never know. What we do know is that the Neanderthal folk must have been organized in families and groups of families that hunted together, that such an organization required good verbal communication, and at least an informal kind of leadership and obedience, and that these hunters seem to have concentrated on killing single animals rather than on butchering migrating herds, as their Cro-Magnon successors seem to have done.

A favorite quarry, at least in Europe, was the giant cave bear. After the hunt, the men handled the skulls of the bears with ceremony, stacking them in special compartments in the caves, like limestone coffins or altars. It is possible that the European Neanderthals captured baby bears in the spring, fed and played with them during the summer and killed them with ceremonies in the fall.

Ceremonies and rituals have little or no part to play in the lives of insensate brutes as portrayed in the Neanderthal image, but the presence of such rites indicates foresight, solicitude, anxiety and even tenderness.

La Chapelle, a nearly toothless, arthritic cripple, was kept alive by his fellows, who must have fed him, and must even have softened his food by pre-chewing it. To have merited such attention suggests that his cavemates were not simply sorry for him, but that he may have symbolized something to them, or even have been an artificer of symbols, a priest, healer, reciter of ancient tales, or all these things rolled into one.

One of the Shanidar Neanderthals had suffered a grievous birth injury which rendered his right arm useless. His face had been injured at the same time, and it is possible that he could see out of only one eye. Somewhat later in life, someone amputated his useless arm above the elbow, presumably with a flint knife.

Not only did he survive this operation but he, like La Chapelle, apparently, lived by the efforts of others, reaching the same ripe old age of 40 to 50 when a rock fell from the roof of the cave and killed him.

For decades, scientists and literary camp-followers of science have speculated on why the Neanderthals disappeared. Did the damp cold of the Ice Age overtax their ability to get food in the winter? Was their clothing inadequate? We know that they went barefoot in caves because their footprints have been found, but the later Cro-Magnon peoples also went barefoot in caves, and they did not become extinct. In Spain and Italy, the weather was never cold enough to kill the Neanderthals off, and they inhabited those peninsulas.

Many of the Neanderthal skeletons show evidence of disease, particularly arthritis, but arthritis usually sets in too late in life to interfere with reproduction. Perhaps the Cro-Magnons who followed them brought new diseases to which the Neanderthals had no immunity, just as the Europeans gave smallpox to the Indians in many parts of the United States.

In the history of interracial contacts with which we are familiar there is no certain record of complete extinction. The last native Tasmanian died in 1876, but several hundred persons of mixed

European and Tasmanian ancestry still live. The tribes of Tierra del Fuego are nearing extinction as separate peoples, but plenty of mixed-bloods will survive them. Their genes will not be lost forever.

In the case of the Neanderthals, evidence is growing that some of the Ice-Age peoples of the Near East who, rightly or wrongly, bear that label, survived and evolved, with or without mixture, into certain modern white populations. The European Neanderthals can have survived only in mixture, but it is possible that some of their gene-borne capacities, such as hardihood in the cold, turned out to be advantageous to those who absorbed them.

There is almost certainly no living person who duplicates in all visible physical features the lineaments of Neanderthal men, but when we look over our fellow citizens en *masse*—as, for example, in the subway—we see not a few who, in one way or another, would not be out of place in a Neanderthal cave. These are not all humble people or failures in life. The Neanderthal stamp also turns up in exclusive clubs, and on the stage.

Physically, the Neanderthals represented an archaic stage of human evolution, more advanced in some organs and systems of organs than in others, but we have no sound reason to believe them to have been mentally inferior to many people living today.

Culturally they had reached an advanced stage of hunting, making better tools than some living people do, and softening skins for clothing by chewing, Eskimo-fashion. Should we find a camp or settlement of Neanderthals living in some hidden valley, we would probably see nothing cruder about their way of life than Darwin did when he saw his first wild Fuegians from the decks of the *Beagle*.

Few persons unexposed to anthropology may realize how vast was the range of human cultures which survived the vicissitudes of conquest and mechanization into the present century. Even the simplest of them managed to survive because cultures are just as subject to natural laws as are plants and animals. Geographical laws, for example, indicate where the most primitive types of organisms are to be found, tucked away in odd corners of the world, while evolution progresses in the centers of geographical regions.

So with cultures. In both the Old World and the New, agriculture began in centers of land masses, and it was followed in the same locations by the rise of villages, towns and cities, along with the inventions of writing and metallurgy.

On the peripheries of land masses, primitive folk continued to lead simple lives without much disturbance until the white man surprised them with his ships, cannons, Bibles, diseases and, eventually, his aircraft and bomb tests. These disturbances reduced the numbers and displaced the hunting grounds of peoples like the Australian aborigines and South African Bushmen, but no sizable group has become "extinct" except the Tasmanians.

Within the past half century, some such peoples still went naked, even in chilly climates. All had fire, but some did not know how to rekindle it if it went out. Many had not yet learned the use of the bow.

Even the most primitive of them—in a material sense, more primitive than the Neanderthals were 40,000 years ago—are organized into families and bands of families, following elaborate rules of who marries whom and who gives food to which women, children and old people. Because Neanderthal men were just as successful in hunting large animals that fed dozens of mouths apiece, they must have obeyed comparable rules.

As human societies have become more and more complicated during the past ten thousand years or so since our ancestors left simple hunting behind them, the human animal has been gradually selected, not for an increase in compassion and solicitude for his fellows, which he had already, but for an ability of his nervous and endocrine systems to tolerate the pressure of being organized into groups or structures—economic, political, military, religious and the like—of ever-increasing size and complexity. Each man has had to tolerate the presence of more and more other men, and to withstand increasing invasions of his privacy.

Intermediate stages which our ancestors passed through in running the cultural gamut may still be seen in what were once remote places in Asia, Africa and elsewhere. Peoples who forge iron, build houses and breed cattle are still organized into tribes, and even kingdoms, and the impact of Western civilization has hit them hard only in our own lifetime.

Many of them are now attempting—in freedom from colonial protection, guidance, suppression, or whatever it be called—to pass in one generation through cultural stages that took our ancestors hundreds, if not thousands, of years, and this attempt is causing tremendous pressures which in some places are intolerable.

The acquired capacity of individuals living in modern mechanized and highly organized states to stand such pressures can carry with it a chain reaction. What goes in must come out. In the history

of civilized man, the usual outlet has been war. From spears, to
bows, to cannon, to atoms is a progression of sorts. But we have
no mammoths to kill, and few of us can afford to kill our bosses.

In the ways in which we release our tensions we cannot come
out very far ahead of the company of Neanderthal men—whom,
if we are not careful, we may join in the valley of extinction.


# NEANDERTHAL RE-EVALUATED


Ancient Neanderthal man, long believed an ape-like creature
from a dead branch on man's family tree, could turn out to be an
ancestor of modern man.

Dr. T. Dale Stewart, head curator of the department of anthropology at the Smithsonian Institution, told *Science Service* that
the Skhul people found in Skhul Cave in Mount Carmel, Pales-
tine (now Israel), could have evolved into a modern man during
the time gap between 50,000 years ago when Neanderthals disappeared and 35,000 years ago when modern man appeared.

Dr. Stewart said Neanderthals, when first discovered, were pic-
tured as much more primitive than they actually were. He said
these primitive men were not too much different from modern man.

According to Dr. Stewart, Neanderthals fall into two populations:

1. The primitive type who has been found in Shanidar Cave in
Iraq, Tabun Cave at Mt. Carmel, and in Europe. He is believed to
have died out as he became increasingly primitive.

2. A more modern type such as the Neanderthals from Skhul
Cave who probably lived about the same time as the Shanidar
man, 45,000 to 60,000 years ago or earlier. This type could have
evolved into a modern man.

Apparently the two types lived at the same time; the primitive
type is most often associated with the idea of Neanderthals, having practically no forehead and very large eyebrow ridges.

From *Science News Letter*, Vol. 80 (Nov. 4, 1961), p. 301. Reprinted, with permission, from *Science News Letter*, now titled *Science News*, the weekly news
magazine of science and the application of science, copyright 1961 by Science
Service, Inc.

Dr. Stewart said that so far is is now known no Neanderthals lived later than 45,000 years ago. The exaggerated features now associated with Neanderthals were mainly found in the sidelines of the primitive types while the evolutionary mainstreams of these men were more in the direction of modern man.

Neanderthals have been credited by some anthropologists with the inventon of sewing, and the first known evidence of surgery was found in a Neanderthal whose arm had been amputated.

The first suggestion of man's humanity to man was seen in this same individual who had been allowed to grow up and live for some 30 years despite the fact that it was necessary to protect and wait on him.

Dr. Stewart reported on the evidence of human evolution and the evolution of modern man from Neanderthals at the Washington Academy of Sciences.

# Chapter Nine

# "Race": Problems
# of
# Definition

The trouble with the word "race" is that modern population genetics has changed its meaning. To some this warrants discarding the term, or at least recognizing it as a fossil, while others find little difficulty in using a word which now has a new definition. Scientists of both persuasions agree that the concept of a subgroup within a species having eternally fixed characteristics which absolutely distinguish it, part and parcel, from all other such groups is totally erroneous, describing an entity that does not exist. That old typological definition of "race," which had anthropologists as recently as the 1940's describing a given human group as consisting of X numbers of "negroid" traits and Y numbers of "caucasoid" traits, has now been totally abandoned. In fact, most physical anthropologists investigating living human groups today confine themselves to Mendelian or breeding populations, the *minimum* unit that actually evolves. Any group larger than that, but smaller than the whole species, (the *maximum* population) is a definitional no-man's-land. Thus research on "geographical races" (the old familiar reds, blacks, whites, and yellows) is no longer undertaken.

Anthropologists and geneticists agree that human variation is not equally distributed throughout the species, and that to some degree different human groups may have had somewhat different evolutionary experiences. Anthropologists also agree that while research tends to be focused on the cultural and biological differences between human groups, the similarity of all subpopulations of this most widespread of all species is much more striking than the differences.

# THE DEBATE OVER RACE: A STUDY IN THE SOCIOLOGY OF KNOWLEDGE

*Leonard Lieberman*

Leonard Lieberman is an Assistant Professor of Sociology at Central Michigan University, Mount Pleasant, Michigan.

The sociology of knowledge invites us to discover how reason is shaped by social factors.[1] The sociological imagination suggests that the social function of reason is "to formulate choices, to enlarge the scope of human decision in the making of history."[2] The concept of race provides a case study in the growth of distorted reason and the formulation of choices within changing social structures.

In the seventeenth century, following the era of worldwide exploration, Europeans awoke to renewed awareness of the fact that there were many other peoples and cultures. The concept of race emerged in the effort to assimilate this new information. *Race* was introduced into common usage and scientific taxonomies. In common usage it became racist ideology, and in scientific circles it was first debated whether the races had separate origins; then in the nineteenth century the debate shifted to emphasize the issue of equality. Scientific and popular ideas influenced each other and both served the cause of justifying ideologically European colonialism, slavery, nationalism and imperialism.

In the first decades of the twentieth century, anthropology, sociology and psychology took up the issue of inequality, debated it, and with the aid of a changing social structure suceeded in shift-

From *Phylon*, Vol. 29 (Summer 1968), pp. 127–41. Reprinted by permission.

ing the majority opinion of scientists and educated persons from racism to equalitarianism. Having helped persuade many that races are not unequal, many anthropologists began to argue that races do not exist. They argued that race is a fiction or a myth which must be exorcised like ghosts, the humors, instincts, and phlogiston.

The debate has been underway among physical anthropologists for three decades. The affirmative states that races exist, the negative claims that race is a myth. Their discussion was the most recent in a tournament lasting over two centuries. In this paper, this debate will be analyzed from the perspective of the sociology of knowledge, which leads to the question of how ideas have been shaped by existing ideology, social structure, social problems, and the debating process itself.

### The Current Debate: Splitters vs. Lumpers

The splitters, adherents of the position that races exist, include Dobzhansky, Garn, Laughlin, Mayr, Newman, and others. The lumpers, who argue that races do not exist, include Livingstone, Montagu, Brace, Hiernaux, Hogben, and Fried.

The splitters claim that:

1. Races are the taxonomic unit below the species level, and if such units are not called race, "it still has exactly the same taxonomic meaning."[3]
2. Races vary from populations "differing only in the frequencies of a few genes to those groupings that have been totally isolated for tens of thousands of years and are at least incipient species."[4]
3. Clines (gradations) exist but it is necessary to distinguish clines between subspecific populations and clines within subspecific populations. Interracial clines are found in intermediate populations between subspecific populations or races.[5]

The No-Race position of the lumpers holds that:

1. Biological variability exists but "this variability does not conform to the discrete packages labelled races."[6]
2. So-called racial characteristics are not transmitted as complexes.[7]
3. Human differentiation is the result of natural selection forces which operate in ecological zones and such forces and their zones do not coincide with population boundaries. Furthermore, different selective forces may operate in overlapping ecological zones.[8] Thus geographic distributions of more than one trait have no necessary correlation.[9]

4. Races do not exist because isolation of groups has been infrequent; populations have always interbred.[10]
5. "Boundaries between what have been called 'races' are completely arbitrary, depending primarily upon the wishes of the classifier."[11]

The debate over an issue helps clarify it by generating finer distinctions. Thus among the lumpers and splitters it is possible to distinguish polar positions and moderate views about the number of races and their existence:

1. No races exist now or ever did.[12]
2. Very few races have existed.[13]
3. In its anthropological sense, the word *race* should be reserved for groups of mankind possessing well developed and primarily inheritable physical differences from other groups. Many populations can be so classified but, because of the complexity of human history, there are also many populations which cannot easily be fitted into a racial classification.[14]
4. The number of races varies with the size of unit studied and/or the scope of the definition.[15]
5. A race is a breeding population, hence there are thousands of races.[16]

The first thought that occurs to an observer of this debate has to do with the arbitrary nature of definitions. Similar problems have been discussed by distinguishing realism and nominalism, absolutism and arbitrariness, reality and ideal types. But in this debate both sides accept essentially the same definition. The common meaning of their definitions is a population which can be distinguished from other populations on the basis of inherent physical characteristics. There must be some identifiable boundary, therefore, where one population ends and another begins. The general acceptance of boundary lines in fact or as an arbitrary necessity leaves the two sides contending over the issue of whether or not one can locate boundaries and thereby prove that races exist. One of the problems discussed later in this paper considers why the contending sides do not resolve the issue by simply calling it a matter of definition.

The debate sketched above is not an argument in which a minority is opposed to a majority or in which experts oppose non-experts. Both debate teams include widely recognized specialists in physical anthropology. Briefly, the argument hinges on the significance of the gradation of genetically based physical characteristics. The race-exists supporters argue that these genetic gradations are intergradations between races; the no-race position holds the gradations are not intergradations but are overlapping gradients which are not confined to the boundaries of particular populations.

Although the early physical anthropologists were aware of the conflict between their taxonomy and the question of validity, the issue lay dormant until the 1950's. The eruption of the debate has been stimulated by the availability of new data. The dispute has been concentrated in the pages of *Current Anthropology*, where in three issues in 1962–64 some twenty-four 8 x 11 triple-column pages in small print were given over to the topic. Paradoxically, while the new data are better and more abundant, they have intensified the issue rather than resolved it.

Race as a concept appeared before there were techniques for measuring physical attributes. For some time the major source of information on race characteristics depended upon whatever struck the fancy of explorers and travelers, and often this was skin color and hair texture. Several biometric techniques were developed before Darwin's publication of the *Origin of Species* in 1859. Camper (1722–1789) developed the facial angle, "the interior angle the face makes with the horizontal."[17] In 1842 Retzius introduced the cephalic index, the ratio of head length to width. By 1900 A. Von Torok had found enough techniques available to take 5,000 measurements on a single skull.[18]

The old data were external phenotypical traits; the new data are genetic in character. Examples of genes which have been identified and used in studying taxonomy and variations in man include: the Rh series of alleles, the ABO system, the sickle cell trait, the gene for M blood type in the MNS series, and frequency of tasting phenylthiocarbamide by females.[19]

Examples of the uses of this kind of data will indicate how they can be used to support either position. Glass and Li compared blood types of Negroes in the United States with those of African Negroes and concluded that North American Negroes have about 30 per cent genes from white populations. The authors estimated that at the same rate of gene flow Negro North Americans will be indistinguishable from white Americans in about a thousand years.[20] In this way the authors use the new genetic viewpoint to investigate change but do so with the old taxonomy of races.

The most ambitious taxonomic undertaking so far attempted is that of Edmondson, who uses 124 populations from all over the world and classifies 24 genetic traits to construct a measure of population distance.[21] The lumpers argue that he ignores clines and that the 24 genes are not a random representation of the assumed 10,000 to 40,000 genes.

The studies relating to the no-race position include the classic study on sickle cell anemia in which one sickling gene gives resistance to malaria and inheritance of two sickling genes causes anemia and early death. The West African populations studied revealed a series of clines ranging from a population where 29 per cent of the genes are of the sickling type to a population without any sickling genes.[22] Livingston interprets these clines as indicating that boundaries between races are nonexistent, hence races are nonexistent.

Another study in Africa by Hiernaux questions the general validity of race taxonomies. Hiernaux asks if "human populations . . . form clusters within which the distances are less than the inter-cluster distances?" Hiernaux answers the question with research on 15 populations in central Africa. He finds "one cluster of two closely related populations (the Tutsi of Rwanda and those of Burundi) is clearly apart, but the remaining thirteen populations allow no further clustering. . . ." Hiernaux believes a similar situation would apply to published data on Asia or America.[23] The splitters would argue that Hiernaux has identified at least two races, perhaps three, and thus races do exist and better techniques might reveal the existence of still more.

The response of the splitters and lumpers to the improvement in data is not unlike that of debaters. The splitters are on the defensive and argue that more data and methods are needed to identify races properly. "There are valid races but biology is only beginning to properly discern and define them."[24] New mathematical models are needed better "fitting the human condition."[25]

The lumpers, on the offensive, find that present data provide sufficient ammunition to argue that mankind cannot be split into races. "The theoretical analysis of clines has barely begun but there seems to be no need for the concept of race in this analysis."[26] From their strategically superior position the lumpers generally do not concede that further data are needed to clarify the taxonomic question of the existence of races. Instead, they view further data as necessary to study current processes of evolution. On this point the lumpers seem to have the splitters on the defensive since more data tend to show more overlapping clines, to which the splitters can only reply that new methods and data are needed.

One possible position which neither side seems to use is that that there are not yet sufficient data to determine whether races do exist or do not exist. Not enough data are available because too few groups have been studied, and too few genetic traits have been measured. These are all traits controlled by one allele; and since most traits are controlled by interaction of multiple alleles, then the present collection of data is based on a biased sample.

If science were a self-correcting inquiry, then checking concept against better data in time should clarify the question of race. But science is not free of social influences; and while a theory is pulled towards validity by data, it may be pulled back by ideology, social structure, and social problems. Even the best of data must be interpreted by inquiring into the social process in which ideas are formulated.

## The Sociology of Knowledge

The formation of ideas is a process influenced by many social factors. For analytical purposes it is possible to group these factors into five classes:

1. Ideas may emerge from existing ideology, philosophy, science, or common sense.
2. Ideas are shaped by existing social structure. The range of theoretical influences includes the position of scientists or intellectuals in the social stratification system of their society, the nature of systems of social stratification established between nations or societies in contact, and the nature of their economic and political relationships.
3. Ideas are also shaped in answer to social problems.
4. Scientists and intellectuals, working independently or in cliques, debate with each other and from their dialectic emerges differing views. They also debate the popular conceptions held by nonscientists and this debate influences their position.
5. New techniques of measurement and new data shift the bases of argument.*

---

*One example of how the existence of more data has shifted interpretations is seen in the lumping trend in classification of fossil hominids. *Paranthropus robustus* is increasingly being classified as an *Australopithecus*, *Pithecanthropus erectus* has been raised to the status of *Homo*, and Neanderthal is being considered for promotion to *sapiens*. This trend is partly the result of increased data which change taxonomies by presenting a fossil series ranging over 1.75 million years and thereby reducing the relative time span and physical differences between fossils.

The perspective of the sociology of knowledge is not intended to mean that a statement cannot be examined for its logical and empirical value. A statement is not proven false if one points outs that its author was expressing his group perspective, vested interests, or personality characteristics. Yet it is useful to examine how thought is distorted in order to improve reason and its effectiveness. The race concept illustrates how reason may shift and change in relation to changing social structure.

### Changing Social Structure and Changes in Concept and Ideology: The Emergence of "Race"

The idea of inherited differences is ancient, but men have not always been classified into races. The notion of race is a comparatively recent development which has existed according to historians only since the sixteenth century.[27] The emergence of the idea of "race" occurred in the seventeenth century following upon the exploration of the preceding two centuries, in which Europeans ranged the globe, established themselves as conquerors and colonizers, and brought back reports of aborigines and sometimes the aborigines themselves. The effect was to create vivid awareness of physical and cultural differences between men.

The first known use of the word *race* was in 1606 by Tant in *Thresor de la Langue Française*. The seventeenth century was a period in which race was not yet a concept in wide use. Montagu claims that during the whole of the seventeenth century only five discussions relating to the varieties of mankind were published.[28] In the eighteenth century the idea of race was introduced into the scientific literature by Linnaeus in his *Systema Naturae* (1735). He saw the human species as a fixed and unchanging entity made up of four varieties or races identified primarily by color. His contribution to the race concept was primarily to place man in the animal kingdom and thereby make a scientific problem of racial classifications.

### European Exploitation and the Growth of Racism

During the two centuries from 1700 to 1900 Europe completed its worldwide colonization. By the year 1900 European nations and the offshoots of Western civilization controlled 85 per cent of the earth's land surface. During this period of time the awareness of race was converted into an ideology of racism.

*Racism* is defined here as the emotional conviction that race and behavior are linked in heredity and that some races are superior to others. An *ideology* is defined as a cluster of ideas that is widely shared and emotionally defended by the members of a society as a justification for their activities.

The ideology of racism took a mild form in the course of the eighteenth century and became particularly intense in the second half of the nineteenth century.* Other major phenomena in Western civilization which intensified the existing racism were the slavery issue and the emergence of nationalism, both in the nineteenth century. These forces later in the century received the assistance of Europe's last adventure in imperialism, and, in the United States from 1890 to 1920, a pattern of events known as nativism.

During this period of time the race concept held by scientists went through two debates which helped influence the growth of the ideology of racism and was in turn influenced by it. The polygenic-monogenic debate occurred in eighteenth century scientific circles and helped support and develop racist ideology. The polygenic view held that races had separate origins and were possibly separate species. Having looked at the world through taxonomic glasses, the debaters explained taxonomy in terms of existing cosmology and so in the eighteenth century they asked if God had created these races all at once or if he had created them separately.

The monogenic view had been held earlier by Linnaeus and came to be the position of the leading naturalists and intellectuals of the eighteenth century and the early nineteenth century, including Buffon, Blumenbach, Kant, Cuvier, Camper, and Heider. They were in agreement that there was one common source for the races, and most of them held that race differences intergraded.[29] Blumenbach described the intergradation in 1793: "No variety of mankind exists, whether of colour, countenance, or stature, etc., so singular as not to be connected with others of the same kind by such an imperceptible transition, that it is very clear they are all related, or only differ from each other in degree."[30]

Today Blumenbach would be classified as a splitter, but in his time he was a lumper. The splitters of that day held the polygenic

---

*Interpreters of the development disagree as to the starting point for racism, and suggestions range from the age of exploration to the slavery controversy, the French Revolution, and nationalism late in the nineteenth century. The basis for disagreement seems to be in the fact that the intensity of racism increased during the period in question.

view. Usually they were nonscientists such as Voltaire, or lesser scientists such as Nott, Gliddon, Morton and others[31] who held that the different races were products of creation and that changes occurred by hybridization.[32] Gliddon, Morton and Nott in the first half of the nineteenth century expressed the polygenic position dominant in the United States among scientists and laymen. It fitted their reading of Genesis and helped justify their view of themselves as children of God among the barbaric Canaanites—the Canaanites being any Indians occupying desirable land. But many Southerners found the polygenic view too much at odds with their fundamentalist interpretation of Genesis and so they took the monogenic stance. Their virtue was rewarded by the discovery that one of Noah's sons had seen his father's nude body and been cursed for it, and that his descendants had turned black and become the servants of man.

The debate over the inequality of man grew out of the monogenic-polygenic debate. During the latter portion of the nineteenth century it was hardly a debate at all since inequality of races was the predominant view of scientists and intellectuals. According to Gosset, American thought from 1880 to 1920 "generally lacks any perception of the Negro as a human being with potentialities for improvement. Most of the people who wrote about Negroes were firmly in the grip of the idea that intelligence and temperament are racially determined and unalterable."[33] In 1925 Sorokin wrote that: "perfect agreement of all these tests: the historico-cultural, the mental, the absence of geniuses . . . seems to indicate strongly . . . that the cause of such a difference in the Negro is due not only, and possibly not so much to environment, as to heredity."[34]

Scientific racism extended also to psychologists. G. Stanley Hall, a pioneer psychologist, held that primitive races were at earlier evolutionary stages.[35] By 1916 the Binet intelligence test was regarded as perfected and "a powerful school of psychologists appeared which took up the old argument that intelligence is largely hereditary and little affected by environment."[36] Racists found support in the idea that some persons could not benefit from education as much as others.[37]

In literary circles the list of those believing in the inequality of races included James Fenimore Cooper, Henry Adams, Frank Norris, Jack London, Owen Wister, and Henry James.[38] In Europe a comparable group of writers included Kipling and Sir Walter Scott, whose *Ivanhoe* converted a feudal class struggle into an affair of "self-conscious racial conflict" between Saxon and Norman.[39]

The majority of intellectuals and scientists had ideas which helped give racism respectable veneer. But there were some intellectuals and scientists who were not racists. Most of the opponents of racism were humanitarians and intellectuals such as George Washington Cable, Winslow Homer, Mark Twain, Stephen Crane, and J. S. Mill. Among the scientists there were a few men who were not racist in their thinking. The list includes Adolf Bastian, Rudolph Virchow, William Ripley, Theodore Waitz, Friedrich Ratzel, Henry Rowe Schoolcraft, Lewis Henry Morgan, and John Wesley Powell.[40] They were not active anti-racists. They were forerunners of a reformed view of race who generally held races differed only in minor respects.

The debate over the inequality of races was largely one-sided until the 1920's. The historian Gossett writes that the stemming of the tide was the work of "one man, Franz Boas, who was an authority on several fields which had been the strongest sources of racism." He asked for proof that race determines mentality and temperament. From then on "it would be the racists who were increasingly on the defensive . . . it was clearly Boas who led the attack."[41]

The techniques used by Boas were based on research he carried out or stimulated in physical and cultural anthropology. In 1912 he published work in physical anthropology demonstrating changes in head shape in children of immigrants. It weakened the older concept of the fixity of race[42] and the implication that mentality was also racially determined.

But Boas' influence on racism was even more significant through his leadership in cultural anthropology. According to Gossett, the ethnographic work his students began "had the utmost importance for race theory because the close and detailed knowledge of . . . primitive peoples showed how directly ideas and customs are interrelated and how fallacious is the idea that any society can be meaningfully interpreted in terms of its racial inheritance."[43] Gossett holds that what was needed to break through the dominant misconception was a way to explain character as an outcome of institutions, history, and environment. Boas and his students did that by building on the foundation left by Tylor, by their development of the relativistic approach to cultural differences, and by the insistence on masses of evidence. Gossett believes "it is possible that Boas did more to combat race prejudice than any other person in history."[44]

A broader explanation is needed in terms of how Boas' ideas came to be part of anti-racist theory in the social sciences and then how they gained wide popular acceptance. Boas' influence on his students explains the spread of his views into anthropology. One of Boas' most prominent students was Kroeber, whose 1917 article, "The Superorganic," was one of the influential statements calling for a social rather than an organic interpretation of human behavior.[45]

Psychologists began to shift their position. Otto Klineberg[46] was one psychologist who had contact with Boas and his students. He later gathered experimental support for the culture concept through his work in the changing I.Q. of Negro children as they moved from South to North.

In sociology the same trend occurred but under differing influences:

> Racial explanation disappears from serious sociology with the great generation of the early twentieth century: Pareto, Durkheim, Hobhouse and Max Weber made the issue of race irrelevant by the introduction of rew canons of analysis and by their attempt to explain the social by the social. . . .[47]

What the social sciences had done was to respond to racism with a scientific rebuttal. Scientific anti-racism came to be the accepted position in the social sciences and among intellectuals. The idea was soon to spread and become a new popular ideology partly replacing racism and engaged in competing with it.

But a set of ideas does not become an active ideology simply because it is scientific. It spreads when cultural conditions are appropriate. The earlier ideas ran against the tide of conditions causing racism. But in the 1940's a social base for anti-racism was emerging.

Gossett lists several of these conditions and comments that: "We owe something to impersonal forces in the decline of racism, but the trouble with impersonal forces is that they can as easily work one way as another. We owe far more to the people and the organizations motivated by a concern for equality of all."[48]

Gossett's position seems to be that of the historian and humanist: men and ideas make history. The view that must be added concerns the influence of culture conditions. Boas' ideas could only spread when the social structure was ready. Men may make history, but they do not do so unilaterally.

In the early decades of the century the forces for equality began to develop in the United States in the emergence of the social sciences as organized disciplines and in the advanced growth of urbanism and industrialism. To these must be added the transcendent influence of World War II. The propaganda developed during the War was based on the fact that Nazi Germany was totalitarian and racist. Since the enemy was racist America had to become anti-racist. The massive anti-racist propaganda and the racist enemy undermined the strength of the racist groups in the United States that had been so vocal in the 1930's. Racism began to recede on the surface and to be replaced by an appearance of genteel tolerance as a public policy, a trend aided by the shift in the American social classes in which the middle class increased in size and in its level of living.

## The Current Debate and its Relationship to Past and Present Ideology

The major debates of the past two centuries were over the issues of separate or common origins for races and the equality or inequality of races. Both these issues still persist within the current debate over the existence of races. The three debates all pivot on one common problem: equality. Each emphasized a different aspect of equality: equality of origins, equality of intelligence, and taxonomic equality, but in each debate the same issue of equality of rights has been present.

The influence of ideology in the current debate can be discovered in the statements of two men who take opposite positions as lumpers and splitters. Consider the position of Montagu, who for decades has held that race is a myth:

> How many times will it have to be reiterated that human beings are not "races" or for the simple principle that all men, by virtue of their humanity, have a right . . . to fulfill themselves. None of the findings of physical or cultural anthropology . . . can in any way affect this principle, this is an ethical one—an ethical principle which happens in every way to be supported by the findings of science.[49]

Montagu's statement is one that expresses values with which the author fully agrees, but they are nonetheless values which influence his particular interpretation of the available data. The fact remains that the data do not adequately support his position. Too few hereditary characteristics have been studied for too small a segment of world populations for one to be able to conclude that races do not exist.

Carleton Coon, who is a willing splitter, takes a position opposite to Montagu. Coon's thesis is that 500,000 years ago man was one species, *Homo erectus*, which perhaps already was divided into geographic races or subspecies. *Homo erectus* then evolved into *Homo sapiens* five times as each subspecies or race living in different territories passed a threshold from *erectus* to *sapiens* state. In this parallel evolution the races passed over the threshold from *erectus* to *sapiens* species at different times: Caucasoid was first at 250,000 years ago, then Mongoloid, 150,000 years ago, Australoid, 40,000 years ago, Congoloid (Negroes and Pygmies) 40,000 years ago, and then the Capoid (Bushmen, Hottentots).[50]

Coon's values may be inferred from several scattered statements in *The Origin of Races:*

> ... it is a fair inference that fossil men now extinct were less gifted than their descendants who have larger brains, that the subspecies that crossed the evolutionary threshold into the category of *Homo sapiens* the earliest have evolved the most, and that the obvious correlation between the length of time a subspecies has been in the *sapiens* state and the levels of civilization attained by some of its populations may be related phenomena.[51]
>
> ... the Australian aborigines come closest, of any living peoples, to the *erectus-sapiens* threshold.[52]
>
> [If Africa was the cradle of mankind] it was only an indifferent kindergarten. Europe and Asia were our principal schools.[53]
>
> As far as we know now, the Congoloid line started on the same evolutionary level as the Eurasiatic ones in the Early Middle Pleistocene and then stood still for half a million years, after which Negroes and Pygmies appeared as if out of nowhere.[54]
>
> Genes in a population are in equilibrium if the population is living a healthy life as a corporate entity. Racial intermixture can upset the genetic as well as the social equilibrium of a group, and so newly introduced genes tend to disappear or to be reduced to a minimum percentage unless they possess a selective advantage over their local counterparts.[55]
>
> It is a common observation among anthropologists who have worked in many parts of the world in intimate contact with people of different races that racial differences in temperament also exist and can be predicted.[56]

The polar position of Montagu and Coon on the question of the existence of races and their statements indicate opposite positions on the equality of populations or races. But most anthropologists who take a position on this matter are equalitarians. A racist can only be a splitter, a lumper can only be an equalitarian, but an equalitarian has the choice of being a lumper or a splitter. Since lumpers can logically be only equalitarian, it is worth noting that the debate over the existence of races can be kept active only by the lumpers. There would be no issue if the lumpers as challengers of the status quo did not contend that races do not exist. These lumpers, represented by Ashley Montagu, express the values of equalitarianism.

The division of anthropologists into lumpers and splitters when most of them are equalitarian requires further explanation. The general liberal orientation of most anthropologists may relate to their selection of anthropology as a career. It is also supported by group definition and pressure in the social organization of the professions. A related condition might be the change in social climate about race since World War II; an atmosphere of tolerance means that the battle to fight racism is not so pressing to some intellectuals. It is no longer necessary to minimize race by arguing there are only three or only a few very similar races; and then, too, the argument that there are many races is a way of quietly saying that race is not important. Thus equalitarians can comfortably be either lumpers or splitters. Their equalitarian values are shown in their opposition to racism. Lumpers generally oppose splitting as invalid and playing into the hands of bigotry, and splitters generally oppose lumping as unrealistic and playing into those same hands. Dobzhansky takes this latter view:

> Nowadays, a scientist cannot ignore the uses and misuses of his findings by politicians and special pleaders. He certainly cannot and should not refrain from recording the facts which he discovers, but he had better see to it that the language he uses to describe the facts does not invite misrepresentation. To say that we have discovered that races of man do not exist is such an invitation. It is far better to find out, and to explain to others, the real nature of the observable phenomenon which is, and will continue to be, called "race."[57]

Can racism be fought by persuasion, semantics, and data? Fried, Montagu, and others think so. Race is an evil concept, says Montagu, and therefore should be fought. It is too ambiguous to be redefined, and so he proposes to substitute the concept of ethnic group. He claims that *ethnic group* being noncommittal and of uncertain meaning would raise questions about meaning.[58] Unfortunately, Montagu's semantic magic is likely to raise evil spirits already thought dead, since the term *ethnic group* is given cultural meaning by sociologists to clarify the idea that many groups are unified by nonbiological characteristics. If not semantics, then perhaps data will solve this problem, but the concept of race may be one that is so sensitive to social pressures that mere data will never resolve the issue.

### The Future of Race and Racism

Men can most easily change ideas in directions which express their social structures. If social structure can facilitate the idea that races exist, then it can also facilitate the disappearance of the idea. If the idea of race was invented and transformed under the influence of social structure, it can be asked whether current changes support the lumpers or the splitters, or neither.

The notion that mankind consists of populations with different hereditary taxonomic positions may disappear during the next century if certain trends in world social structure continue. The European notion that mankind consisted of races developed as Europeans became aware of the great variety of human differences. It became an ideology of racism to justify colonialism, slavery, imperialism, nationalism, wars, and genocide. Currently the leaders of many of the nations of the world desire to move their nations from subordinate status as underdeveloped former colonies into the status of industrialized nation-states where their members will be the equal of all men, especially white men of Western civilization. At present nationalistic ideology in new nations is intense in its insistence upon equality, but insistence is not enough. If they succeed in adopting and developing the new technology, their nations become important beyond their present role as allies or votes in the United Nations; they then become power centers and their economies become interdependent with those of other nations. This kind of structural equality puts direct pressure upon the concept and ideology of race.

Within nations that value equality and are able to reach a stage of industrialization and high mass consumption, it is possible that segregated stratification systems will break down and racism will be reduced. During that future, if racism is thus dissipated, the race concept will either become as forgotten as phlogiston or will be used without its present undesirable connotation. If these events occur it should not be viewed as the unfolding of the law of progress so much as indicating that old problems are replaced by new ones.

During these changes the role of the intellectuals will be to transform the clash of power groups and vested interests into intellectual issues. They can carry out their role in such a way as to hasten a change and perhaps avoid some of the pitfalls in the change. The present debate between lumpers and splitters offers two alternative ways of expressing a future social structure of interdependence and coordinate status: the lumpers say there are no races, the splitters say there are thousands. The author takes the position that the data and the assumed future world social structure are better formulated in terms of the lumpers' position. If pressed to explain, the answer is that by using the splitters' definition of race, races can exist, but they are no more typical of the human species than hermits are of human societies.

## Conclusion

Several generalizations are suggested by the above review of the debate over race:

1. The race concept developed in a dialectic that has been controlled largely by the same structural forces that generated the growth of racist and equalitarian ideology.
2. The specific issue debated has shifted with changing social structure.
3. Whatever the specific issue under discussion, the underlying theme has been the equality or inequality of different populations.
4. With one exception it is possible to take any side of the issue and debate for or against equality. The exception is that of the nonexistence of races, which makes all men equal.
5. Improvement in data has not helped bring consensus about the nature of race because the concept is polarized between two groups influenced by the ideology of equality. Splitters believe that equality of man is a matter of values and that the idea of the existence of many overlapping races will erode racism faster than the idea of the nonexistence of races. The lumpers accept the unity of man and argue against race as man's most dangerous myth.
6. The existence or nonexistence of races remains a problem to be explored empirically as better data are gathered and better techniques devised. A crisp answer to the question may be obtained if adequate data are available for longitudinal as well as contemporaneous comparisons. Gathering data of this kind over a century may also answer a far more important question than the taxonomic; it may answer the question of how the species is changing.

7. Although the data push towards greater similarity of taxonomic groups, it is argued here that the short-run fate of
race as a concept and racism as an ideology will depend upon
the range of possibilities created by changes in social
structures.

8. The role of scientific data in past disputes over race and the
present dispute over the existence of races has been largely
controlled or made possible by changes in social structure.
The role of science in this view is that of a catalytic agent
which can speed and channel the change by developing one
or another of the possible alternative formulations for con-
ceptualizing biological differences. It is the hope of action-
oriented intellectuals that adopting one formulation rather
than another will lead to changes in man's future which
transcend the limits of the social structure that made the
formulation possible.

## References

1. Lewis A. Coser and Bernard Rosenberg, "Sociology of Knowledge,"
   in *Sociological Theory* (New York: Macmillan, 1964), pp. 667–84.
2. C. Wright Mills, *The Sociological Imagination* (New York: Oxford
   University Press, 1959), p. 174.
3. Stanley Garn, "Comment," *Current Anthropology*, Vol. 5 (Oct. 1964),
   p. 316.
4. *Ibid.*
5. Carlton Coon, *ibid.*, p. 314.
6. Frank B. Livingstone, "On the Non-existence of Human Races,"
   *ibid.*, Vol. 3 (June 1962), p. 279.
7. Ashley Montagu, *Man's Most Dangerous Myth: The Fallacy of Race*
   (New York, 1942), p. 33.
8. C. Loring Brace, "On the Race Concept," *Current Anthropology*, Vol.
   5 (Oct. 1964), p. 320.
9. *Ibid.*, p. 313.
10. Morton H. Fried, "A Four Letter Word that Hurts," *Saturday Review*,
    Oct. 2, 1965), p. 22.
11. Brace, *op. cit.*, p. 313.
12. Fried, *op. cit.*
13. Jean Hiernaux, "The Concept of Race and the Taxonomy of Man-
    kind," in Ashley Montagu, ed., *The Concept of Race* (Glencoe, Ill.:
    Free Press, 1964), pp. 42–3.
14. "Statement on the Nature of Race and Race Differences by Physical
    Anthropologists and Geneticists," June, 1951, reprinted in *Current
    Anthropology*, Vol. 2 (Oct. 1961), pp. 304–06.

15. Stanley Garn and Carlton Coon, "On the Number of Races of Mankind," in Stanley Garn, ed., *Readings on Race* (Springfield, Ill.: Charles C. Thomas, 1960), p. 9.
16. *Ibid.*, pp. 9, 13–14.
17. W. Stanton, *The Leopard's Spots: Scientific Attitudes Toward Race in America, 1815–59* (Chicago: University of Chicago Press, 1960), p. 25.
18. Jacques Barzun, *Race, a Study in Modern Superstition* (London, 1938) p. 117.
19. A list of genetic traits is presented by Munro S. Edmondson, "A Measurement of Relative Racial Differences," *Current Anthropology,* Vol. 6 (April 1965), pp. 167–98.
20. Bentley Glass and C. C. Li, "The Dynamics of Racial Intermixture— An Analysis Based on the American Negro," *American Journal of Human Genetics,* Vol. 5 (March 1953), pp. 1–20.
21. Edmondson, *op cit.*
22. Frank B. Livingstone, "Anthropological Implication of Sickle Cell Gene Distributions in West Africa," *American Anthropologist,* Vol. 60 (June 1958), pp. 533–62.
23. Hiernaux, *op cit.,* pp. 36–7.
24. M. T. Newman, "Geographic and Microgeographic Races," *Current Anthropology,* Vol. 4 (April 1963), p. 189.
25. Stanley Garn, "Comment," *ibid.,* Vol. 4 (April 1963), p. 197.
26. Livingstone, "On the Non-existence of Human Races," *op. cit.,* p. 279.
27. Louis L. Snyder, *The Idea of Racialism* (New York: Van Nostrand Reinhold, 1962), p. 25.
28. Ashley Montagu, *The Idea of Race* (Lincoln: University of Nebraska Press, 1965), pp. 9–10.
29. John C. Greene, *The Death of Adam* (New York: Mentor Books, 1959), pp. 222–4.
30. Johann Blumenbach, cited in Montagu, *Man's Most Dangerous Myth,* p. 15.
31. John C. Greene, "Some Early Speculations on the Origins of Human Races," *American Anthropologist,* Vol. 54 (Feb. 1954), p. 22.
32. Stanton, *op. cit.,* p. 195.
33. Thomas F. Gossett, *Race: The History of an Idea in America* (Dallas, Texas: Methodist University Press, 1964), p. 286.
34. Pitrim Sorokin, *Contemporary Sociological Theories* (New York, 1928), pp. 297–8.
35. Gossett, *op. cit.,* p. 154.
36. *Ibid.,* p. 363.
37. *Ibid.,* p. 368.
38. *Ibid.,* p. 198.
39. Donald G. MacRae, "Race and Sociology in History and Theory," in Philip Mason, ed., *Man, Race and Darwin* (London, 1960), p. 80.
40. Gossett, *op. cit.,* p. 245.

41. *Ibid.,* pp. 429–30.
42. Harry L. Shapiro, "The History and Development of Physical Anthropology," *American Anthropologist,* Vol. 61 (June 1959), p. 376.
43. Gossett, *op. cit.,* p. 416.
44. *Ibid.,* p. 418.
45. A. L. Kroeber, "The Superorganic," *American Anthropologist,* Vol. 19 (April-June, 1917), pp. 163–213.
46. Otto Klineberg, *Negro Intelligence and Selective Migration* (New York, 1935).
47. MacRae, *op. cit.,* p. 84.
48. Gossett, *op. cit.,* p. 445.
49. Ashley Montagu, *Race, Science and Humanity* (Princeton, N. J.: Princeton University Press, 1963), pp. 144–5.
50. Carleton Coon, *The Origin of Races* (New York: Knopf, 1962). Coon's argument can be questioned on the basis of the difficulty of distinguishing race in fossils, and the flow of genes between populations.
51. *Ibid.,* pp. ix–x.
52. *Ibid.,* p. 427.
53. *Ibid.,* p. 656.
54. *Ibid.,* p. 658.
55. *Ibid.,* p. 661.
56. *Ibid.,* p. 116.
57. Theodosius Dobzhansky, "Comment," *Current Anthropology,* Vol. 4 (April 1963), p. 197.
58. Ashley Montagu, "The Concept of Race," *American Anthropologist,* Vol. 64 (Oct. 1962), pp. 919–28.

# SCIENCE ON RACE

*Patricia McBroom*

Patricia McBroom is a Staff Writer on the weekly *Science News* of the Institution for the Popularization of Science, Washington, D. C.

For eight hours last week, 20 scientists alternately denied and upheld the concept of human races. When all had been said, Dr. Theodosius Dobzhansky, professor of genetics at Rockefeller Uni-

From *Science News,* Vol. 91 (Jan. 14, 1967), pp. 44. Reprinted, with permission, from *Science News,* the weekly news magazine of science and the application of science, copyright 1967 by Science Service, Inc.

versity, took the podium and in measured tones offered his opinion
of the symposium: "I am known as a compromiser," he said, "but
the conflicting opinions tonight are beyond my ability to com-
promise."

"To deny the existence of racial differences is futile," he told
the American Association for the Advancement of Science panel
on "The Utility of the Construct of Race."

If races did not exist they would have to be invented in order to
deal with the "wild variety" of three billion people, said Dr.
Dobzhansky.

At the same time, he noted, there is "no careful, objective definition" of race that permits grouping people into discrete categories.
If such separation existed, mankind would be composed of distinct
species, not different races.

Dr. Dobzhansky said the number of races the human species can
be divided into is a completely arbitary matter. It could be three,
four, five or 35.

Brazil, in fact, recognizes 40. A current textbook lists five while
another acknowledges 65.

Herein lies the scientific controversy: Because the races overlap,
creating a continuum, and because that continuum can be broken
into as many parts as one wishes, some scholars are maintaining
that races do not exist at all.

Mankind is a single continuous species, said Dr. Morton H.
Fried, an anthropologist from Columbia University. So loose are
the divisions below the species level, that it is impossible, he said,
to sensibly relate race to any other variable. Studies which attempt
links between race and such things as intelligence and adaptability
are "destructive and antisocial," he charged. They cannot even
define accurately what they wish to study, he said.

Dr. Fried called for an end to the "pseudoscientific investigation
of race."

Dr. Fried's comments served to point out the miasma that often
distorts racial studies in the United States. Several speakers acknowledged that the American concept of race is a product of
"hyperconflict." It is so loaded with emotional connotations that
many scientists have shied away from the subject altogether, fear-
ing that their work, particularly work on genetics, would be misinterpreted and misused.

Also any attempt to study races in the United States encounters
environmental inequality which makes basic racial distinctions
virtually impossible.

To some scientists such distinctions are mythical in any case.
Heredity and environment interact so completely that the two are

forever inseparable: "Any work that tries to separate them is scientifically worthless," said Dr. Herbert G. Birch of the Albert Einstein College of Medicine.

In this view, a concept of race that rests on genes alone is invalid as a basis for study.

Dr. Birch recalled an experiment in which rats were supposedly bred for brightness and dullness. The trouble was they were selectively bred according to how well they ran a particular maze. When the maze—the rat's environment—was changed to highlight visual cues, the dull rats became bright and the bright ones, dull. Applied to humans, the rat test simply means that many tests of intelligence do not ask the right questions. Nor do human environments always ask the right questions; change the conditions and very subtle differences, perhaps even racial differences, in sight, hearing and touch, make large differences in the ability to learn and achieve.

Two symposium members, however, did venture out on a racial limb. Substituting the word "populations" for "races," Drs. Benson E. Ginsberg of the University of Chicago and William S. Laughlin of the University of Wisconsin said that the differences between human groups are more than skin deep.

The human species is not genetically uniform, either in physical appearance, physiology or behavior and was probably less so in the past than it is today, said geneticist Ginsberg.

Human populations have been separated by distance, geography, language, religion and other cultural factors—all of which helped to determine which human traits were valued and therefore which genes were multiplied.

"It would be nothing short of remarkable if we were to find that the Ainu (Japan) and the Zulu (Africa) were alike in genetic capacities and therefore in behavioral characteristics."

Dr. Ginsberg and Laughlin contended that the different populations of the earth are not in fact equal genetically, but all have equal potential. Every reasonably large human group possesses the full spectrum of human genes, in so far as talent and behavior are concerned, they said.

The two men estimated that any group of 30,000 people on earth is genetically capable of recreating every accomplishment of mankind, without genetic crossing from any other group.

The number, 30,000, is a guess based on the achievements of past civilizations such as the Mayan which, while isolated from outside genes, generated mathematics, astronomy, writing, architecture and the concept of zero—all from a base of primitive hunters.

Genetic potential was probably pulled out by population density, said Dr. Laughlin. Density allowed the gifted to seek each other out, marry selectively, and thus accentuate the genes responsible for memory, intellect and talent.

While "positive" selection took place, "negative" selection did not. There was no attempt to breed out talent, simply a failure to exploit potential. And genetic potential does not atrophy from disuse, said Dr. Ginsberg, "The deuces remain in the deck."

Recognizing these genetic differences between populations "offers the major scientific hope for upgrading our biological condition," Dr. Ginsberg told the symposium. He estimated that the full human potential can be pulled out of any population within seven to ten generations. This will occur naturally, through the tendency of gifted people to marry each other, once society offers full educational opportunity.

Since the Ginsberg-Laughlin thesis was treated with near total silence throughout, it is questionable whether other panelists considered this construct of race to be a "major scientific hope" for upgrading the human species.

But some areas of agreement emerged, the most important one being that no superiority or inferiority can be attributed to race and that the word "race," no longer useful, should be replaced with "population."

# Chapter Ten

# *Racial Differences*

While no two individuals are ever exactly alike, members of the same population who share the same gene pool and the same environment, are apt to be more similar than two individuals who come from different populations. Thus a given population is characterized by a number of "concordant" traits—traits that hang together. The following articles describe some of these traits. But more important than noting the incidence of a certain disease in this group and a blood group frequency in that group is the very fundamental question of why population X manifests trait Y in the first place. If it is a genetic trait we must assume that it was established there by the action of evolution. Or perhaps it is a trait which could presumably be developed in any population of the species, but is not because it takes a particular environment (natural or cultural) to call it forth. In most cases, of course, the existence of a trait is due to genetic *and* environmental factors which are notoriously difficult to separate into their component and interacting parts. Moreover, gene frequency change is a slow, conservative business compared to cultural changes and the genetic constitution of a population today is the product of a long evolutionary history.

In the end, we must admit that we don't know why human populations are different. In fact, for the most part, we really don't even know how to identify and measure the differences. Yet we have learned a few things—that most differences between groups of humans are differences in degree; that the differences don't lend themselves to good or bad classifications, since traits are relative to the environment in which they evolved or developed; that some differences are evidently the fortuitous by-products of the action of some evolutionary force which we usually cannot identify; and that any human population is only operating on a small proportion of its hereditary and environmental potential—i.e., that there are a tremendous number of successful ways of "being human." Humanity is a constant for the species although its biological and cultural expression is variable.

# ADAPTATION AND RACE

*Jean Hiernaux*

Jean Hiernaux, a professor of physical anthropology at the Free University of Brussels, is an authority on human races. He has written numerous articles on the significance of biological differences in man.

Before developing the theme of this paper, it is necessary to define what is meant by the terms "Race" and "Adaptation."

The adjective "racial" refers to the hereditary patrimony. Two groups will be said to differ racially in skin color, for instance, if they differ in their collective hereditary patrimony, or "gene pool," for this feature. "Racial" is thus synonymous with "genetical" when the latter adjective is applied to groups of people. "Genetical" should be used in preference to "racial" because it is unequivocal.

An observed difference between two groups may be a matter of a difference between the gene pools, or of different environments

From *The Advancement of Science*, Vol. 23 (April 1967), pp. 658–62. Reprinted by permission of The British Association for The Advancement of Science, and the author.

influencing the expression of identical gene pools, or the combined effect of differences in environment and in gene pool. For, in most features, the individual's heredity determines only a range of possible values, within which his real value depends on his environment. Skin color, for instance, is influenced by sun-tanning, and weight by diet. It is of great theoretical and practical importance to distinguish how much in a difference is genetical, and how much is expressional.

In the matters that concern us now, we look to groups of people as to gene pools. We must therefore define them in genetical terms. The unit of study is called the breeding or mendelian population, or, in short, the population. This unit denotes a group of people who share in a common gene pool because they intermarry without internal geographical, social or other barriers while an effective barrier—usually a relative one—separates them from other populations.

Many anthropologists are interested also in larger units, called races. It has however been questioned whether human diversity can objectively be cut into such large discrete units, and an increasing number of biological anthropologists are convinced that the arbitrary element in any subdivision of mankind into races is such that the procedure entails more confusion than simplification. As a matter of fact, classificatory schemes of mankind currently proposed number nearly as many as the classifiers themselves; they differ greatly in the number and their method of delimitation of races. A group of 22 biological anthropologists from all over the world, assembled in 1964 by UNESCO in order to give their views on the biological aspects of the race question, stated that "many anthropologists, while stressing the importance of human variation, believe that the scientific interest of these classifications is limited, and even that they carry the risk of inviting abusive generalizations." This risk is evident. For instance, you may find an African population more similar to an Asian one in its ABO blood group frequencies, and to a European one in its fingerprints frequencies, than to another African population near to it by its total gene pool. What is observed in a population is valid only for that population. Extrapolation is not permissible in anthropology because each population is unique in its combinations of gene frequencies.

Turning now to the term "adaptation"—this will be understood here as a modification leading to a better performance in a specific environment. In this sense, it does not include those modifications of behavior which are aimed at avoiding a stress, for instance a lowered muscular activity in the heat. How important such behavioral responses are compared with adaptation as defined above will not be discussed here. In many situations, man has evolved the capacity to achieve adaptation through nonbiological, or cultural, changes. He can resist cold, for instance, by clothes and house-heating. Biological adaptation, usually interwoven with cultural adaptation, presents as several different categories. The adult retains a limited plasticity which allows him, for example, to increase his performance during a period of hard work in a hot environment, a phenomenon usually called acclimatization. It is reversible, though its effects may be of long duration. Plasticity is much more pronounced during development, and may then affect morphology as well as function. In some situations, environment induces deviations in the morphological development which are adaptive to it, and which are irreversible once growth has stopped. Such an adaptation through developmental plasticity, like acclimatization, is not transmitted by heredity.

There is only one way by which an adaptation can become fixed in the gene pool of a population: it is through selection. In this case, "perfomance" in the stated definition of adaptation means survival. Suppose that, for a given hereditary trait, a population possesses two genes, A and B, in its gene pool. Since genes go by pairs, an individual may be AA, AB, or BB. If the AA adults contribute more to the next generation than the AB's and BB's (by having more children, dying less often before reproducing, or by both mechanisms), gene A will increase in frequency from one generation to the next until the frequency of B is reduced to nil. If AA is advantageous only in certain environments, while other environments favor BB, the absence of gene B in the former environments, and of A in the latter ones, are cases of genetic adaptation. Such an extreme contrast of 0 and 100 per cent gene frequencies is probably very rare amongst human populations, if it even exists. On the contrary, what seems quite common is the case in which genotype AB is favored, in some environments at least, compared with both AA and BB, by a value depending on a variable of the environment. In this situation, selection leads to an equilibrium between the frequencies of A and B, the level of which depends on the intensity of the selective agent. The result is called "balanced polymorphism," and the process responsible for it is called "heterosis." The best known example of it in man, and the only one that seems really elucidated today, concerns the chemical composition of the hemoglobin, the red pigment of the blood. Some populations possess two variants of hemoglobin, each determined by a single gene: the so-called "normal" hemoglobin A, and the sicklemic hemoglobin S. SS individuals usually die before reaching puberty, and therefore leave no progeny, while the AS's display a higher genetic fitness than AA's by being more resistant to malignant malaria, a great killer of children in a large part of the world. In a malarious population in which these genes are present, the frequencies of A and S genes tend to an equilibrium which represents an adaptation to the severity of malaria.

Since we are dealing with the theme "Adaptation and Race," and the concept of race having been reduced to that of gene pool, the question is: "How much of the differences in gene pool between human populations represents genetic adaptation?"

For evaluating the extent of genetic adaptation, we must first consider the other factors making for differences between gene pools, and weigh their possible importance in the genesis of current human diversity. They are: mutations, hybridization, and random fluctuation or genetic drift.

Mutations, which produce new genes, are rare phenomena, and are incapable of generating notable frequencies of the mutant genes unless they are backed by adaptive selection, the mechanism of which has been just described, or unless genetic drift or related mechanisms happen to multiply the mutants. It is important to note that mutations might provide different materials for building equivalent balanced polymorphisms in different parts of the world. For example, the A–S hemoglobin polymorphism is present in malarious areas of Africa, Arabia, India, and Southern Europe. An A–E hemoglobin polymorphism is present in malarious southeastern Asia and maybe represents an adaptive equivalent of the A–S polymorphism, in an area where the hazards of mutations created gene E but no gene S as mutants from gene A. A more complex A–S–C hemoglobin polymorphism is found in a western African area, with an extension through the Sahara up to North Africa and Sicily. It is not clear whether E and C compete or respond to different environmental stresses (even for S, it now appears that resistance to malaria is not the whole story; resistance to leprosy has also been evidenced). Still other genetic polymorphic systems, like thalassemia and an inherited enzyme (glucose-6-phosphate dehydrogenase) deficiency are also suspected as responding to malaria. In some populations, they coexist with the A–S polymorphism; how they interact with it is still unclear. As all this shows, the effect of genetical adaptation depends not only on the nature and intensity of the environmental stress, but also on the genes present in the gene pool. It is the very rarity of mutations that makes them play a role—an indirect one—in the diversity of human populations.

Hybridization of a population means immigration of genes from a different mendelian population. This process shifts the gene frequencies of the first population in the direction of those of the second, by an amount proportional to the relative influx of genes. Hybridization unceasingly changes the pattern of differences between the world's populations, but its levelling effect excludes it as a source of the human diversity.

Random fluctuations in gene frequencies, or genetic drift, increase with a decrease in population size. The theory of probability shows indeed that large populations are likely to keep stable in their gene frequencies, while restricted ones tend to show fluctuating frequencies, a tendency possibly leading to the loss or fixation of genes. Until the discovery and diffusion of means of food production (agriculture and stock raising), a recent event indeed when compared with the duration of man's evolution, mankind was composed of small bands of hunter-gatherers, disposing each of a large territory. In those circumstances genetic drift surely met favorable opportunities of acting all over the world. Two kinds of events are capable of producing sudden changes in gene frequencies, which are similar to the generation-to-generation genetic drift by the fact that they are nondirectional and only statistically predictable. In the first one, a small group of individuals leaves a large population and founds a new one. The resulting "founder effect" had many opportunities to operate in the past. Most African tribes, for instance, claim to have originated by such a process. The second kind of event is a sharp reduction in the number of a population by war, epidemics, or natural cataclysms, all events which repeatedly struck mankind.

Genetic drift is much more powerful on these traits which are determined by one gene, like blood groups and hemoglobin types, than on traits whose hereditary component consists in a number of independent genes acting additively, like body size, proportions, and most descriptive traits. These multifactorial traits, however, show no less diversity between human populations than monofactorial traits. This suggests that adaptation is a paramount factor in the genesis of the genetic diversity between human populations.

This conclusion has been reached by exclusion of other factors as main sources of diversity. To demonstrate cases of selective adaptation is by no means easy in the human species. Man is unique in his cultural capacity for modifying his environment, and in the extent and frequency with which his populations migrate or change the size of their territory. An observed polymorphism may very well reflect an adaptation to an environment quite different from the one in which the population now lives: gene frequencies can change but slowly; the population may be a relatively recent newcomer in its current environment, or it may have modified its environment recently by cultural means (think of the effects of eradicating malaria on the hemoglobin polymorphism). Thanks to a technological innovation giving it advantage over the surrounding ones, a population may have enormously spread its size and territory over a variety of environments and replaced local populations which were better adapted biologically to their milieu. Given mankind's history, even a moderate association between a gene frequency and an environmental variable, like the one between S hemoglobin gene and malaria, looks highly suggestive of genetic adaptation.

The search for such associations between a gene frequency and a quantified aspect of the environment is actively pursued by a number of anthropologists. It is impeded by the fact that few aspects of the environment are properly quantified on a world scale yet. The best known attributes of the milieu are climatic variables, yet it seems probable that blood hereditary characteristics, which constitute today the vast majority of known monofactorial traits, are sensitive mainly to pathological factors, the intensity of which remains to be scientifically established in large parts of the world. Moreover, some data suggest that infectious agents themselves change their properties as a genetic adaptation to the human host, at the rapid rate permitted by their short life cycle. It might therefore be that selective pressure from pathology is highly variable in time on some systems. In the field of monofactorial traits, the evidence for adaptation as the main source of human diversity still rests more on theoretical grounds than on factual verification.

Demonstrating genetical adaptation is still more difficult in the case of multifactorial traits, like stature, weight, and bodily proportions. Most, if not all of them present an "expressional" component in their diversity, the isolation of which is no easy task. For instance, body weight, a feature partly determined by heredity, manifests a statistical tendency to be lower in human populations living in the tropics. There are theoretical reasons to believe that a low weight is physiologically advantageous in a hot climate, and some experimental verification of this advantage has been made. On the other hand, we know that nutrition is poorer, as an average, in the tropical zone than in the temperate one, and that diet directly affects weight. How much is genetical and how much is expressional in the association of mean weight with latitude? Two African populations of different origin living side by side in Rwanda for

several centuries and eating similar diets today show largely different weight to stature ratios. A genetical component is here evidenced in the difference, but we do not precisely know in which
climate the two groups have lived in the past; this prevents us from
testing any hypothesis identifying a specific climatic variable to
which genetical adaptation would have occurred. Research into
the association of several anthropometrical variables with climate
in sub-Saharan Africa is now in progress. It has revealed many
significant associations, many of which convincingly involve some
genetical adaptation. Weight shows a significant correlation with
several climatic variables, but human plasticity for it is so marked
that one can but hesitate to identify those variables as selective
agents on the basis of such evidence. At the same time, we must
keep in mind that climate is only one aspect of the environment.
A poor diet lowers mean weight by influencing the expression of
the population's hereditary patrimony for weight. On the other
hand, a low weight is advantageous for somebody doomed to a low
caloric intake. Selection favoring genetically light people is therefore conceivable; it would produce a genetical adaptation adding
its effects to the expressional influence of poor nutrition in lowering mean weight. If one remembers that climate strongly influences
diet in simple farming communities, one sees how complex is the
interpretation of the observed relations between climate and
weight. It will need a multidisciplinary and international effort,
like the one currently planned by the International Biological Programme, for us to advance beyond our limited understanding of
the question.

Another example. There is a tendency in related mammals to
show larger protruding organs in hot climates. A similar tendency
has been found in man for the relative length of the lower limbs.
The physiological advantage of such an association has been elucidated. Bodily proportions are, for a large part, determined by
heredity. We are therefore strongly tempted to interpret the relation between climate and the trunk to lower limb ratio in terms of
genetical adaptation. Rightly so indeed: European children born in
the tropics do not develop the long legs usual in Africans. Part of
the association might however be due to developmental plasticity:
mice reared in the heat develop a longer tail.

However large our ignorance, the more we know, the more important appears the role played by genetical adaptation in those
differences between human populations which strike the eye, and
are usually referred to as "racial" differences, as well as in less

visible ones. Differences in skin color and in nose shape, for instance, appear to result mainly from genetical adaptation.

How deep is genetical adaptation of human populations? In other words, what is the price of biological adaptation to an environment in terms of capacity to success in another one? History and biology give us ample evidence for answering this question. We know of many historical cases of successful transplantation of a population into a strikingly different environment. A widespread distribution of an initially restricted group is repeatedly recorded by historians, prehistorians or human palaeontologists. The works of environmental physiologists show that all human populations are alike in their modes of reaction when faced with a given climatic stress; the differences in efficiency in their reaction once they are acclimatized are slight, if they appear at all. Contrasting with most animal species whose subdivisions tend to adapt strictly to specific environments, man is characterized by a general adaptability. The 22 UNESCO experts referred to above were unanimous in stating that "general adaptability to the most diverse environments is in man more pronounced than his adaptations to specific environments." How man did escape partitioning and local specialization is clear: by the extent of his migrations and interbreeding.

The roots of this distinction of man lie in the unique nature of his progress. To give the word again to the 1964 UNESCO statement: "For long millenia, progress made by man, in any field, seems to have been increasingly, if not exclusively, based on culture and to transmission of cultural achievements, and not on the transmission of genetic endowment." Biological success of a population, which means its increase in number, is achieved in man essentially through cultural advance, most often of a technological nature. Cultural advantage is also the mover to faraway implantation and possible replacement of a population genetically better adapted to the local conditions but less advanced by some aspects of its culture. Culture again provides man with more and more efficient nonbiological means of coping with the departure from optimal genetical equilibrium which migration in a fresh environment may involve. Success in this cultural adaptation lightens or possibly annuals the selective pressure for genetical adjustment.

If we now consider man's place in nature, what made him so successful on earth is his genetic capacity for culture. This major distinction is so essential for his survival in any environment that, at the light of current knowledge at least, all populations seem to be equal in this respect. Adaptation to local environment was and still is a paramount factor in the genesis of genetical or "racial" differences between human populations, but these differences are minor and unessential compared with man's general physiological adaptability and his general capacity to find nonbiological means of coping with the variations of his environment, including the new biological challenges which cultural evolution itself unceasingly generates.

# RACE MIXTURE

*Francisco M. Salzano*

Francisco M. Salzano, a professor at the Institute of National Sciences, Porto Alegre, Brazil, has recently written *Problems in Human Biology*.

## Process and Consequence

The expected consequences of race mixture are different according to the genetic structure of the populations in question. We simply do not know if human populations can best be described in terms of what is called the *classical hypothesis* or if the contrasting *balance hypothesis* fits the known facts better. According to the classical hypothesis evolutionary changes consist principally in gradual substitution and eventual fixation of the more favorable gene alleles and chromosomal structures in place of the less favorable. Superior alleles are established by natural selection and supplant inferior ones. Most individuals in a Mendelian population should, then, be homozygous for most genes. Heterozygous loci will be a minority. According to the balance hypothesis the adaptive norm is an array of genotypes heterozygous for more or less numerous gene alleles, gene complexes and chromosomal structures. Homozygotes for these genes and gene complexes occur in normal outbred populations only in a minority of individuals, and

From *International Social Science Journal*, Vol. XVII, No. 1 (1965), pp. 135–38. Reprinted by permission of UNESCO.

make these individuals more or less inferior to the norm in fitness.

It is clear that if human populations follow the second model the consequences of race mixture, with its consequent increase in heterozygosity, will be less drastic than otherwise.

Furthermore, the historic past of the groups involved is important. Darlington studied selected British families and European royal families through three generations and demonstrated the fact, well known in the animal and plant kingdom, that inbreeders suffer by outbreeding and outbreeders by inbreeding. In Darlington's material this is true for the average of each of the successive reproductive tests in the progeny: viability after birth, marriage frequency and numbers of the second generation.

Another basic question which remains to be answered for a proper understanding of the consequences of race mixture is concerned with the nature of the racial differences. Are they adaptive or did they result from the action of genetic drift? The great majority of human biologists favor the first hypothesis but Lasker is of the opinion that natural selection has not been satisfactorily demonstrated as a significant factor in racial differentiation and that small groups would come to differ racially by the purely random process of primarily endogamous mate selection. Subsequent rapid increases in population size based on cultural advantages or historical opportunities would be mainly responsible for the kind of racial pattern manifest today. This is a view which I cannot accept, especially in view of the large amount of evidence now available on the influence of race on the response to cold or heat stress; but it is possible, as stressed by Dobzhansky that in some special cases genetic drift in conjunction with natural selection may have played an important role in human populations descended from small numbers of "founders."

This problem has a direct bearing on the prediction of the consequences of race mixture. If race formation in man was a purely random process, the consequences of race mixture will be small; if it was built through a sometimes slow process of gene coadaptation, the breakdown of such systems can lead to decreased fitness.

## The Evidence

Intercrossing of inbred lines in corn restores the vigor found in crossbred parental varieties and even improves it. The term *heterosis* was proposed by Shull to describe this phenomenon. Although hybrid corn represents the most important practical application of genetics to date, the genetic mechanisms that bring about heterosis are by no means completely understood. Some generalizations, however, can be made: (a) many but by no means all heterozygous combinations contribute to increased fitness of these genotypes: (b) this superiority prevails only on certain genetic backgrounds and in specific physical and biotic environments; (c) viability is strongly affected by the internal balance of the genotype. A disturbance of this balance may override favorable effects of heterozygosity.

The studies on human populations have developed through several lines of research. Trevor surveyed all the morphological data available up to then and selected for analysis nine studies. The general conclusions of his analysis can be summarized as follows: (a) comparisons of the mean measurement of metrical characters possibly suggest that the average for a crossed population always tends to lie between those of the parental populations in cases where the latter themselves differ significantly; (b) most of the groups studied stand closer to the non-European parental type; (c) there are no great differences in variability between hybrid groups in general and the populations from which they were derived; and it cannot be said that all hybrid populations tend to be equally variable; (d) the hybrid series as a whole tend to be slightly more variable than the European parental and the latter slightly more variable than the non-European parental; (e) it can be categorically stated that the material available does not suggest that the distributions of metrical characters in populations derived from the crossing of distinct racial groups, are in any way peculiar when compared with populations of unmixed origin.

The fitness of human population hybrids in terms of reproductive success were considered by several authors. Snell reviewed the older literature. He interprets part of the data as indicating heterosis but pointed out that some crosses have not led to favorable results. Freire-Maia and Quelce-Salgado reported important work in this connection. Their studies in populations of the southern region of the State of Minas Gerais, Brazil, suggested that the Negroes there had a number of lethal equivalents per individual significantly higher than Caucasians. The Mulattos showed intermediate values. However strictly equivalent results are not being observed in other populations (Freire-Maia, personal communication). As pointed out in the above-mentioned papers, the findings and conclusions refer exclusively to the populations of the area and no generalization can be uncritically made. Salzano, Marçallo,

Freire-Maia and Krieger, on the other hand, presented data which indicated that Brazilian Indians, Mestizos and Whites seem to have the same amount of genetic load as revealed in the offspring of consanguineous marriages.

Another important investigation about the reproduction of a hybrid population was recently reported by Chung and Morton. Their study is based on 179,285 babies born in Hawaii during the period of 1948 to 1958, together with samples of blood types from the Hawaii Blood Bank and records of maternal weight and height from the Straub Clinic. Their results can be summarized as follows: (a) there is no evidence of an increased obstetrical hazard in outcrosses; (b) there is no effect of hybridity of child or parent on birth weight or height. This supports the conclusion of Trevor that hybrid populations are intermediate for metrical traits, without detectable heterosis or recombination effects; (c) there is no effect of hybridity of the child on post neonatal infant death, stillbirths, early fetal death, or previous fetal death; (d) hybridity of the father has no detectable consistent effect; but previous fetal death and late fetal death are reduced by maternal hybridity.

## Retrospective and Perspective

The studies reviewed here sometimes showed contradictory results. It should be pointed out, however, that the amount of work done in this direction is clearly out of proportion to the importance of the problem. Some of the discrepancies observed could be due to differences in methodology; others to the different genetic structures of the populations investigated. Careful and standardized studies in large hybrid human and animal groups are needed in order to provide a broader framework of reference from which generalizations could be made with more confidence. But a general answer to the question of the biological consequence of race mixture in man has to await the elucidation of two basic questions: the nature of the main component of genetic load occurring in the majority of the human populations; and the nature (if adaptive or not) of the majority of the racial differences. However, the evidence does show that the biological consequences of intermixture are not sufficiently large to determine any general policy either against or in favor of such marriages among humans. The money spent in such enterprises or in the dissemination of discussion between racists and nonracists might more profitably be used in the financing of the needed research.

# VITAMIN D AND THE RACES OF MAN

The very existence of the essential vitamin D, or "sunshine vitamin," was not established until the present century, but its imprint upon history goes back a million years or more. According to a theory now elaborated by Brandeis University Biochemist W. Farnsworth Loomis, it is because of the human body's need to take in a certain amount of vitamin D, but not too much, that the human species has developed into three principal racial groups distinguished by skin color and loosely called black, yellow and white.

Loomis points out in the journal *Science* that vitamin D is no ordinary vitamin. Unlike the others, it occurs in virtually no natural foods.* It is synthesized in the skin under the influence of ultraviolet rays. The body needs vitamin D if it is to process calcium from food to make bone. Consequently, children need proportionately more vitamin D for their growing bones, and a D deficiency causes rickets.

D differs from most other vitamins in a second important respect: too much of it is as bad as too little. Severe or long-term excess causes chalky calcium deposits in arteries, notably the aorta, and in the kidneys, with stone formation and loss of kidney function. Eventually, this can be fatal. To guard the U.S. child against rickets, health authorities recommend a daily vitamin D intake of 400 international units (ten micrograms), which is easily obtained from milk. If the youngster's system makes more vitamin D as he plays in the sun, it is usually not enough to be dangerous. If he is given more than 20,000 units, a child becomes severely ill. In northern climes, most white adults make all the vitamin D they need from casual exposure of their face and hands to the sun and need no dietary supplement. They get ill on 100,000 units a day. But in the tropics, Loomis figures, the white man's unpigmented skin could make a deadly dose of D: up to 800,000 units, he calculates, in a six-hour exposure of his whole body to the equatorial sun.

Reprinted from *Time*, The Weekly Newsmagazine, Aug. 19, 1967, pp. 52–3. Copyright Time Inc., 1967.

---

*Exceptions: the liver oils of some fish, notably cod and halibut; egg yolks (small quantities) and milk (minute amounts). Milk and many other foods are now "vitamin D enriched" by ultraviolet irradiation.

## Origin on the Equator

The control of skin color over vitamin D synthesis, says Loomis, explains the distribution of the races of man in prehistoric and early historic times. As far as anthropologists can tell, "human beings" originated in Africa near the equator. Almost certainly, they had black skins. Many anthropologists have argued that dark skin evolved as a protection against sunburn and skin cancer. On the contrary, says Loomis: dark skin came first, and light skin evolved as a protection against a deficiency of vitamin D. Black skin allows only 3 per cent to 36 per cent of ultraviolet rays to pass, while white skin passes 53 per cent to 72 per cent. As early man moved north from the equatorial region, beyond the 40th parallel (roughly, the latitude of Madrid and Naples), Loomis argues, he got into a zone where black skin filters out too much ultraviolet. He encountered rickets. The darkest-skinned young male hunters were so crippled that they could not keep up: the darkest-skinned females died in childbirth because of pelvic deformities. Those who happened to be lighter skinned, of both sexes, survived.

Thus, by the classic Darwinian process of evolution by natural selection, the farther north man went, the more completely did the light-skinned survive and the dark-skinned die out.

The layers of the skin involved in the sun-screening process are visible under a microscope. Below the skin's outermost horny layer, or *stratum corneum*, lies a germinative layer where, on exposure to sunlight, the pigment-producing cells are stimulated to produce more melanin—and a suntan. The black races (Negro, Bushman-Hottentot and Australoid), with a more abundant supply of melanin, are in effect, perpetually tanned. Members of the white race are transparent-skinned in winter, when they must make the most of the limited ultraviolet available to synthesize vitamin D, but they take a tan in summer, when they might suffer from an excess. There are other bits of confirmatory evidence: the only relatively dark-skinned people in high latitudes are the Eskimos, who get all the vitamin D they need from fish-liver oils. Until the 1930's, when irradiation of milk to enrich its vitamin D content became prevalent, U.S. Negro childen suffered far more commonly from rickets than white children.

## Reverse Selection

There remains the question of why the Mongols and related peoples are "yellow." Biochemist Loomis explains this on the basis of additional keratin (horny material) in the outer skin layers—

though dermatologists deny this and say that the Mongol's sun screen is melanin, like the Negro's, but in smaller amounts. Loomis surmises that the yellow races may have developed their coloration after having gone through the white-race depigmentation phase. If migration away from the equator produces lighter skins, says Loomis, reverse migration could have the opposite effect. In the mere 10,000 to 20,000 years since relatively light-skinned Mongols crossed from Siberia to Alaska and spread southward to Tierra del Fuego, there has been a natural selection in favor of the darker-skinned Amerindians between 40° north and 40° south latitude. Outside these boundaries, and in most of the dark rain forests of Brazil, the Indians are not appreciably darker than most Asiatic Mongols.

Loomis' theory is not entirely new, but he has honed it to a greater sharpness than have previous investigators. Every human being of every race lives through a cycle of supporting evidence for at least part of it and carries some in his hand throughout life. Babies of all races are lighter than adults, presumably reflecting nature's provision for early vitamin D needs. And people of all races have pale, unpigmented palms and soles. Since these parts have extra keratin and are not exposed to ultraviolet, they need no melanin protection against excess vitamin D synthesis.

# BIOLOGY, SOCIETY, AND CULTURE IN HUMAN ECOLOGY

*Frederick Sargent II and Demitri B. Shimkin*

Frederick Sargent II, an ecologist, is a professor at the University of Wisconsin at Green Bay; Demitri B. Shimkin, an anthropologist, is a professor at the University of Illinois.

*All creatures have a specific nature, all represent wholes having the character of individuality.* (From *The Organism*, by K. Goldstein, p. 476.)

Human ecology seeks to understand man and his problems by studying individuals and populations as biological entities pro-

From *Biological Science*, Vol. 15 (Aug. 1965), pp. 512–16. Reprinted by permission.

foundly modified by human society and culture and by studying the effects of physical, biological, and cultural environments upon man and those of man upon his environments. The viewpoint of ecology is at once statistical and typological.[8] The observational reality is always a set of tolerances pertinent to the physics and chemistry of an individual's metabolism and behavior and to those of his behavioral products. Yet this reality persists only through genetic and social mechanisms that transcend individual life sequences to provide the continuities, feedback stabilities, and progressive adaptations of biological and cultural evolution.

## General Concepts

Biologically, man has both generic and unique characteristics as an organism. Among the former, the phenomena of distinctiveness and of persistence over time, through physiological and morphological changes, are central.

By what processes is this constancy maintained? To answer this question we must have some concept of a free-living organism in its natural life-situations. Many biologists prefer to view organisms as systems of self-regulatory processes.[13] By this view alone one cannot really understand organisms. Equilibrium and constancy are important, but a more fundamental organismic characteristic among free-living animals is direction.[13] Direction arises both from the organism and the environment, for the survival of the organism depends upon its finding an environment which is adequate for it.[13] To succeed in this search the organism must select, from all sorts of environmental stimuli that act upon it, only those events that are pertinent to it. This milieu is certainly not "definite and static"; rather it forms continuously as the active organism grows, matures, and ages.[13] Thus organism and environment are in essence inseparable.[1] It is this bond that gives rise to directions in organismic behavior and to selection in evolution.

In finding this adequate environment, the free-living animal organism exhibits preferred behavior.[13] To determine whether a particular phenomenon which seems to be preferred behavior is essential and genuine, one must consider the entire organism. As Goldstein states it (p. 364), "We are dealing with genuine attributes or constants if we find, by examining as many fields as possible, order and 'adequate performance' in the rest of the organism.... In this way we apprehend certain characteristics of the organism with which we are dealing, certain norms and constants of its nature."[13]

Among these "constants" of the nature of the organism are ways of behaving; sensory and motor thresholds; intellectual characteristics; affectivity; psychic or mental and physical traits; physiological attributes such as temperature, respiration, pulse, blood pressure; chemical qualities of the blood; blood types; and reactivity to noxious and stressful circumstances. The living organism tends to approach these relative constants or the "average mean." Thus, Goldstein remarks (pp. 364–5), "We are only in position to speak of one and the same organism, if, in spite of temporary changes, these constants become manifest."[13]

There are two groups of "constants": those which express "the essential nature of the species" and the "individual constants." Goldstein emphasizes the fundamental significance of the "individual constants" (p. 365): "On the basis of the constants of the species, the life of the normal and especially of the defective individual cannot be sufficiently comprehended, notwithstanding certain congruencies between the individuals of the same species. For that objective, an acquaintance with the nature of the individual, that is with the *individual's normal constants*, is prerequisite."[13]

Merely enumerating innumerable constants, however, does not define the essential nature of the organism. The constants themselves are equivocal because they are measured under isolating conditions. To determine which phenomena are biologically relevant and which are not, we need "a conception of the organism in its qualitative organization and holistic function" (p. 400).[13] This conception is *"the capacity of the organism to become adequate to its environmental conditions. . . .* Whenever we speak of . . . the organism, we have in mind these essentials for the realization of adequacy between the organism and its environment. And these are the principles of composition of that picture which biology has to grasp. . . ." (p. 403).[13]

## Species Constants

Man is a species that has proved unique in its fitness to survive and multiply under extremely varying selective pressures.[7] In the Pliocene, the protohominids appear to have been brachiating dwellers in tropical forests, a habitat which favored depth perception, color vision, sound production and hearing, and truly prehensile hands. Increasing drought in the late Pliocene and early Pleistocene forced adaption to a forest-edge and grasslands environment, in which both escape from predation and increasingly successful predation were basic elements of survival.[18] During this period, the precursors of man (Australopithecenes) become effective runners, in consequence of mutations and selection leading to the human heel, the reduced jaw, and the S-shaped spine. In general, less robust and more juvenile body builds sacrificing strength for endurance were evidently favored. These factors, jointly with the direct advantages of better perception, memory, symbolization, cerebral inhibition, learning and communication, fostered the absolute and relative growth of the brain.

Over the past half-million years, man has adapted to a wide range of nontropical climates, as a consequence both of migrations and climatic fluctuations during the ice ages.[17] These events must have been associated with periods of population growth and dispersal alternating with others of decline and concentration. Mechanisms such as these account, in fact, for the extraordinary combination of long-persistent geographical variability and full reproductive unity characterizing man.[9] Even more important have been the selective advantages of variability, role specialization, and cooperation in human society. These and other expressions of polygenesis even in small populations of man are undoubtedly related to the propensities toward out-breeding and mating stability ubiquitous in man. The prolonged mobility and self-sufficiency, in primitive conditions, of preadolescent children, in combination with taboos on parent-child and sibling intercourse and the continuous sexual receptivity of the human female, seem to have been the behaviors crucial to expressing these propensities.

The increasing range and effectiveness of taught behavior—culture—have vastly altered selective pressures during the past half-million years. It limited the restrictions of cold through fire, shelter, and clothing. Effective cooking ended the limitations of unaided human digestion. Thus, with seed-gathering and, later, agriculture, hunger became less of a control on human numbers. But sedentary life, land clearance, the elimination of other potential pathogenic hosts, and symbiosis with dometic animals made disease immunity and behavioral safeguards against infection basic selection mechanisms. The significance of this later selection has been insufficiently stressed. Larger populations made more mutations possible, while group survival became far less random than earlier. On one hand, new technology in some areas radically increased population-bearing capacities. On the other, endemic diseases (parasitism, malaria, tuberculosis) systematically induced childbirth and infant mortality, while epidemics carried off entire susceptible populations (e.g., smallpox and measles in North America and Oceania). Thus, intense growth in favored areas—the Near East, India, China,

Middle America—and stagnation or decline elsewhere, have predominated since the rise of agriculture.[5]

Associated with control of food and the increasing size of human populations has been the increasing importance of management: the determination of goals, the discovery of means, the organization of efforts, and the distribution of gains—in human societies.[33] An allied process has been the increasingly high evaluation of play and symbolic expression as ever more structured societies have repressed wider areas of biological desire. At the same time, the change from simple face-to-face communities to stratified states brought with it lessened capacity to identify and harness individual variation. Social criteria, such as the accidents of conquest or defeat, urban or rural residence, white skin or black, have dominated role choices. The significance of complex individual variations in human adaptation has thus been diminished through feedbacks from history. This diminution has also lowered man's evolutionary adaptability.

At his present stage of evolution, man as a species has many distinctive characteristics. He matures slowly; some 25 per cent of his life span is occupied with maturing. This long period of maturing is, however, merely an exaggeration of a primate phenomenon. Bolk has called the slowing "foetalization."[19] Another term is neoteny.

Neoteny has had several important consequences. First, it is advantageous for learning and social cooperation to be taught while the organism is docile and sexually nonaggressive.[34] Second, neoteny may be the cause of nakedness in man. According to Huxley (p. 13), "The distribution of hair on man is extremely similar to that on a late foetus of a chimpanzee, and there can be little doubt that it represents an extension of this temporary anthropoid phase into permanence."[19] Hairlessness is, except for desert inhabitants, unique among terrestrial animals. The hairless state, Huxley speculates,[19] must have encouraged humans to protect themselves against their enemies and the elements and thus have been a spur to intelligence.

Perhaps this hairless state has played a role in man's dependence upon evaporative cooling as a method of heat economy. This physiological regulation, of course, is not exclusively human, for many terrestrial animals employ evaporative cooling as a defense against overheating. What is unique about man in this respect is that he is an "eccrine animal." He is probably the only animal utilizing active sweat secreted by the eccrine sweat gland as a process of evaporative cooling.[36] Other animals sweat but their sweat derives from apocrine glands.

One might speculate that the long period of maturing of the young has been genetically related to the postmature longevity characteristic of man. The survival of animals beyond the reproductive period is unusually brief. In man, long survival allows the species to utilize social benefits accruing from speech and tradition.[19] The menopause of the human female is unusually complete and sudden, and her long postreproductive period is exceptional among mammals.[4] Williams suggests that these features may have developed in man because of the selective advantages offered to the slowly maturing offspring.[37]

Man exhibits great reproductive variability.[19] The differential fertility among men is enormous, ranging from infertility to families of one to 12 and even 20. This differential fertility is of greater selective advantage than differential mortality; it provides a basis for rapid changes in human gene pools.

The rapid and profound evolution of man's brain (primarily encephalization) allowed for plasticity and potential variety. This plasticity has had several different consequences. With encephalization and growing cortical dominance, man's power of attention has shifted to self-stimulative phenomena. As a result he experienced not only tensions, e.g., memory tensions of inhibition, but also symbolic satisfaction. These satisfactions have allowed survival and adaptation to stresses, e.g., through ascetism and celibacy, not withstood by animals. Because of the tensions, however, "... man is the only organism normally and inevitably subject to psychological conflict" (p. 22).[19] While experimental neurosis can be produced, under natural conditions avoidance of conflict is the general rule. "Only the peculiarities of the human mind," according to Huxley (p. 23), "have forced its partial abandonment upon man."[19] Association mechanisms bring into relation knowing, feeling, and willing. Both unified mental life and mental illness result. Repression is a device for resolving conflicting impulses, but this repressed input may become harmful and lead to mental disturbance.[23]

Taraxis or disorder[27] has come to dominate the lives of men. Events appear to be overwhelming and incomprehensible; everything appears to be in disorder. We suffer confusion, defeat, frustration, failure, remorse, humiliation, grief, and so on. Richards writes (pp. 250–51):

If one looks . . . at biology and the biological species, it is curious that the human being should be so sensitive and subject to external events and tormented by things that do not physically hurt; that it cannot accept adversity with the same philosophy that rabbits, rats, and guinea pigs can. To be sure, experiments can be set to torture the rat, the dog, possibly even the rabbit in taraxic patterns, but they have to be most deviously contrived. With man these things happen daily by themselves.[27]

Thus creativity and disorder, distress and sublimation, are complementary properties of man in society and culture.[15]

## Consequences and Implications

Man's unique endosomatic, and particularly his exosomatic, evolution have brought him to a position as the dominant animal. In almost all environments, he dominates the ecosystem and holds much of his own evolution in his own hands.[10,22] Cultural evolution —so inexorably interwoven with man's unique psychoneurological traits—has brought him to this position of power. He not only dominates but also consciously manipulates ecosystems.[35] By virtue of this power he has created a biological revolution directed primarily toward the immediate enhancement of human welfare at the expense of competing species and often with reckless disregard for long-range consequences. Only in recent decades has there developed a broad awareness of the need for a continuing strategy of resource management.[6]

A few examples will illustrate the problems man now faces. He has created what Rostlund appropriately terms "the domesticated landscape,"[28] that panorama of domesticated plants and animals, cultivated fields and pastures, and monosystem reforestations. This domesticated landscape (anthroposphere may be suggested as a technical term) comprises a series of artificial ecosystems designed to assure man of plentiful food and raw materials to meet his domestic and industrial requirements. The domesticated plants and animals selectively bred to inhabit these ecosystems depend upon the continuing intervention of man for their survival. Because of competition with other organisms which continually invade these ecosystems man has been forced to institute control measures. These measures have been chemical more often than biological. The use and misuse of the biocides, moreover, have often complicated the problems of management, for not only do these chemicals have their intended effects but also unintended ones, ofttimes remote. Through his actions man tends to create a negative balance in the nutrient cycles of ecosystems. He extracts more than he returns. For example, he has caused a definite species reduction. Furthermore, since his artificial ecosystems are most susceptible to erosion through the agencies of water, wind, and fire, he must treat his fields and pastures with concentrated chemicals—the fertilizers. These fertilizers must be applied with care else more undesirable reactions accrue. There has resulted what in essence is a continuing managerial struggle to maintain the artificiality of the domesticated landscape.

The capture of energy is another problem for resource management strategy. It can be argued, for instance, that cultural advance is directly dependent upon an increased ability to capture energy. In the United States today, man's consumption of energy outside of the food chain exceeds that used directly and indirectly in food by some 25 times. While this energy has been vital in the support of man's technological establishment, there have resulted two profound consequences. In the first place, the disposal of technological waste has become an increasing problem. Water and air have provided ready vehicles for discharge. The exponential increase in man's domestic and industrial use of energy has now demonstrated that the vital natural resources are not unlimited in their capacity to dilute and degrade his wastes. Water pollution and air pollution have become central problems of our times and there is ample evidence accumulating that these pollutants exert diverse and profound disturbances throughout ecosystems.

In the second place, this capture of energy has brought to him enormous power, power with which man can destroy himself as well as all other forms of life. This power will necessitate a drastic revision of his mode of thinking. He must turn from traditional views of ingroup survival to concern for the survival of mankind. Chisholm (p. 319) states the matter precisely:

The whole method of survival by groups in competition to the death with other groups has broken down. The survival group, for the first time in human experience, has become the human race itself. From now on we will survive as members of the human race or not at all, but we have no previous experience of this situation and no traditional concern or education for survival of the human race. The occasion for such concern had not arisen until about fifteen years ago and was not foreseen or provided for by our parents or ancestors. Now we are all threatened with extinction by our own traditional survival patterns, a position which most of us still find impossible to accept as real, because we have been taught from infancy to depend upon our "conscious" values, and even to consider changes in them is commonly felt to be immoral and disloyal.[3]

This same view was eloquently expressed by Lord Brain (p. 194) in a recent article entitled "Science and Antiscience":

> The evolution of the human race is now threatened by a failure of integration. [By "integration" Lord Brain means bringing man into *adequate* relation with the ecosystem.] That integration is a social function, necessary both within individual national societies and, in the interest of our common humanity, between those societies.[2]

The magnitude, speed, and imbalance of cultural advances over the past century have created other problems. New levels of anticipation have spread more rapidly than productive skills and technology. The control of epidemic diseases has had insufficient returns, too often in work opportunities for a growing, healthier labor force. More unemployment and more pressure on resources have been the tragic results. In addition, the world's population is already so large and the rates of growth are seemingly so rapid that the prospect of Malthusian limits has become real.[25] Vast increases in productivity, better systems of international exchange, and drastic increases in birth control are essential. These problems involve complex moral as well as technical issues. In a world of prejudice, the problems of eugenics, except for overwhelming diseases, can scarcely be broached. This is especially true since traits of selective value in some environments, such as the sickle-cell gene and perhaps diabetes,[21,26] are very deleterious in others.

## Individual Constants

A basic question in human ecology is thus a clarification of relationships and values. What is "health"? How does one measure health? No one really knows the answer to either question. Why must we understand health so that we can measure it? As man more and more rapidly disturbs his ecosystem, he makes it increasingly difficult for each individual to find an adequate environment. The rapidity of environmental changes may soon exceed the norm of reaction, the adaptability, or the human organism. Thus it becomes urgent that we gain some insight into the limits of the adaptability of individual organisms.[29]

The disturbances which man has created in the ecosystem are manifold. He has polluted the water and the air and has contaminated his food. His gregariousness has led him to live in congested urban agglomerations where, if he is well off, his private quarters and place of work are air-conditioned. His physician administers to him an increasing array of chemicals designed fundamentally to assist him in coping with illness but which take their toll in iatrogenic diseases.

Problems such as these have led to an increasing concern about "environmental health."[14] Attention is now turning to controlling the environment so that it will not become inadequate. Questions that now confront those working on problems of environmental health include: (1) What are the long-term effects on human health of low levels of toxic chemicals such as biocides and water and air pollutants? (2) What are the long-term effects of living in atmospheres with closely regulated temperatures and humidities? (3) What effects accrue from such labor-saving devices as the automobile which eliminate the necessity of walking? (4) What impact do these man-made changes have on the ecosystem and how do these impacts affect the health of man?

To provide answers to these questions we must be able to measure health with sufficient precision to detect deviations from the healthy state before there is morbidity and mortality. To do this means a radical reorientation of our thinking, for health has heretofore been defined in terms of lack of evident morbidity and mortality. To arrive at a productive model of health we must begin with the individual's normal constants, needs, and requirements.[29]

Several features of individuality must be integrated in this model. One particularly characteristic constant of individuality is "the constant in the temporal course of processes." Goldstein writes (p. 366):

> Every human being has a rhythm of his own, which manifests itself in various performances. . . . A performance is normal when an individual can accomplish it in a rhythm which is his adequate rhythm for this performance. Just as for physiological processes, like heartbeating and respiration, this is valid for physico-chemical processes. The time constant indicates a particular characteristic of the personality.[13]

In addition, there is a relation between biochemical and physiological individuality and sensitivity to noxious environmental influences and susceptibility to illness. Individuality is largely quantitative rather than qualitative;[16,38] each individual mobilizes different configurations or patterns of component homeostatic processes in making adjustments to environmental change. This diversity is probably polymorphic.[30] Through systematic study of the diversity will emerge knowledge of the individual's adaptive capacity, which is required to deal constructively with the problems of environmental health.[29]

Some examples may be given to illustrate these general points. Without a doubt, air pollution is a serious problem. The acute disasters serve to emphasize the grim prospects. Low levels of air pollution are now present in many urban centers. How do these low levels affect the health of the population? The individuals we should be most concerned about are those most sensitive to air pollution.[12] If attention is devoted only to the "individual at the mean," many persons will be severely incapacitated or dead before the group within the "normal range" are affected. The most susceptible persons must be identified, for their individuality is a matter of fundamental importance in establishing criteria for air quality and other environmental standards.

The human being has a propensity to store excess energy as fat.[24] This propensity creates significant health problems for a segment of the population identified as obese. Obesity predisposes to a variety of illnesses—for instance, diabetes mellitus, hypertension, and coronary artery disease. There is an individuality in the matter of fat storage.[24] The ectomorph stores fat more readily than the endomorph. This fact suggests that the configuration of the component physiological regulations of the ectomorph differs from that of the endomorph. The needs and requirements of these types are not the same. That these types exist suggests that there are probably polymorphisms of physiological regulations in the population. These polymorphisms can only be elucidated through systematic studies of individuality. Such studies should contribute to an explanation of why some people have a high frequency of illness and others have a low frequency, why some persons are successful in finding an adequate environment and other are not.[15]


Epilogue

Human ecology is, above all, a way of asking questions that may be productive in understanding man's evolution, nature, and problems of adaptation. It recognizes that, in man, biology, society, and culture are deeply interrelated. Culture and society have transformed man's environment but, in doing so, have changed rather than eliminated the selective pressures to which he must adapt effectively if he is to survive.

The problems posed by human ecology are very difficult. In fact, until the theoretical structure of operations research[11] and the modern armament of instrument and data processing had become available, few of these problems could be effectively attacked. Today, both the necessity for, and possibility of, effective human ecological research present great challenges for the biological and behavioral sciences. It is to be hoped that such forthcoming scientific undertakings as the International Biological Programme will meet these challenges.[31, 32]

References

1. Bernard, C., Introduction to the Study of Experimental Medicine, H. C. Greene, trans. (New York: Schuman, Inc., 1949).
2. Brain, W. R., "Science and Antiscience," Science, Vol. 148 (1965), pp. 192–8.
3. Chisholm, B., "Future of the Mind," in G. Wolstenholme, ed., Man and His Future (Boston: Little, Brown & Co., 1963), pp. 315–21.
4. Comfort, A., Ageing. The Biology of Senescence (rev. ed.; New York: Holt, Rinehart & Winston, 1964).
5. Committee on Human Ecology, Introduction to Human Ecology: Syllabus (Urbana: University of Illinois, 1964), Lecture 32.
6. Committee on Natural Resources, Natural Resources, Publication No. 1000 (Washington, D.C.: National Academy of Sciences-Natural Research Council, 1962).
7. Dobzhansky, T., Mankind Evolving: The Evolution of the Human Species (New Haven, Conn.: Yale University Press, 1962).
8. ———, "Evolutionary and Population Genetics," Science, Vol. 142 (1963), pp. 1131–5.
9. ———, "Genetic Entities in Hominid Evolution," in S. L. Washburn, ed., Clasification and Human Evolution (Chicago: Aldine, 1963), pp. 347–62.
10. Dubos, R., Mirage of Health (New York: Anchor Book A-258, Doubleday & Co., 1961).
11. Flagle, C. D., W. H. Huggins, and R. H. Roy, Operations Research and Systems Engineering (Baltimore: Johns Hopkins Press, 1960).
12. Goldsmith, J. R., "Effects of Air Pollution on Humans," in A. C. Stern, ed., Air Pollution, Vol. I (New York: Academic Press, Inc., 1962), pp. 335–86.
13. Goldstein, K., The Organism (Boston: Beacon Press, 1963).
14. Gross, P. M., Report of the Committee on Environmental Health Problems to the Surgeon-General, Public Health Service Publication No. 908 (Washington, D.C.: U.S. Government Printing Office, 1962).
15. Hinkle, L. E., Jr., and H. G. Wolf, "The Nature of Man's Adaptation to his total environment and the Relation of this to Illness," AMA Archives of Internal Medicine, Vol. 99 (1957), pp. 442–60.
16. Hirsch, J., "Individual Differences in Behavior and their Genetic Basis," in E. L. Bliss, ed., Roots of Behavior (New York: Harper & Bros., 1962). pp. 3–23.

17. Howell, F. C., "Pleistocene Glacial Ecology and the Evolution of 'Classic Neanderthal' Man," Southwestern Journal of Anthropology, Vol. 8 (1952), pp. 377–410.
18. ———, and F. Bourliere, eds., African Ecology and Evolution (Chicago: Aldine, 1963).
19. Huxley, J. S., Man Stands Alone (New York: Harper & Bros., 1941).
20. Johnston, F. E., "Racial Taxonomics From an Evolutionary Perspective," American Anthropologist, Vol. 66 (1964), pp. 822–8.
21. Livingstone, F. B., "Anthropological Implications of Sickle Cell Gene Distribution in West Africa," American Anthropologist, Vol. 60 (1958), pp. 553–62.
22. Medawar, P. B., The Uniqueness of the Individual (London: Methuen & Co., Ltd., 1957).
23. Menninger, K., The Vital Balance: The Life Process in Mental Health and Illness (New York: Viking Press, 1963).
24. Mitchell, H. H., Comparative Nutrition of Man and Domestic Animals, Vol. I (New York: Academic Press, 1962).
25. Mudd, S., ed., The Population Crisis and the Use of World Resources (Bloomington: University of Indiana Press, 1964).
26. Neel, J. V., "Diabetes Mellitus: A 'Thrifty' Genotype Rendered Detrimental by 'Progress'?" American Journal of Human Genetics, Vol. 14 (1962), pp. 353–62.
27. Richards, D. W., "Homeostasis: Its Dislocations and Perturbations," Perspectives in Biological Medicine, Vol. 3 (1960), pp. 238–51.
28. Rostlund, E., "Taming Trees," Bulletin of the Atomic Scientists, Vol. 17 (1961), pp. 326–30.
29. Sargent, F., II, and D. M. Barr, "Health and Fitness of the Ecosystem." Mimeograph, 1964 (Travelers Research Center, Hartford, Conn.).
30. Sargent, F., II, and K. P. Weinman, "Physiological Individuality," in J. E. Brozek, ed., Conference on Biology of Human Variation (New York: New York Academy of Sciences, 1965).
31. Special Committee for International Biological Programme, IBP News, No. 2, 1965 (International Council of Scientific Unions; IBP Secretariat, 2 via Sebenico, Rome).
32. Stebbins, G. L., "International Horizons in the Life Sciences," AIBS Bulletin, Vol. 12 (1962), pp. 13–19.
33. Steward, J. H., and D. B. Shimkin, "Some Mechanisms of Sociocultural Evolution," Daedalus, Summer 1961, pp. 477–97.
34. Tanner, J. M., Growth at Adolescence (Springfield, Ill.: Charles C Thomas, 1955).
35. Thomas, W. L., Jr., ed., Man's Role in Changing the Face of the Earth (Chicago: University Press, 1956).
36. Weiner, J. S., and K. Hellman, "The Sweat Glands," Biological Review, Vol. 35 (1960), pp. 141–86.
37. Williams, G. C., "Pleiotropy, Natural Selection, and the Evolution of Senescence," Evolution, Vol. 11 (1957), pp. 398–411.

38. Williams, R. J., *Biochemical Individuality: The Basis of the Geneto-tropic Concept* (New York: John Wiley & Sons, 1956; paperback ed., 1963).

# THE ETHNIC DISTRIBUTION OF DISEASE IN THE UNITED STATES

*Victor A. McKusick*

Victor A. McKusick, a professor of medicine at the Johns Hopkins University School of Medicine, is a specialist in medical genetics. He has examined a number of small human population isolates.

Except for the Amerindians among us, we Americans have come to this continent from all parts of the globe in the last 400 years or so—more from some parts than from others. Furthermore, despite the melting-pot metaphor, we have remained to a considerable extent in separate groups according to ethnic* extraction. In part this results from the fact that insufficient time has elapsed for mixing, but to a considerable extent from religious and other sociocultural impediments to mixing.

That we Americans differ in many physical characteristics according to ethnic extraction is a commonplace and no one can question that these physical differences are based mainly on genetic differences. That the genetic differences according to ethnic extraction extend to pathogenic genes can be heavily documented.[1]

Valuable opportunities for studying the distribution of genetic disease and uncovering clues as to the factors which have led to a relatively low or high frequency of specific genes are afforded by the population structure in the United States. Such studies can

From *Journal of Chronic Diseases*, Vol. 20 (March 1967), pp. 115–18. Reprinted by permission.

*Here I use the word *ethnic* to refer to both sociologic and racial groupings. Since the two, one biologically based, one culturally based, are essentially always indistinguishable, one term is indicated. Derived from the Greek for nation, the word avoids the odium of *race* and is sufficiently general to be appropriate to the usage here.

take several forms. The frequency and distribution of genetic diseases in specific ethnic groups can be determined. Although the Amish have characteristics, such as the level of inbreeding, which distinguish them from most groups in this country, the surveys of genetic disease conducted in these groups by my colleagues and myself illustrate this approach.[2]

In the second place all cases of a specific genetic disease can be ascertained in the United States or a section thereof and the ethnic extraction of the cases determined. This approach we have used in relation to homocystinuria (which appears to have a rather uniform ethnic distribution)[3] and Riley-Day familial dysautonomia which is almost completely confined to Ashkenazic Jews).[4]

Two other approaches are variations on the first two. In a given geographic area where, as in most areas of the United States, the population is of heterogeneous extraction all (or many) genetic diseases can be surveyed and their frequency in the several component ethnic groups can be determined. Finally, the frequency of diseases can be determined in an ethnic group in this country and in the parent population in the old country.

The diseases whose ethnic extraction can be usefully studied can be either the simple inherited "Mendelizing" disorders or common conditions of multifactorial causation in which the role of genetic factors is important but complex. Tables 1 and 2 summarize information on the distribution of disease of these two types. Among the Mendelizing disorders (Table 1), recessives particularly show nonuniform ethnic distribution. Many more instances of above average frequencies are known than below average frequencies. This is largely because most of the conditions listed are rare and detection of a low frequency necessitates differentiating "very rare" from "rare." Many of the instances listed are based on impressions which although probably valid have in the case of most not been quantitatively corroborated.

To achieve a picture of the ethnic structure of the American population as background for a comprehensive understanding of the distribution of genetic disease, it is essential to get for each group information of the following types:

1. The demography in the Old World;
2. The history of migration, both immigration and internal migration;
3. The sociologic factors which make for cohesion or dispersion of the group; and, of course,
4. The contemporary demography of the group.

## Table 1. The Ethnicity Of Disease: Simply Inherited Disorders*

| Ethnic group | Relatively high frequency | Relatively low frequency |
|---|---|---|
| Ashkenazic Jews | Tay-Sachs disease<br>Pentosuria<br>Gaucher's disease<br>Familial dysautonomia<br>Stub thumbs<br>Bloom's disease<br>Factor XI (PTA) deficiency<br>Niemann-Pick disease<br>Abetalipoproteinemia<br>Dystonia musculorum deformans<br>Spongy degeneration of brain | Phenylketonuria |
| Mediterranean peoples<br>(Italians, Greeks, Sephardic Jews) | Thalassemia (mainly β)<br>G6PD-deficiency, Mediterranean type<br>Familial Mediterranean fever | Cystic fibrosis |
| Africans | Hemoglobinopathies, esp. HbS, HbC, α<br>and β thalassemia, persistent HbF<br>G6PD-deficiency, African type | Cystic fibrosis<br>Hemophilia<br>Phenylketonuria<br>Wilson's disease |
| Japanese (Koreans) | Acatalasia<br>Oguchi's disease<br>Dyschromatosis universalis hereditaria | |
| Chinese | α thalassemia<br>G6PD-deficiency, Chinese type | |
| Armenians | Familial Mediterranean fever | |

*For references on individual conditions, see McKusick, Ref. 7.

## Table 2. The Ethnicity Of Disease: Disorders With Complex Genetics Or In Which Genetic Factors Are Not Proved

| Ethnic group | High frequency | Low frequency |
|---|---|---|
| Ashkenazic Jews | Hypercholesterolemia | Cervical cancer |
| | Diabetes mellitus | Tuberculosis |
| | Polycythemia vera | Alcoholism |
| | Hyperuricemia | |
| | Ulcerative colitis and regional enteritis | |
| | Kaposi's sarcoma | |
| | Pemphigus vulgaris | |
| | Buerger's disease | |
| | Leukemia | |
| Northern Europeans | Pernicious anaemia | |
| Chinese | Nasopharyngeal cancer | |
| Japanese | Cleft lip-palate | Otosclerosis |
| | Cerebrovascular accidents | Acne vulgaris |
| | Gastric carcinoma | Breast cancer |
| | | Chronic lymphatic leukemia |

| Group | Conditions | |
|---|---|---|
| Filipinos | Hyperuricemia | |
| Polynesians (Hawaiians) | Clubfoot | |
| Africans | Polydactyly | Major CNS malformations (anencephaly, encephalocele) |
| | Prehelical fissure | |
| | Sarcoidosis | |
| | Tuberculosis | Skin cancer |
| | Hypertension | Osteoperosis and fracture of hip |
| | Esophageal cancer | |
| | Uterine fibroids | Polycythemia vera |
| | Corneal arcus | Pyloric stenosis |
| | Cervical cancer | Gallstones |
| | Ainhum | |
| | Keloids | |
| American Indian and Mexican | Gallbladder disease | |
| | Tuberculosis | |
| Am. Indian, Lapps, No. Italian | Congenital dislocation of hip | |
| Icelanders | Glaucoma | |
| Eskimos | Salivary gland tumors | |

The factors which influence the frequency of genes in populations are mutation, selection, drift and gene flow. Consanguinity increases the frequency of recessive diseases in a population—it "brings out" homozygotes—but *per se* consanguinity does not influence the frequency of genes. There is a prevailing misconception that it does, that inbreeding causes a "build-up of genes," usually it is stated as a "build-up of bad genes," in a population. In fact if the homozygote is at a disadvantage as is true for essentially all recessives, especially those listed in Table 1, inbreeding causes a fall in the frequency of the particular gene in a population. This is the principle of the "inbreeding bottleneck" which at least theoretically could account for a low frequency of recessive genes in a population.

No evidence of differences in mutation rate in different races has come to light; such is unlikely to account for differences observed in frequency of hereditary diseases.

Selection is quite well established as the basis of the relatively high frequency of hemoglobin S and C genes, thalassemia genes and glucose-6-phosphate dehydrogenase genes in selected populations. Selection in all these instances seems to have operated through the advantage which the gene in heterozygous state endowed on its possessor *vis-à-vis* malaria.

Random genetic drift refers to the change in gene frequencies which can occur in small populations by chance alone. Founder Effect is a special case; the founders of a particular group, i.e. the immigrants, may by chance carry particular genes, which as a result have a higher frequency among their descendants than in the parent population. Founder Effect and drift appear to account for the high frequency of some genes in certain closed population groups in the United States: e.g. the high frequency of blood type A (75 per cent of persons) in the Lancaster County (Pa.) Amish[5] and of the gene for the Ellis-van Creveld syndrome (about 0.07) in the same group.[6] However, drift or Founder Effect has not been established as the cause of any of the atypical frequencies shown in the table.

Gene flow resulting from mixture of peoples of different ethnic extraction is an obvious cause of change in the genetic structure of a population. The present-day American Negro has derived 10–30 percent of his genes from European ancestors. The occurrence in American Negroes of some diseases such as cystic fibrosis (which is very rare in native Africans) is probably attributable to gene flow.

For most of the atypical frequencies shown in the tables, the reasons are completely unknown.

Information on the ethnic distribution of genetic disease has practical usefulness in connection with diagnosis and with the design of screening programs. Anemia in someone of Mediterranean extraction has different diagnostic significance from that in a person of Scandinavian extraction. Furthermore, quantitative information on the ethnicity of disease can be the point of departure for studies of population genetics in man, elucidating the cause for atypical frequencies. Certainly whenever a "new" inborn error of metabolism is discovered, the ethnic extraction of the patients should be recorded. Ethnic extraction can be a clue to genetic heterogeneity. Glucose-6-phosphate dehydrogenase deficiency occurs in Americans of African, Mediterranean and Chinese extraction, but a different allele is involved in each. Phenylketonuria may be different in Irish and Italians; at least a more benign phenylketonuria-simulating condition ("hyperphenylalaninemia") has been found particularly in persons of Mediterranean extraction.

## References

1. A. Damon, "Some Host Factors in Disease: Sex, Race, Ethnic Group, and Body Form," *Journal of the National Medical Association*, Vol. 54 (1964), pp. 424–31.
2. V. A. McKusick, J. A. Hostetler, J. A. Egeland, and R. Eldridge, "The Distribution of Certain Genes in the Old Order Amish," *Cold Spring Harbor Symposia on Quantitative Biology*, Vol. 29 (1964), pp. 99–114.
3. R. N. Schimke, V. A. McKusick, T. Huang, and A. D. Pollack, "Homocystinuria: A Study of 20 Families with 38 Affected Members," *Journal of the American Medical Association*, Vol. 193 (1965), pp. 711–19.
4. V. A. McKusick, R. A. Norum, H. J. Farkas, P. W. Brunt, and M. Mahloudji, "The Genetics of the Riley-Day Syndrome with Observations on Survivorship: An Interim Report," *Israel Journal of Medical Science*, in press, 1967.
5. V. A. McKusick, W. B. Bias, R. A. Norum, and H. E. Cross, "Blood Groups in Two Amish Demes." To be published.
6. V. A. McKusick, J. A. Egeland, R. Eldridge, and D. E. Krusen, "Dwarfism in the Amish. I. The Ellis-van Creveld Syndrome," *Bulletin of Johns Hopkins Hospital*, Vol. 115 (1964).
7. V. A. McKusick, *Mendelian Inheritance in Man—Catalogue of Autosomal Dominant, Autosomal Recessive and X-Linked Phenotypes* (Baltimore: Johns Hopkins Press, 1966).

# GIVING THE OLYMPICS
# AN ANTHROPOLOGICAL ONCE-OVER

*Marshall A. Smith*

Marshall Smith is a senior editor of *Life* magazine, and has been a reporter for *The Providence Journal*, a news writer for NBC, and editor of *Time* magazine.

A physical anthropologist could presumably ask for nothing more in the way of a professional field day than a visit to the main Olympic stadium in Tokyo this week. In the clusters of coiled sprinters leaping from their starting blocks, in the milling hurdlers, high jumpers and discus throwers, he would find the world's most varied and superbly conditioned assortment of the human species, in all shapes, sizes and colors. By applying his knowledge of the physiological and anatomical differences among the athletes, he might also become a successful prognosticator of Olympic results. Past performance charts of Olympic Games do seem to offer an "anthropological" pattern of achievement.

For example, Mongoloids, headed by the competitive Japanese, have done particularly well in gymnastics, swimming and wrestling. Negroids, particularly those from the U.S., have dominated the shorter foot races, the jumps and hurdles. They have been outstanding in boxing and basketball, sports which call for quickness of hand and foot and for sudden, explosive bursts of effort. But in past Olympics they have been conspicuously absent from the list of leaders in the marathon and other long-distance runs. No Negro has ever qualified for the U.S. swimming team. (On the U.S. men's track-and-field team presently competing in Tokyo, 18 of 67 are Negroes; 15 of the 20 members of the women's team are Negroes. There are nine Negroes on the ten-man boxing squad and five of the 12 basketball players are Negroes.)

While Olympic records show that Negroids and Mongoloids have seldom excelled in the same events, they offer less of a guide to the performance of members of the white (or Caucasoid) race.

White athletes, though they are the complete masters of some competitions (rowing, sailing, fencing, for example), have ranged all the way from being the best to the poorest in nearly every sport on the calendar.

Most observers justifiably are far more concerned with the real differences between individuals than with interpolations based on studies of the races by groups. Furthermore, they are inclined to attribute the apparent domination of certain athletic events by certain races to cultural and sociological factors, such as differences in interest, motivation, tradition, opportunity. Certainly the breakthrough of the Japanese swimmers in the Olympics of the 1930's and of the Australians in the late 1950's gave major impetus to later efforts by the young swimmers of both nations. The international fame won by one of the great American sports heroes of the 1930's, Jesse Owens, encouraged young Negro athletes in the years since to emulate his feats. And the absence of Negroid or Mongoloid competitors in the Olympic 5.5-meter-class yachting event surely must have something to do with simple lack of opportunity.

Nonetheless, the scientific fact that there are, in general, basic physical differences between races of people plus the widening appreciation that there is an apparent correlation of body build to achievement in sports has raised the intriguing question: what, if any, bearing do these various racial differences have on athletic performance?

There are strong arguments over the question, as this article will show, and there are those who refuse to argue the question at all because of the hotly controversial implications. Most physical anthropologists prefer to keep their opinions to themselves and concentrate on their growth studies, blood group analyses and similar unexplosive areas of racial research. But two distinguished anthropology professors whose special field of study is race, and who do believe there is a connection between racial characteristics and athletic achievement, are Dr. Carleton S. Coon, formerly of Harvard and the University of Pennsylvania, now retired, and Dr. Edward E. Hunt, Jr., of Harvard. Drs. Coon and Hunt believe: "Inherited physical adaptations seem to play a part in the abilities of members of different races to excel in different sports. That is one reason why Negro athletes have achieved such outstanding success in certain fields in addition to whatever social factors or motivation may be involved." However, the professors emphasize that their conclusions about athletic performance do not imply any overall "superiority" or "inferiority" of the races.

The juxtaposition of athletics and anthropology made news some 30 years ago when former Yale Track Coach Albert McGall suggested that maybe Negro sprinters got better leverage—and a little advantage over white sprinters—because of the projecting heel bone (*calcaneus*) that is frequently found among Negroids. That did it.

There were reproving rebuttals from coaches and scientists. One of the more convincing arguments against Coach McGall's theory was made by Professor W. Montague Cobb, prominent physical anthropologist at Howard University and now president of the National (Negro) Medical Association. In the *Journal of Health and Physical Education*, January 1936, Cobb reported that he had measured X-rays of Jesse Owens' heel and found it did not conspicuously protrude. He also observed and measured Owens' calf structure and found that it was shaped more like the Caucasoid type than the Negroid.

Cobb explained that the Negro (as a group) is indeed long of limb; "that is, he has long legs and arms relative to the length of his trunk as compared with the white. In addition, the leg of the Negro is said to be long in proportion to his thigh. Possibly," commented Cobb, "this might be of significance in broad jumping, as leaping animals, such as the kangaroo, have extremely long shins and very short thighs."

But the anthropologist was unconvinced that "Negroid physical characteristics are anatomically concerned with the present dominance of Negro athletes in national competition in the short dashes and the broad jump. There is not a single physical characteristic," he concluded, "which all the Negro stars in question have in common which would definitely identify them as Negroes."

Since Dr. Cobb's study, American Negroes have shown remarkable prowess in nearly every major spectator sport, as the opportunity to participate was gradually given them. Their success could not have been achieved without enormous motivation. It was made against discouraging odds—hostility, inadequate facilities, and inferior training and instruction methods. Of course, American Negroes were particularly motivated toward athletic achievement because, for a long time, the sports and entertainment worlds were about the only fields where they were permitted to compete on an equal basis with whites.

The most impressive example of American Negroes' reaction to opportunity came in organized baseball, after Jackie Robinson joined the Brooklyn Dodgers in 1947 and finally opened the door for other members of his race. Negroes have come to occupy approximately 20 per cent of all regular major-league positions and it is now taken for granted that Negroes will be at the top or among the leaders in the most significant individual achievement categories, such as batting and base-stealing.

The boom in professional football has been accompanied by the growing prominence of Negroes—in the line, where muscle and power count strongly, and in the backfield, where speed and quickness are needed. In basketball there is some question whether Bill Russell or Oscar Robertson is the game's best all-around player. Both are Negroes and so are many of the other superior shooters and ball-handlers in the pro and college ranks. And the sport where desire and motivation are most required—boxing—has been dominated for the last quarter of a century by Negroes.

American Negroes, who have produced so many outstanding athletes in recent years, form just one branch of the Negroid race, of course. And it is a quite special branch. For one thing, "they are a mulatto population with an average of one-quarter white blood," says anthropologist Jean Hiernaux of the University of Paris. "There are very few pure African Negroes left [in the U.S.]." As a result, American Negroes tend to have both Negroid and Caucasoid physical characteristics.

Also, Dr. Cobb suggests, there is logic in the theory that American Negroes are a select Negroid strain. In the process of choosing slaves in Africa to be sent to the New World, only good physical specimens were taken. Cobb points out: "The weak did not survive to embark from the African ports. The rigors of the voyage... further decimated the ranks, so that only the toughest survived to land on our shores."

But the physical characteristics that distinguish the basic groupings—the Mongoloid, Negroid and Caucasoid races—have been fairly well established. Just how these differences came about is a question that scientists are still researching and debating.

Anthropologist Coon has suggested that "many racial differences reflect the adaptations of human beings to differences in temperature, sunlight, altitude, humidity and local diseases in parts of the world where the different races of man evolved."

As an instance, the original home of the Mongoloids was China at a time when its climate was chilly. Some Mongoloid characteristics, developed over countless generations, seem to be designed to conserve body heat. Their body fat is evenly distributed; their eyelids have a fatty fold which protects the eyeballs in severe temperatures. Their trunks are relatively long; their arms, legs and neck, short; and their hands and feet small.

Negroids, on the other hand, adapted over the millenniums to other extremes in equatorial Africa. Their bodies evolved to dispel heat, not conserve it, and also to accommodate a high degree of ultraviolet radiation and a formidable array of tropical diseases. As a result, they tend to have less fat. Their wrists and ankles are slender and they have long arms and legs to go with relatively short bodies. Long extremities are a principal means of dissipating heat —a thin pipe being a more efficient radiator than a thick one.

Anthropologists are a long way from piecing together a complete natural history of the races of man, but over the years they have come up with increasing evidence of man's varying physical characteristics. For example, they have determined that Negroids have trunks relatively shorter than whites, with smaller chest circumferences. Negroids have relatively longer arms, particularly the forearms.

In measuring lower arm lengths of Europeans, German anthropologists Rudolf Martin and Karl Saller have reported that the figures ranged from 14.3 per cent to 15.9 per cent of total height; the forearms of African Negroes from 15.9 per cent to 17.7 per cent. The same procedures applied to leg lengths have produced measurements, which, in proportion, parallel those of the arms. It is obvious that, as groups of people, Caucasoids and Negroids have contrasting sets of locomotive levers. Anthropologists do not necessarily conclude that Negroids have an advantage over whites in running because their lower legs are longer in relation to their thighs.

However, U.S. Olympic Swimming Coach Jim Counsilman, who tested Negroes and whites in the vertical jump, found that the Negroes in the group averaged about two inches better than the whites.

The weight of bones also has been found to vary between Negroids and Caucasoids. In 1957 the anthropological team of Paul Baker and Russell Newman, working out of the U.S. Army Quartermaster Research and Engineering Center at Natick, Mass., reported on their study of the skeletons of Negro and white soldiers who had died during the Korean war. They found that the Negro skeletons were approximately 7 per cent heavier than the white skeletons, even though Army records showed that the weight of the Negroes at the time of induction had been an average of 5 per cent (or seven pounds) lighter than that of the whites.

In separate studies, Newman discovered that young Negroes in good physical condition had, on the average, 38 per cent less protective fat than comparable whites, and Baker learned that what fat they did have insulated them less. This consideration, it would seem, puts Negroes at a disadvantage in cold weather and in the water, and may be a factor in explaining why they participate less than whites in swimming and winter sports.

Over the years Olympic coach Counsilman has also conducted a number of buoyancy tests in swimming pools at the University of Iowa and at the State University College at Cortland, N.Y. Counsilman says the results showed that the Negro swimmers had low buoyancy compared to the whites.

"I know that they don't have the opportunity as far as pools go, especially in the South," says Counsilman, "but apparently lack of buoyancy makes it more difficult for them to learn to swim and harder to stay up once they do."

Mongoloids, though not particularly buoyant as a group, have lighter bones than Caucasoids do, which could be a factor in water sports. In addition, as already noted, their body fat is more evenly distributed, which provides a comfort factor in terms of better insulation in the water.

At the current games in Tokyo one would not need an anthropologist's eye to recognize some of the more obvious variations in muscle structure among the races represented. The Japanese athlete tends toward thick calves and general compactness; the Negroes, slender calves with tendons proportionately longer than those of the white and an overall appearance of loose-jointedness —characteristics, says Dr. Coon, of living things (cheetahs, for instance) known for their speed and leaping ability.

Negroid feet vary in structure from that of other races. In a famous study of Bantu, Bushmen and Europeans of South Africa, made by anatomist L. H. Wells, it was determined that in whites the great toe was generally longest, whereas in Negroids the second toe was longest. The center of weight for white men went mainly through the first toe; on the Negroids, more of the weight was on the outside of the foot. Further, the heel bone of the tribesmen was slightly longer than that of the whites, but the additional length was not so much bone as a hard, fat pad that ran the length of the foot.

Caucasoids have a fat pad, too, but only beneath the heel and the ball of the foot. The arch of Negroids is less visible because it is filled with fat and the bottom of the foot is shaped more like a wedgie shoe, as Coon describes it. Coon, on the other hand, describes this Negroid foot as "a marvelous organ for mobility, leaping, jumping and landing with a minimum of shock."

Other studies of the physical differences between African Negroes and whites have concentrated on lung capacity. The results have led some scientists and coaches to speculate on the effect this difference may have on long- and short-distance runners. The chest cavity and the lungs of West Africans, for example, were found to be smaller on the average than those of the whites. At rest their respiratory rate was found to be 20-a-minute compared with 16 to 18 for Caucasoids.

The size of the lungs, in terms of how much air they can hold, is called "vital capacity." Physiologists relate this measurement to the body's total skin area, and the resulting ratio may be important in sports requiring endurance and stamina. Tests have shown that the ratio for adult U.S. Negroes falls 25 to 35 per cent below the ratio for adult whites while the average ratio of Congolese falls as much as 40 per cent below that of Europeans.

Lower vital capacity has been cited by anthropologists as a possible reason why American Negroes, so superb in explosive sports (basketball, boxing), have been less prominent in competitions that call for unusual amounts of stamina (marathon running, amateur wrestling).

Although slender calves, long, thin forearms and a smaller chest sometimes give Negroes a gangling appearance, they tend to be more muscular than other racial groups. This has been studied by Dr. William Sheldon, formerly of Columbia University, who has invented three overall human classifications: endomorphic (fat), ectomorphic (skinny) and mesomorphic (muscular and athletic). He finds that, on the average, Negroes are significantly more mesomorphic than whites. Mongoloids show up on his graphs as moderately endomorphic.

But attempts to cite any one racial characteristic—size of lungs, length of forearm, amount of body fat—as a factor in the performance of any one individual inevitably leads to apparent scientific contradictions, if not total confusion. Jesse Owens' foot demonstrated that differences between individuals are far greater than those between racial groups. Anthropological classifications are constantly being revised because racial characteristics are forever changing as a result of intermingling of blood, migrations of peoples, new diets, variations in climate and other factors. Four years ago Ethiopian Abebe Bikila, who might be presumed to have both Negroid and Caucasoid characteristics, ran off with the Olympic marathon—in his bare feet. Also in the 1960 Games, the decathlon event became a dramatic duel between two tall, husky athletes representing racial extremes—C. K. Yang of the Chinese Nationalists and Rafer Johnson, an American Negro.

Any discussion of the role of race in athletics threatens controversy. But the scientific inquiry goes on. The anthropologists
supply us with fascinating data; and the coaches and the sports
experts and the sociologists will continue to argue their significance. In the end, of course, there is no dispute at all. Every athletic
performance depends on what the individual brings to the contest.
The sprinter, tensed in the starting blocks, must rely upon a whole
complex of human factors to take him across the finish line—
muscle and sinew, and mind and heart, too.

# Chapter Eleven

# Race and Intelligence

Intelligence is the one human trait beyond all others that promotes emotional discourse. Twin studies have shown that whatever it is that "intelligence tests" measure, in our culture at any rate, "it" has a genetic, i.e., heritable, component. But having demonstrated that individual intelligence test performance differences within one culture have a genetic component, it does not then follow that populations are different genetically for intelligence. There are, after all, many traits for which there is great individual variation, but not populational variation. But the same non sequitur that any trait with a hereditary component is also a "racial" trait has unfortunately become well established in the minds of some people. Add to that the fact that an intelligence test may really be a test of an individual's knowledge of a given culture, or even a subculture, and the confusion on the topic of "racial intelligence" is complete.

Today's anthropologists find it difficult to accept intelligence as the one trait that enables us to grade human populations on a high to low scale. This is partly because the anthropologist's experience of living in another culture has convinced him that it takes as much intelligence to live as a "native" as it does to live as a New Yorker. Moreover, most anthropologists are not as apt to be impressed with Western European technology, which is the common yardstick by which most people in our society measure the degree of primitiveness of another group. In fact, compared to the complexities of a people's belief systems, language, or social organization, technology takes a very definite back seat. But since it is in the area of technology that Western society is most distinctly different from non-Western society, its elaboration has mistakenly been taken as an index of a people's intellectual worth.

Finally, anthropologists tend to view "intelligence" as a whole complex of abilities which are species' traits that vary in expression, but without which survival would not be possible. All peoples use language; they all have complex systems that organize human behavior; they all puzzle over and variously explain man's relationship to nature; they all experience a long period of childhood dependency in which the cultural novices are taught the accumulated knowledge of their ancestors, or how to cope with a given environment. It seems unnecessary to suppose that any single human way of life requires less intellectual capability than any other. Since the chief characteristic of the human species is his brain, it seems unlikely that its function would be graded across populations. All men have upright posture, all men speak; whether they slouch or strut, whether they ramble on in Japanese or English does not indicate "better" walking or "better" talking.

# MIGRATION, RACE AND MENTAL HEALTH:
# A REVIEW OF SOME RECENT RESEARCH

*Christopher Bagley*

Christopher Bagley is a member of the Medical Research Council's Social Psychiatry Research Unit at the Institute of Psychiatry, London.

In a review of the literature on delinquency and immigration, A. E. Bottoms in *Race* (Vol. 9, No. 2, April 1967) has suggested the need for further research in this area. Two subjects discussed by

---

From *Race*, Vol. IX, Number 3, January 1969, published for the Institute of Race Relations, London, by the Oxford University Press © Institute of Race Relations, 1968.

Bottoms were the relevance of the Mertonian theory of the gap between culturally prescribed goals, and culturally available means for reaching these goals (creating the condition of "anomie") as a cause of delinquency; and the possibility that emigrants from Commonwealth countries contained a higher proportion of the mentally abnormal, for example schizophrenics, so that in the host community this factor might predispose immigrants to higher delinquency rates than the rest of the population.

The purpose of the present note is to discuss these two questions, in the light of recent American and British research on deviance taking the form of identifiable *mental illness*,* rather than delinquency. At the same time, the review of recent research should indicate the direction of work in this area.

### Race and Mental Health in America

The literature on race and mental health is much more numerous in America than in Britain, and is often written from the standpoint of several disciplines. Earlier literature on the subject has been reviewed by Pettigrew (1964) who concluded that the American Negro manifested "a deterioration of mental health through a combination of poverty and persecution."

In an outstanding piece of research, Zahra (1965) showed that the concept of the self was intimately connected with mental health. Children who had a poor self-image, or perception of themselves, also had poorer mental health. This finding is of obvious relevance for race relations: if the majority race asserts, strongly and silently through the processes of national socialization (such as school textbooks, Bennett, 1967) that the Negro race is naturally inferior, Negroes themselves will hold this view.

There seems to be strong evidence that Negroes have a poor self-image. Drake (1966) has pointed out that Negroes reject their own body image by using the skin whiteners regularly advertised in *Ebony*. Roberts and Robinson (1965) showed that in intelligence tests, the performance of Negro subjects was artificially depressed by their perceptions of the views held by the white tester about their performance. Gibby and Gabler (1967) showed that Negro

---

*The problem of defining mental illness is a complex one, involving issues such as defining actual cases, and differential diagnosis. However, the problem is now much less since papers appearing after 1964—on which most of this article is based—generally use the internationally agreed World Health Organization classification of mental illness, by which an illness is defined by salient and apparently unequivocal signs and symptoms.

children, in comparison with white control subjects, had significantly poorer self-concepts in relation to intelligence and worthiness. Chethik *et al.* (1967) who treated disturbed Negro children at a predominantly white Psychiatric Clinic indicated that the Negro could hardly avoid the internalization of feelings of inferiority, equating blackness with dirtiness, aggressiveness and loose sexuality, while whiteness becomes equated with superior qualities. They suggest that in the treatment situation the Negro child needs identification models different from his own degraded ones or from that of the clean, restrained and friendly, but always sad, "white man's negro." Instead, successful and civic minded Negro men and women, or Negro figures from the civil rights struggle were used. A further factor in successful treatment was the self-examination of the consciously nonprejudiced staff themselves, since the staff had inevitably internalized something of the prevailing image of the Negro: while recognizing this image as an unjustified stereotype they could not always control their reactions. In this context it is of interest to note that Banks *et al.* (1966) found that in a psychotherapy clinic, two-thirds of the Negroes who initially saw a white counsellor said they would not return; while all of those seeing a Negro counsellor said they would return.

Vosk (1966) made a depth study of slow-learning Negro children. These children came to school with a particular vulnerability to failure. "Fearful and discouraged, they are unable to surmount the difficulties the average child must surmount in the learning situation. Before they learn tool subjects they must be helped to a sense of their own worth and constructive capabilities through appropriate and meaningful school activities." Morland (1966) found that Negro children identified with the white race, as did white children. This preference and identification was more marked in the Southern states.

Mental illness in the urban Negro community of Philadelphia has been studied in the monograph of Parker and Kleiner (1966). Their object was to test the relation of the degree of psychosis and neurosis to "goal-striving" in the Negro population. A random sample was made of areas with a high proportion of Negroes. Negro subjects thus obtained were given a mental health assessment, and assigned to a "community" or healthy group, or to an ill group. A second sample of mentally ill Negroes was obtained from clinics, psychiatrists and hospitals. These procedures gave 1,489 subjects in the community or healthy sample, and 1,423 in the mentally ill sample. All subjects were given questionnaires on attitudes to goal striving, by Negro interviewers.

The results of this procedure showed clear and significant differences with regard to goal-striving, between the mentally ill and
the community samples. The mentally ill had higher levels of
aspiration—they set themselves higher goals—than the non mentally ill. Markedly more of the mentally ill denied that being a
Negro constituted any barrier to achievement: "Almost every
clinical study of psychopathology among Negroes indicates that the
Negro who is not identified with other members of his group, or
who aspires to 'be white,' is relatively more prone to manifest
various forms of mental ill health."

The mentally ill had significantly more "low self-esteem," which
was related to the large gap between an internalized ideal and perception of the self's success. There was a significant and positive
correlation between the number of psychiatric symptoms and
lower self esteem. The highest rates of mental illness were found in
those who were upwardly mobile. The findings in this respect are
consistent with the anomie theory of Durkheim and Merton:

> Individuals at the highest level, who have risen in the occupa-
> tional status hierarchy despite the considerable barriers facing the
> Negro, are probably characterized by chronic achievement striving
> and dissatisfaction with self—an inability to reduce their striving
> even after they have achieved considerable success. This continued
> achievement striving suggests the anomic effects of the differen-
> tially restricted opportunity structure the Negro faces in American
> society. A high level of goal striving in the context of a relatively
> restricted opportunity structure apparently takes its psychological
> toll.

The authors point out that downward mobility was not a significant factor in the experience of the subjects in this sample, since
the parents of the Negroes were so often in the lowest occupational
class anyway. However, those who do succeed in rising occupa-
tionally for a time, but fail to keep high status jobs and retain a
high level of goal striving, had high psychiatric symptom stress
scores, and high rates of mental illness.

More goal-striving was found in the psychotics (a more seriously
mentally ill group) than in the neurotics. Men were more often
mentally ill, and younger rather than older men. The authors
conclude:

> Despite the relatively closed nature of the opportunity structure
> for the Negro in American society, the patients were more prone
> than the community respondents to perceive the system as open.

Along with this perception, they rigidly maintained high levels of goal-striving stress. The existing dysjunction involved high levels of goal-striving orientation in the context of an objectively limited opportunity structure.

Goldberg (1966) studied the differences in response to drug treatment (phenothiazine compared with a placebo) of Negro and white schizophrenics and found that on the placebo, the Negroes improved more than did whites, but on phenothiazine (a powerful tranquilizer) there were no differences between the improvement of the two racial groups. Goldberg suggests that this indicates that psychosis in Negroes is likely to be due to psychological stress, while in whites it is more often due to genetic factors. These findings are in keeping with those of Parker and Kleiner. It is interesting to compare the psychosis in their sample of Negroes to Laing and Esterson's account of schizophrenia (1964) in the individual placed in a logically impossible interactive situation within the immediate social environment of the family. The Negro is an analogous situation: his belief in the desirability of striving, and the "openness" of the opportunity structure are at odds with the reality situation.

Hartog (1967), reviewing "the mental health problems of poverty's youth" points out that a substantial proportion of the poor in America are Negro, so that a discussion of this problem has direct relevance to the question of race and mental illness. Hartog showed that the young poor are particularly at risk: they have poorer nutrition, more birth injuries, and more mental retardation and neurological illness. They have a heavier load of psychotic illness. When they are ill, they are treated less well than the middle-class, and the rich.

Maas (1967) reviewed the post-war literature on the treatment of Negroes by the psychiatric services, and concluded that the Negroes were more reluctant than Caucasians to go to hospital when mentally ill; once they were there, they were not released as quickly or as often as whites. Psychiatric services seemed to assume that the Negro male was less accessible to psychotherapy.

Singer (1967) reported an investigation of the treatment received by 160 white and 160 Negro schizophrenics during the period 1956–62. The latter were given only drugs as treatment 50 per cent more often than white patients, while receiving psychotherapy less than half as often. In contrast to some earlier studies, Singer found that the Negroes were discharged more quickly than whites, apparently because the physicians were pessimistic about the response of Negroes to treatment.

## Race and Mental Health in Britain

British research has concentrated on the study of illness rates of recent immigrants in comparison with those in the host population; and the special nature and content of the mental illness of the immigrants. This research has been carried out by physicians and psychiatrists, without the use of any explicit sociological concepts.

Pinsent (1963) studied the morbidity of 127 West Indians in Birmingham (66 men, 61 women), compared with morbidity (illness rates) in a similar number of English control subjects of similar sex and social class, using a General Practice register. The illness rates were studied for a period of three years. The West Indians were found to have illness rates, including mental illness, twice those of the English controls. The West Indians were also more accident prone; two exceptions to the general rule were that West Indians had fewer skin diseases, and fewer illnesses of the central nervous system. Mental illness in West Indian women was found to be particularly high in relation to their controls. One possible explanation of the higher West Indian morbidity advanced by the author is that the Birmingham working class are traditional users of patent medicines, whereas West Indians tend to report an illness to their doctor, rather than attempting self-treatment.

Kiev (1963) studied the beliefs and delusions of ten psychotic West Indian patients in London. He found that a common belief was the acceptance, in a vivid fundamentalist way, of God and the Devil having personal control of one's health and disease. A belief in the existence of ghosts and the spirits of the dead was also common. The power of the Obeah, an individual having special control over health and disease, was now absent, since it was assumed that his power could not survive the distance between the West Indies and Britain. Obeah, apparently, does not emigrate.

Tewfik and Okasha (1965) studied the pattern of mental illness in 124 West Indians (74 men, 50 women) at an English mental hospital. They found a relative excess of paranoid illnesses (characterized by false fears and suspicions of persecution) and illnesses with paranoid somatic symptomatology, compared with English patients. A comparison with the figures from the Mental Hospital Census for the West Indies indicated, however, that the paranoid illnesses are probably similar to the pattern of mental illness seen in West Indians in their native environment—"The illness may occur more frequently following migration, but it does not seem to alter in character." The authors attribute the increase in the incidence of mental illnesses to the difficulties of adapting to a new environment.

Gordon (1965) studied mental illness in 112 West Indian patients at a mental hospital serving part of South London. His finding on the excess of paranoid illnesses was similar to that of Tewfik and Okasha. However, Gordon cites previous literature to show that paranoia is a common reaction of many immigrant groups to being placed in an alien and perhaps hostile culture. Other factors which were sources of possible stress were the separation from close relatives or family in 70 per cent of cases; difficulties in finding adequate housing; and the stress following the change in the customary role of the West Indian woman, with new freedoms and responsibilities.

Kiev (1965) studied the prevalence of mental illness over a six-month period in West Indians in a Group Practice in Brixton. In this period, 83 West Indians (36 men and 47 women) became mentally ill. This incidence was compared with that in the English people registered with the practice. This comparison showed that West Indian men had a significantly higher rate of mental illness than English men; the excess of mental illness in West Indian women was not so marked as that in men, a finding in contrast to Pinsent, who reported particularly high rates for West Indian women. Pinsent's more careful method may account for this difference in findings. Kiev suggested that the stress involved in changing from a pastoral to an urban way of life, the absence of a stable kinship system to care for the children of the unmarried, and the absence of extensive social controls so prevalent in the West Indies, are contributory causes in the excess of mental illness in West Indians.

Recent research in this area has concentrated on the mental health of West Indian mothers and their children.* Stroud and Moody (1967) studied 100 West Indian mothers in London. They reported: "From our clinical experience it was obvious that many mothers were not able to offer their children the secure and loving home background which we feel is essential as a basis from which the child will progress into our formal, school educational programme." Many of the mothers suffered from severe depression,

---

*No British literature on the subject of race and mental illness published in the year 1966 can be located.

which resulted from overcrowding, poor housing, the fear of pregnancy which would make this problem worse, hostility in the host community, worry about children still in the West Indies, difficulties with employment, and the exhaustion of having to work and look after children. One interesting and alarming syndrome was observed in children of 13 of the mothers: the pre-school child had developed anti-colored attitudes, regarding themselves as pale and white and showing aggressive tendencies towards darker people.

Prince (1967) studied 23 West Indian children who were referred to a London child guidance clinic in 1966. In 21 of them the author observed a syndrome resembling autism, in which the child was aloof, apathetic and withdrawn, and often without the development of speech. The following aetiological factors were observed: 17 of the 23 children had been separated from their mothers for more than a month; 20 of the mothers were quite seriously depressed, because of homesickness, feelings of isolation in their neighborhood, disillusion with life in England, and marital conflict. Ten of the mothers had left behind varying numbers of children in the care of relatives, which was a source of both guilt and financial difficulty to the mother. Fourteen mothers were working, and were exhausted in the evenings. Thirteen had inadequate housing, and financial difficulties. The parents often displayed guilt, knowing that they could not give the child a stimulating and child-like environment.

Hemsi (1967) investigated the first admissions to psychiatric hospitals of West Indian and native-born patients in the London boroughs of Camberwell and Lambeth. Base populations were calculated from the 1961 Census, and the first-admission rates for the year 1961 calculated. Although only 40 West Indian patients were located by this procedure, the rates for West Indians were appreciably greater than those for the nativeborn population, being 31.8/1,000 and 30.4/1,000 for West Indian men and women respectively, and 9.5/1,000 and 12.2/1,000 for nativeborn men and women. Even though the West Indian rate is nearly three times as great as the native rate, it should be borne in mind that these incidence figures give a rate of only three per cent for mental illness in West Indians. Since immigrants represent only under two per cent of the total community, mental illness amongst them cannot be said, in the context of the use of health services, to be anything but a very small problem.

With regard to diagnoses, Hemsi found, as did some earlier writers, that the most common illness of the West Indian men was schizophrenia, and in West Indian women, affective disorder.

Organic syndromes, alcoholism and drug addiction did not occur in the West Indian patients in this study.

## Discussion

This review of recent research on race and mental illness in Britain and America reveals a perturbing picture. In America, the climate of prejudice which assumes the inferiority of the Negro and denies him access to jobs, housing and education, is taking a heavy toll in terms of mental illness. Research in Britain has concentrated on problems of adaption of new immigrants, but here too the effects of discrimination seem to be taking their toll. The effect on the mental health of children is particularly alarming.

Two points remain to be considered. Bottoms has suggested that the Mertonian model of a shortfall between expectations and means of fulfilling these expectations might provide a useful explanatory model for delinquency among immigrants. Clinard's review of research (1964) in the field of anomie theory shows that the deviant reaction to anomie can be in the nature of mental illness, as well as in the form of delinquency. The research of Parker and Kleiner has provided substantial support for the view that Mertonian anomie is a major cause of mental illness among American Negroes. It is an important question to identify factors which differentiate the deviant outcome in terms of mental illness, or delinquency. Gibbs and Martin (1964) provide a possible explanation: using a measure of status isolation as an indicator, they have provided a major explanation of the mental illness leading to suicide. In a further paper Gibbs (1966) points out that when unusual statuses (such as unemployment) cease to become statistically "unpopular," resulting deviant behavior is likely to be in terms of group action rather than in terms of mental illness.

When the deprived form a stable social group, action should be collective, rather than individual. In America this collective action may take the form of street violence by Negroes. At the end of their book, Parker and Kleiner report research which seems to indicate that the consciousness of the Negro is becoming increasingly collective: this, as the authors say, should tend to decrease mental illness as *isolated* Negroes who have internalized the traditional American ethic of individual striving, now adopt a common, and perhaps semi-revolutionary consciousness.

The P.E.P. report (1967) on race relations in Britain has suggested that as colored people in Britain become better educated and qualified they will experience more discrimination, since they will be denied the higher status jobs for which they are qualified. In the light of Parker and Kleiner's study a likely outcome will be an increased load of mental illness among this community. To what extent this will lead, in turn, to unified militant action, or group delinquency is difficult to say, but it certainly seems theoretically possible that race relations in Britain will follow the American path.

A second point made by Bottoms is that it is possible that immigrants may be a selected population, in terms of personality characteristics. He cites a reference to Ödegaard's research (1932) which apparently showed that individuals with a schizoid personality were much more likely to emigrate from Norway to America, so that in America the Norwegian was more likely to be schizophrenic than Norwegians in Norway. In recent research this point has not been considered, and mental illness in immigrant populations has been attributed to stress factors.

The personality characteristics of immigrants may be predicted deductively, from research on the association of mental illness and social mobility. Lowenthal (1967) has shown that migrants from the West Indies to the United States are upwardly mobile. It is an interesting question for further research whether there are any factors differentiating migrants from the West Indies who go to America, Canada and Britain; but assuming that migrants from the West Indies to Britain do so because of upwardly mobile aspirations, this factor should mean that there will be a *dearth* of schizophrenics of the genetic type amongst West Indian immigrants.

Research in recent years (Goldberg and Morrison, 1963; Turner and Wagenfeld, 1967) has demonstrated that schizophrenia occurs with a much heavier frequency than expected in lower social classes; and that this is because the schizophrenics drift *downwards* in the social scale because of their inability to hold jobs. Schizophrenia is an illness of insidious onset, which progressively cripples the individual's capacity to plan rationally and to think ahead.* It seems possible, therefore, that the schizophrenic would be unable to carry out the complex tasks of organizing and financing emigration.

There is additional evidence that manic depression occurs with a higher than expected frequency in *upper* social classes (Hare, 1952;

---

*"Increasing failure to plan," is one of the five diagnostic criteria which distinguished schizophrenics from nonschizophrenic controls suffering from anxiety, in Parfitt's experimental study (1956). However, the fact that schizophrenics may also be restless, if purposeless drifters, does make the schizophrenic's role as a potential emigrant slightly ambiguous.

Rose, 1956). This finding has recently been validated in an Indian province (Rao, 1966) suggesting that it is not an artifact of Western industrial culture. A crucial question which future research must solve is whether this excess of manic depression is associated with the strains of maintaining social or economic position, or whether individuals predisposed to manic depression tend to rise in the social scale. Wechsler's study (1961) which showed that fast growing American communities contained a higher proportion of manic depressives than static communities would support both propositions. From the point of view of immigration, it seems possible either that a predisposition to manic depression may cause individuals to emigrate (for example, in manic phases, when grandiose planning is common); or that the strains of maintaining a social and economic position in those who have emigrated would precipitate this illness. The incidence of depression reported in West Indian women would tend to support the latter view. Research in this field is complicated by the possibility that some depressive pictures may be independent of environmental stress (Kiloh and Garside, 1963; Bunney *et al.* 1967). The exact relationship of manic and depressive aspects of the illness is also problematic.

How far do the studies of immigration and mental illness support this *a priori* model of the connections of mobility and mental illness? An examination of Ödegaard's original study shows that Norwegians who emigrated had a mental illness rate of 6.35 per cent, compared with the rate of 3.7 per cent in those of similar age and sex who remained in Norway. The incidence of manic depression was not significantly different between the two groups, but there was a significant excess of schizophrenics among those who had emigrated. The methodology of Ödegaard's study is highly sophisticated, and his findings cannot be challenged. However, social factors might account for these findings, and Ödegaard considers the hypothesis that the experience of emigration may precipitate an individual to psychosis. His account of this experience is interesting, since it may well summarize much of the experience of the West Indian in Britain:

> Everywhere you are surrounded by people with strange and unfamiliar ways and customs, and you can hardly understand anything of what they say ... they do not seem as friendly and helpful as the people at home, and many of them do their best to profit by your lack of experience. Even if you have not had any disagreeable experience yourself your imagination is stirred by all the stories you heard about how crooked and dangerous they may be. You notice that your own experience, clothing, and language points you

out to everybody as a greenhorn, and a "big Swede" at that, and you are frequently met by a mixture of mirth and contempt. You have no friends, no one to associate with and no money for expensive entertainments—frequently you live under the strain of imminent unemployment. You are forced to live among the least attractive types of Americans, because it is cheap in those sections, and this frequently means a considerable lowering of your previous standard of life. There are hundreds of similar things which tend to make you suspicious and bewildered, anxious and lonely . . .

These factors, the author concludes, might account for a paranoid coloring in affective disorders, which would lead to a diagnosis of schizophrenia, thus accounting for the excess of individuals with this illness. However, Ödegaard finally makes the hypothesis that embryonic schizophrenics are particularly likely to emigrate, on the *a priori* assumption that schizophrenia is essentially an endogenous, constitutional disease, which is only marginally influenced by social factors.

Ödegaard's conclusion has often been quoted as providing proof that schizophrenics are more likely to emigrate; in fact, the evidence does not support this conclusion, which was made under the influence of the Kretschmer school of psychiatry which stressed the endogenous nature of psychosis. Ödegaard's study does receive some support from a more recent study of Mezey (1960), which showed that schizophrenics who fled from Hungary at the time of the 1956 revolution had contracted the illness before this event, and that stress did not contribute to its emergénce after emigration to Britain. However, since the circumstances of emigration were highly unusual, it is difficult to generalize from this finding to the psychological factors in normal emigration. In addition, the incidence of schizophrenia in those who did not emigrate is unknown, so that the connection of schizophrenia and emigration in this study remains uncertain.

Four recent studies have thrown further light on the problem of deciding whether schizophrenia in migrants is due to factors in the illness which motivate migration, or to stresses experienced after migration. The study of Hemsi, referred to above, identified 40 mentally ill West Indians in two London boroughs. In 36 of the cases it was possible to date the onset of symptoms: in four cases the illness anteceded migration, and in six cases the symptoms occurred within three months of arrival. In a further nine cases symptoms began up to two years after migration. In the largest group of 17 cases the illness began at least two years after migration; in ten of these cases, the illness did not begin until four years after migration. The fact that in the majority of cases the illness had its onset some time after migration tends to support the stress rather than the selection hypothesis.

A study by Krupinski (1967) of mental illness in European immigrants to Victoria, Australia, found that the cases fell into two groups: (1) Unstable, single men emigrating from Western Europe who broke down in their first year in Australia, and who were probably schizophrenic before emigration; (2) Migrants from Southern and Eastern Europe who broke down after being in the new culture for a year or more, and in whom stress played a part in the aetiology of the illness, relating to the lack of acceptance found by the immigrant in the host culture. Krupinski's study, like those of others, found much higher rates in the immigrants than in the native population.

Malzberg (1967) has reviewed the literature on internal migration and mental illness in the white population in the United States. The evidence showed that migrants had higher mental illness rates (principally of schizophrenia) than nonmigrants, and the mental illness rate decreased the longer a migrant had been settled, suggesting that assimilation is related to mental health. Evidence from Canada supported this view, since British immigrants to French-speaking Quebec had higher rates of mental illness than British immigrants to English-speaking Ontario.

Barahona-Ferandes et al. (1967) in a study of psychiatric disorders in the Portuguese province of Macao found a high incidence of classical psychotic cases amongst the Chinese who had emigrated from Hong Kong and Mainland China. The authors attributed the occurrence of these illnesses to stresses involved in job-finding, education of children, and separation from family.

The conclusion from this review of literature on psychosis and emigration must be that schizophrenic and paranoid illnesses occur with greater frequency among immigrants than in individuals who do not emigrate, and with greater frequency than in individuals in the host community.

The literature on the association of mental disorder and social mobility would suggest deductively that emigrants would have a higher incidence of manic depression and a lower incidence of schizophrenia, than those who do not emigrate. However, the empirical evidence from studies of the mental health of immigrants does not support this model. This evidence shows that immigrants have a susceptibility to psychotic illnesses of the paranoid or schizophrenic type, rather than manic depression (although an excess of depressive illness in West Indian women in Britain has been observed). An adequate explanation of these illnesses probably lies in the stress to which immigrants are subjected, although in a minority of cases it is possible that mental illness in migrants may itself be the cause of migration.

## Conclusion and Summary

Recent British and American literature on race and mental illness has been considered. The British literature has dealt with the connections of immigration and mental illness; the American literature is more numerous and broadly based, and deals with all aspects of the effects of race on mental health. In both Britain and America the stress of being a Negro in a white community seems to have led to a high rate of mental illness among Negroes. In America a significant factor in this mental illness has been "goal-striving in a climate of limited opportunity." It seems technically possible that this factor may be a future cause of mental ill-health in Britain's colored community. The investigation of the forms and incidence of mental illness in Negro and Asian immigrants in Britain must be regarded as an important area for future research.

The literature on the connections between mobility and mental health, and the particular kinds of illness to which immigrants are subject, has been considered in detail. Immigrants show a higher proportion of paranoid, psychotic illnesses than those who do not emigrate. Nevertheless, the rate is apparently not sufficiently large to pose a serious problem in terms of the overall social situation. These illnesses are most likely to be reactions to living in an alien, hostile culture. The occurrence of depressive illnesses in immigrants may be a replica of the association of manic depression and the occupation of a higher social and economic status, although these depressive pictures can be explained simply as reactions to overwork, financial difficulties, poor housing, and other anxieties.

## References

Banks, G., B. Berenson, and Carkhuff, "The Effects of Counsellor Race and Training Upon Counselling Process with Negro Clients in Initial Interviews," *Journal of Clinical Psychology,* Vol. 23 (1967), pp. 70–72.

Barahona-Ferandes, H., F. Ferreira, and A. Cotta-Guerra, "Portugal—Psychiatric Experience in Europe, Asia (Macao) and Africa (Mozambique, Angola)," *Topical Problems in Psychiatric Neurology,* Vol. 5 (1967), pp. 143–61.

Bennett, L., Jr., "Reading, 'Riting and Racism," *Ebony* Magazine, March 1967, pp. 130–38.

Bottoms, A., "Delinquency Amongst Immigrants," *Race*, Vol. 8 (1967), pp. 357–83.

Bunney, W., J. Davis, H. Weil-Malherbe, and E. Smith, "Biochemical Changes in Psychotic Depression," *Archives of General Psychiatry*, Vol. 16 (1967), pp. 448–60.

Chethik, M., E. Fleming, M. Mayer, and I. McCoy, "A Quest for Identity: Treatment of Disturbed Negro Children in a Predominantly White Treatment Center," *American Journal of Orthopsychiatry*, Vol. 37 (1967), pp. 71–7.

Clinard, M., *Anomie and Deviant Behavior* (Glencoe, Ill.: Free Press, 1964).

Drake, St. Clair, "The Social and Economic Status of the Negro in the United States," in T. Parsons and K. Clark, eds., *The Negro American* (Boston: Houghton Mifflin Co., 1966).

Gibby, R., and R. Gabler, "The Self-Concept of Negro and White Children," *Journal of Clinical Psychology*, Vol. 23 (1967), pp. 144–7.

Gibbs, J., and W. Martin, *Status Integration and Suicide* (University of Oregon Press, 1964).

Gibbs, J., "Crime, Unemployment and Status Integration," *British Journal of Criminology*, Vol. 6 (1966), pp. 49–58.

Goldberg, E., and S. Morrison, "Schizophrenia and Social Class," *British Journal of Psychiatry*, Vol. 109 (1963), pp. 785–802.

Goldberg, S., "Sex and Race Differences in Response to Drug Treatment Among Schizophrenics," *Psychopharmacologia*, Vol. 9 (1966), pp. 31–47.

Gordon, E., "Mentally Ill West Indian Immigrants," *British Journal of Psychiatry*, Vol. 111 (1965), pp. 877–87.

Hare, E., "The Ecology of Mental Illness," *Journal of Mental Science*, Vol. 98 (1952), pp. 579–94.

Hartog, J., "The Mental Health Problems of Poverty's Youth," *Mental Hygiene*, Vol. 51 (1967), pp. 85–90.

Hemsi, L., "Psychiatric Morbidity of West Indian Immigrants," *Social Psychiatry*, Vol. 2 (1967), pp. 95–100.

Kiev, A., "Beliefs and Delusions of West Indian Immigrants to London," *British Journal of Psychiatry*, Vol. 109 (1963), pp. 356–63.

———, "Psychiatric Morbidity of West Indian Immigrants in an Urban Group Practice," *British Journal of Psychiatry*, Vol. 111 (1965), pp. 51–6.

Kiloh, L., and R. Garside, "The Independence of Neurotic Depression and Endogenous Depression," *British Journal of Psychiatry,* Vol. 109 (1963), pp. 451–63.

Krupinski, J., "Sociological Aspects of Mental Ill-Health in Migrants," *Social Science and Medicine,* Vol. 1 (1967), pp. 267–81.

Laing, R., and A. Esterton, *Sanity, Madness and the Family*—Vol. I, *Families of Schizophrenics* (London: Tavistock, 1964).

Lowenthal, D., "Race and Colour in the West Indies," *Daedalus,* Spring 1967, pp. 580–626.

Maas, J., "Incidence and Treatment Variations Between Negroes and Caucasians in Mental Illness," *Community Mental Health Journal,* Vol. 3 (1967), pp. 61–5.

Malzberg, B., "Internal Migration and Mental Disease Among the White Population of New York State, 1960–1961," *International Journal of Social Psychiatry,* 1967, pp. 184–91.

Mezey, A., "Personal Backgrounds, Emigration and Mental Disorder in Hungarian Refugees," *Journal of Mental Science,* Vol. 106 (1960), pp. 618–27.

Moreland, J., "A Comparison of Race Awareness in Northern and Southern Children," *American Journal of Orthopsychiatry,* Vol. 36 (1966), pp. 23–31.

Ödegaard, O., *Emigration and Insanity, Acta Psychiatrica Scandinavica Supplement,* Vol. 4 (1932).

Parfitt, D., "The Neurology of Schizophrenia," *Journal of Mental Science,* Vol. 102 (1956), pp. 671–718.

Parker, S., and R. Kleiner, *Mental Illness in the Urban Negro Community* (Glencoe, Ill.: Free Press, 1966).

P. E. P., *Racial Discrimination* (London: Political and Economic Planning, 1967).

Pettigrew, T., "Race, Mental Illness and Intelligence: A Social Psychological View," *Eugenics Quarterly,* Vol. 11 (1964), pp. 189–215.

Pinsent, J., "Morbidity in an Immigrant Population," *Lancet,* Vol. i (1963), pp. 437–8.

Price, G., "Mental Health Problems in Pre-School West Indian Children," *Maternal Child Care,* June 1967, pp. 483–6.

Rao, M., "Socio-Economic Groups and Mental Disorders," *Psychiatric Quarterly,* Vol. 40 (1966), pp. 677–91.

Roberts, S., and J. Robinson, "Effects of Task Difficulty, Race of Administrator, and Instructions on Digit-Symbol Performance of Negroes," *Journal of Personality and Social Psychology,* Vol. 2 (1965), pp. 53–9.

Rose, A., *Mental Health and Mental Disorder: A Sociological Approach* (London: Routledge, 1956).

Singer, B., "Some Implications of Differential Psychiatric Treatment of Negro and White Patients," *Social Science and Medicine,* Vol. 1 (1967), pp. 77–83.

Stroud, C., and V. Moody, "One Hundred Mothers," *Maternal Child Care,* June 1967, pp. 487–90.

Tewfik, G., and A. Okasha, "Psychosis and Immigration," *Postgraduate Medical Journal,* Vol. 41 (1965), pp. 603–12.

Turner, R., and M. Wagenfeld, "Occupational Mobility and Schizophrenia: An Assessment of the Social Causation and Social Selection Hypotheses," *American Sociological Review,* Vol. 32 (1967), pp. 104–13.

Vosk, J., "Study of Negro Children with Learning Difficulties at the Outset of their School Careers," *American Journal of Orthopsychiatry,* Vol. 26 (1966), pp. 32–40.

Wechsler, H., "Community Growth, Depressive Disorders, and Suicide," *American Journal of Sociology,* Vol. 67 (1961), pp. 9–16.

Zahran, H., *The Self-Concept in Relation to the Psychological Guidance of Adolescents: An Experimental Study,* Ph.D. thesis, London University.

# RACE AND ABILITY

Of all animals, man is the most unpredictable. Toynbee notwithstanding, history makes an uncertain prophet: the same circumstances, involving different times and different men, can lead to war or peace, love or hate, fraternity or murder. The same hereditary material, pooled by the same man and woman in the act of reproduction, can produce children who do not much resemble either their parents or one another. Even identical twins, issuing from the same egg, can vary; for instance, they never possess identical fingerprints or dispositions.

Classifications may not exist in nature, but order does. And the observable differences among men, as broadly varied as the species, have long challenged the orderly human mind to catalogue them— to find a way, in short, to subdivide the fascinating and unruly

Reprinted from *Time,* The Weekly Newsmagazine, Sept. 29, 1967, pp. 46–7; copyright Time Inc. 1967.

diversity of humankind. Within the diversity may lurk patterns, and the patterns may aid man's understanding of himself and his differences.

This prospect has endlessly occupied—and eluded—the inquiring human mind. If the species could be sensibly subdivided into races, then the races could be measured one against another, could be assigned proper places in the hierarchy of mankind. Cultural and geographical isolation, occurring over numberless millennia, could conceivably have bred peoples of widely differing physical and intellectual capacity. And taking Western technological man as the norm, it could be possible, given the right tools, to compare his performance against those of all the other human varieties.

## What Eyes Can See

The problem is far more complicated than that, as any scientist who has tried merely to determine the biological races has discovered. Among the first to try was the German zoologist Johann Friedrich Blumenbach in 1775. On the basis of physical characteristics, he saw five human subspecies or races—a term possibly deriving from the Arabic *râs* (beginning). Blumenbach divided humans into races that he called Caucasian (white), Mongolian (yellow), Ethiopian (black), American (copper) and Malay (brown).

In Blumenbach's century, other naturalists and philosophers disputed his arbitrary racial census; with equal arbitrariness, it has been reduced and expanded many times in the 192 years since. Sorting men into groups according to their differences may seem a simple task. But even now, anthropologists argue heatedly on how to do it. They have partitioned the human species into anywhere from two to 200 races; some anthropologists maintain that humanity cannot or should not be subdivided into races at all. The debate does not particularly concern the great majority of nonexperts. Man's eyes tell him that the species comes in three predominant skin shades, which are chromatically though imperfectly described as white, yellow and black. From much the same evidence, three major divisions are frequently deduced: Caucasian, Mongolian and Negroid.

Not every human being fits neatly into one of those three categories, but most of them do. The system is at least workable, all the more so because the physical disparities in man are not limited to the color of his skin. The so-called Mongolian race, for example, can also be distinguished by the epicanthic fold that gives some Asian peoples, among them the Japanese and the Chinese, a slant-eyed look. Evolutionary hypothesis has traced this feature to its probable source. The predominant theory is that it developed from a mutation—a random change in the elaborate chemistry of human chromosomes, which govern man's biological evolution. For arctic and desert-dwelling people, subjected to blinding blizzards of snow or sand, the eye fold had definite survival value: it increased the eyes' protection against such hazards. Thus the trait endured.

The dark skin that usually, though not invariably, characterizes members of the Negroid race may also be a protective device. If man was first born in tropical Africa, as some anthropologists now suggest, then it is possible that his skin, whatever color it may have been to begin with, took on added pigment—again, starting with chance mutation—as a screen against harmful radiation from the sun. It is a fact that Negroes seldom have skin cancer, though its incidence is rising noticeably in the white population of the U.S. The same pigment, by filtering solar radiation, impedes synthesis of vitamin D, which prevents rickets and is manufactured from the sun's rays by the body. As early man migrated out of the tropical sun—into the green jungle, north to less torrid zones—light skin thereupon conferred an advantage by admitting more vitamin D-producing sunlight. And the lottery of evolution, patiently awaiting the appropriate mutation, then fixed this advantage into place. Thus, over the centuries, environmental factors were producing genetic changes.

Man's extended tropical sojourn appears to have generated other useful or once useful adaptations more frequently found in dark-skinned peoples. A hereditary blood condition known as the sickle-cell trait, which grants resistance to certain types of malaria, is only now beginning to wane among U.S. Negroes, who no longer have any need of it. The Negro's woolly black hair once provided insulation against the heat of the blazing tropical sun; his thick lips, by exposing more mucous membrane, may have increased the body's evaporative cooling powers in torrid climates; his characteristically long legs and lean frame were once distinctly helpful to some prehistoric race of hunters.

The list of apparently Negroid characteristics can be extended, since dark-skinned persons come in so many shapes and sizes, from the storklike Watutsi, to the Pygmies of Central Africa. Generally, Negro skull capacity—affecting the size of the brain—runs about 50 cc. below that of whites. However, before any large conclusions are drawn from that, another fact must be considered: on the average, the skull capacity of modern whites is some 150 cc. smaller than that of Neanderthal man, who lived 50,000 years ago. Some anthropologists go so far as to say that the Negro's attributes, coupled with the ordeal of slavery, have produced in him a physically superior race—a theory that gains strength from the Negro's extraordinary ability in athletics. The strongest African blacks were selected as the best slave material; only the hardiest of these survived ocean transport in slave ships; only the sturdiest of back and spirit endured slavery's arduous, degrading yoke.

## Bitter Division

It is on the issue of racial superiority, physical and mental, that all of mankind bitterly divides. Such value judgments are largely subjective and lack any solid scientific foundation, but that has never stopped men from making them. The Negro, who reached the U.S. in bonds, has ever since been classified in some quarters as a member of an intellectually inferior race. The attitude is not without historical precedent. Segregationists of the U.S. South often quote the *Book of Genesis* 9:25, which relates that Canaan, the son of Ham—whose skin was believed to be black—is accursed throughout time: "A servant of servant shall be he unto his brethren." The eighteenth century Scottish philosopher David Hume suspected "Negroes to be naturally inferior to the whites." Several U.S. Presidents, among them Jefferson and Lincoln, shared the same opinion, at least for a while. As long as the two races lived together, said Lincoln in 1858, "there must be the position of superior and inferior, and I as much as any other man am in favor of having the superior position assigned to the white race." Washington unreflectively accepted slavery as an institution simply because it was there, but before dying he drew up a will emancipating his slaves. The late Albert Schweitzer, who devoted his life and medical skill to African Negroes, went to his grave believing that "the Negro is a child, and with children nothing can be done without the use of authority."

The theory of racial inferiority lurks at the edges of current anthropological thought. In his book *The Origin of Races*, anthropologist Carleton S. Coon suggests that *Homo sapiens*—modern man—evolved not once but five times, in five different places. The last to attain the fully human estate, says Coon, was the Negro—a conjecture that, if accepted, explains why Negro cultures in Africa lag behind the West's and why the Negro is not yet the white man's intellectual peer. According to Coon, he simply has not had enough time. Approaching the subject from closer range, University of Chicago physiologist Dwight Ingle writes: "America is trying to build the Great Society by applying only palliative methods for the correction of cultural handicaps and ignoring possible biological bases of incompetence, indolence and irresponsibility."

## Open Possibility

Few members of the scientific community agree with these points of view, preferring instead merely to keep open the possibility that the races of man can be intellectually ranked. To Curt Stern, a geneticist at the University of California at Berkeley, it seems unreasonable to conclude that "because there is no evidence of inherent inequalities, the situation couldn't exist." Says University of Colorado anthropologist John Greenway: "I would not want to say that an Australian Aborigine is dumber than I am, because there is no way to tell. In their noncompetitive society there is no way to make any tests and hence no way to make comparisons. We don't know what the differences are between different racial groups and there is a strong prejudice against finding out. Suppose you made a study to determine if there are differences between the brains of whites and Negroes and proved it?" Nobel Laureate William Shockley, a solid-state physicist, drew outraged reaction from the scientific community when he charged that "inverted liberalism" raises taboos against research into man's genetic intellectual differences and "paralyzes the ability to doubt."

A scientist who is closer to the pertient field put it in less provocative terms. "The idea that human races differ in adaptively significant traits is emotionally repugnant to some people," wrote geneticist Theodosius Dobzhansky in *Mankind Evolving.* "Any inquiry into this matter is felt to be dangerous, lest it vindicate race prejudice." Undeniably, racial prejudice is social or cultural in origin rather than biological, and it is understandable that anthropologists, who hesitate to make value judgments on the basis of biological fact, would hesitate also to enter what is fundamentally a sociological—and highly emotional—controversy. Anthropologist Morton Fried says that "participation in a 'debate' over racial differences in intelligence, ability or achievement potential is not participation in a scientific debate at all. It means lifting in the public eye the status of studies otherwise disqualified and rejected by science." Interpreted one way, such studies apparently suggest that the U.S. Negro is inferior to the U.S. white. On IQ tests, he generally averages 15 to 20 points lower. The results of World War I alpha intelligence tests have frequently been cited as evidence of the Negro's mental inferiority, since the Negro soldier invariably ranked below the white soldier on a state-by-state basis. But the same test results can be used in another way to demonstrate that Negros are smarter than whites. On the alpha tests, for instance, Negro soldiers from the Northern state of Ohio outscored whites from eleven Southern states. Beyond this, it could be inferred from the tests that Northern whites are superior to Southern whites, because they almost always did better.

Most psychologists have now abandoned the notion that intelligence can be accurately tested; it is difficult even to define the terms. Einstein once confessed to anthropologist Ashley Montagu that in the Australian Aborigine's society, he would rightfully be regarded as an intellectual idiot who could neither track a wallaby nor throw a boomerang. As anthropologist Stanley Garn has dryly noted, if the Aborigine drafted an IQ test, all of Western civilization would presumably flunk it. "It is possible that some of the behavioral differences between human groups may be genetically determined," says University of Michigan anthropologist Ernst Goldschmidt. "These may include differences in intelligence, but such differences may equally be due to cultural determinants. The question simply remains open." Harvard psychologist Thomas Pettigrew points out that "while the intelligence test means of the two races are still divergent, the range of performance—from the most retarded idiot to the most brilliant genius—is much the same in the two groups. Some Negro children achieve IQs into the gifted range (130 or over) and right up to the testable limit of 200." For three years running, the highest scholastic achievement among Australian state schools was registered by one composed exclusively of Aboriginal children.

Those who resist making value comparisons among groups do so on two grounds. The first is that science as yet lacks valid tools to sort mankind into biological races. The second is that even if science possessed such tools, the racial divisions could not conceivably be used to grade human worth. So meager is man's understanding of the complicated biochemistry of evolution and of the nonhereditary influences of cultural environment that no one can confidently assign that portion of intelligence with which man was born and that part he acquired. If heredity bestows his capacity to learn, culture decides what he will learn—in some cases how much he will be permitted to learn. The handicaps under which the

U.S. Negro has existed since he arrived in chains are cruelly reflected in his group achievement.

## Environment & Culture

Physical differences are variations on the universal human theme. All men are different. But all men are also alike, the similarities outnumber the differences, says Morton Fried, on the order of 95 to 5. During man's nomadic residence on earth, a continuum reaching back 2,000,000 years, he has indiscriminately mingled with his own kind, thoroughly scrambling his genes. It may be possible one day to unscramble the human genetic omelet. Until then group distinctions decreeing one race's superiority over another must necessarily be made on nonbiological lines. With only a few dissenting votes, the world of anthropology has swung in this direction. "The peoples of the world today," concluded delegates to a world meeting of ethnologists and anthropologists in 1964, "appear to possess equal biological potentialities for attaining any civilizational level. Differences in the achievements of different peoples must be attributed solely to their cultural history."

It seems probable that before society solves the thorny problem of race prejudice, advancing science—or even the continuing evolution of the human species—will beat society to it. The world's population is already three-fifths colored—that is, other than white. Geneticists Bentley Glass and Ching Chun Li predict that within ten centuries or so, at the present rate of exchange, the U.S. Negro will be genetically indistinguishable from the U.S. white. In far less time than that, says Stanford University geneticist Joshua Lederberg, science will have learned enough about the genetic code to tamper with it—to insert into the human chromosomes artificial chemical commands capable of determining anything from skin color to musical aptitude.

Until the world accepts the proposition that the universality of mankind outweighs the differences, speculation about the meaning of the diversity will continue. The human physical variety is self-evident, so is the wide spectrum of human achievement. It is well-established that the controlling factors are cultural and environmental. Nothing that man has discovered about himself so far provides any sound scientific foundation for the conclusion that one is innately superior to any other. No one knows. And the men of tomorrow, looking back, may wonder why anyone was ever concerned with such comparisons.

# RESEARCHING RACIAL INFERIORITY?

Pursuing scientific inquiry into the applications of solid-state physics, Bell Laboratories physicist William Shockley played a major role in the invention of the junction transistor, shared a 1956 Nobel Prize for his efforts, and made a substantial impact on technology and society. Now on the faculty of Stanford University, he is creating yet another stir by advocating a similar approach in a science far afield from his own. In speeches and interviews during the past three years, Shockley has charged that the scientific community has been ignoring or blocking research into possible differences in the genetic makeup of races. He has been accused, in turn, of fostering racial prejudice.

Shockley cites the increasing problems of Negro ghettos and the failure of one out of four youths—a high percentage of them Negroes—to pass the Armed Forces Qualifications Tests. Shockley asks: "Is environment the only cause? Is perhaps some of the cause hereditary?" After searching for answers in scientific literature, the physicists recently told a meeting of the Commonwealth Club of California that he found "only unconvincing assertions that carry no sense of certainty." This "environment-hereditary uncertainty," he says, prevents an intelligent attack on city slum problems and may be contributing to a decline in the overall quality of the U.S. population.

## Worries, or Plans

Shockley attributes the uncertainty to "inverted liberalism," which he says has resulted in taboos against research on genetic differences. He charges that such institutions as the Federal Government and the American Anthropological Association have discouraged investigation because they might reach "unpalatable" conclusions. "Our intellectuals," he says, "treat this problem like a frightened person who hides an uncertainty even from himself and does not expose a tumor to a doctor's inspection."

To the genetics faculty of Stanford, which accused him of seeking "pseudoscientific justification for class and race prejudice," and to other critics, Shockley says: "Let's ask the questions, do the necessary research, find the facts, discuss them widely—then either worries will evaporate or plans for action will develop."

But many scientists agree with University of California psychologist David Krech, who insists that it is the difficulty involved in measuring racial differences, rather than any taboo, that is responsible for the lack of evidence that Shockley demands. In any such research, says Krech, there must be the fundamental assumption: "If all other conditions are equal." At present, he adds, there is no such situation between large groups of Negroes and whites in America.

# Chapter Twelve

# *The Non-Biological Basis of Prejudice*

If there is in fact no basis for racism in biological terms, why is racism so prevalent? The answer is that racism grows out of a need to rationalize the subjugation of human beings. Somehow meting out misery on subjects that could be considered naturally inferior justifies the treatment and its result. Thus a good deal of time and effort was (and in some cases still is ) devoted by the subjugator group to find conclusive evidence that the subjugated are in fact a biologically and evolutionarily inferior group, a group not made inferior by the subjugator but simply found that way by him and then put to "proper" use. If the result is inhumane it is nature, not man, that is cruel.

It would please anthropologists greatly if racists would desist from using the "nature" argument to support their prejudices. But evidently the need for a natural rationalization is so great that modern-day racists rely on such arguments with increasing rather than decreasing fervor. It is perhaps naive to hope that anthropological-biological facts will influence and change cultural values. It seems increasingly clear that only "cultural facts" can change a cultural phenomenon like racism. When it becomes culturally disfunctional to practice racism, a change will come about and the death of the biological rationalization will come as a mere side-product of that change. Thus this Reader on Physical Anthropology has the following totally cultural section on race prejudice.

# RACE RELATIONS AND HUMAN RIGHTS

*Philip Mason*

Philip Mason is Director of the Institute of Race Relations.

What I have to say is a summary of an argument which really demands much more space and will, I hope, eventually appear as a book, with several supporting books as evidence. I hope it will not seem too bare a skeleton in its present form.

Relations between races present perhaps the supreme example of the immense effect which confused thought can have on human lives and happiness. A modern society can be divided into many different groups; there will be trade unionists and employers, liberals and conservatives, men and women, materialists and idealists, young and old—groups united by profession, by religious belief, by economic interest. These are groups between whom there is a common link which has some meaning for their lives. But in Britain at the moment there are people who speak of "the blacks," linking together under this one irrelevant heading not only Pakistanis, Indians, Somalis and Jamaicans, but factory-workers and university professors; Muslims, Sikhs, Hindus, and Christians; the latest arrival and those born in the country. It is as meaningless a category as can be devised, worse even than those with bald heads. It is about the diversity of human groups that I wish to speak, about social injustice and about the dangers to the future of humanity that social inequality presents when it is perceived and resented. These are matters we need to think about deeply if something more than rhetoric and vague goodwill is to emerge from Human Rights Year. What do we really mean by Human Rights?

I want first to emphasize the relationship between myth and reality, between social and psychological factors. We need not linger on the difficulty of defining what we mean by race; we know that there are broad divisions of the human species distinguished from each other by various biological characteristics. They were

From *Race*, Vol. 10 (July 1968), pp. 1–16. Published for The Institute of Race Relations, London, by The Oxford University Press. © Institute of Race Relations, 1968.

all produced by the processes of evolution and in some cases we can see that, at earlier stages of man's history, they had some value in relation to environment. But they do not, as physical traits, make much difference to man's ability to live in a modern city. On the other hand, what we *think* and *feel* about them makes a great difference. There is a set of facts—different skin color, a different culture three hundred years ago, exploitation on one side and slavery on the other; those facts have combined to produce a set of associations—something in the human mind, a convention supported by a myth—which has in its turn produced a new set of facts—segregation, bad housing, poor schooling, discrimination over jobs—the vicious downward spiral with which we are all familiar, the familiar tale of the self-fulfilling prophecy that expects nothing and therefore gets nothing. Facts of geography, evolution, and economic needs produce circumstances which have a psychological effect, which in its turn produce physical realities.

I have been thinking as I speak of the Negro in the United States; but in fact only a few words need be changed to apply what I have said to many other groups—to the ex-untouchables of India, to the poor of England a century ago, to women in most of the world for most of history, to the Indians of the Andean region. Race differences and the inequality associated with them are only one special case of group inequality in the widest sense. I need not enlarge to this audience on the many special aspects of discrimination on racial grounds—the deep humiliation it inflicts, its wastefulness, the harm it does—morally and materially—to the prejudiced dominant group, the fact above all that there is no escape. Chromatic mobility is almost unknown.

Let us try—however sketchily in so brief a period—to plot a curve showing the growth of human inequality; we will then make some attempt at estimating the resentment and damage it causes and at predicting how inequality and resentment will develop in the next few years. But let me first make a point about human rights.

It seems to me that we use the word "right" in a very different sense when we speak of a legal and justifiable right, enforceable at law within a sovereign state, and when we speak of "rights" which we think *ought* to exist. The United Nations Declaration of Human Rights constantly uses the phrase: "Everyone has the right" . . . to a variety of activities which in fact are denied to a great many people. Women in Switzerland have no right—in the legal sense— to vote. In South Africa, Africans have hardly any legal rights at all—neither to vote, nor to free speech, nor to free movement, nor to marry, nor to combine for bargaining purposes. A declaration of rights by a sovereign body when embodied in a statute conveys a legal right; a declaration by a nonsovereign body merely expresses an aspiration. This emphasizes the primitive character of international society. I shall try here to distinguish between these two senses of the word "right" by saying either "legal rights"—meaning something which *is*—or "just rights"—meaning something which *ought to be*.

Now let me turn to the curve of growth of human inequality and to the forces that muster for and against it. You will recall that famous saying of Sir Henry Maine that "the movement of the progressive societies has hitherto been a movement from Status to Contract."[1] He meant, of course, a progress from a personal legal status derived from birth and position in the family or clan to a status deriving from some kind of contract, such as an employer enters into with the person employed, or a landlord with a tenant. And his proposition was true for the stretch of history he was thinking of, for Europe from early Roman times to the late nineteenth century. But if one goes back earlier, one could say that progress was from societies that were undifferentiated by birth to societies that were highly stratified, in which status was generally determined by birth and in which there was very little chance to rise in the world. In the earliest human groups—primitive food-gathering groups, such as those of the Bushmen of the Kalahari desert—there was no doubt inequality—as among groups of animals—but it was based on strength, skill, age, or wisdom; there were no slaves, no serfs, no untouchables. But from the beginning, progress was towards increasing stratification, first to primitive states—and I think of African examples, such as the Bemba and Barotse of Zambia—and thence to empires, such as Egypt, Assyria and Peru. The men who dragged the stones into position on the pyramid of Cheops or on the great fortress of Sacsahuaman at Cuzco were hewers of wood and drawers of water for life.

I want to emphasize that specialization seems everywhere to have been essential for progress—in the arts and knowledge of our environment; in geometry and astronomy. It does not follow in logic that specialization had to be rigid and ant-like but in history this was usually the case, and everywhere the first movement was towards inequality and social stratification, before contrary forces began to produce the opposite movement noted by Sir Henry Maine.

The forces making for stratification were of two different kinds. As a means of organization, stratification was efficient; it got things done. A gathering of tribal elders could not build a pyramid or make people store grain against a drought. Also, it was psychologically satisfying; you knew where you were, you knew how to behave, everyone else knew how they were expected to behave to you. There was often a rationalizing myth which explained the system and made it seem part of the order of things. And the myth demanded its own hierarchy of servants. These forces are not dead.

The contrary forces were old by the time the Spaniards reached Peru; they had lain dormant for centuries, only occasionally showing brief signs of life. Forgive me for reminding you of obvious points, but they are essential to my synthesis. There was a set of religious ideas embodied in Judaism and another set of social, legal and political ideas embodied in Athens—but both, from the outset, carried with them such far-reaching consequences that even those who accepted them immediately hedged them about with limitations which nullified them, while there were always people who opposed them. It was like the working of a vaccine which carries with it its own antibody.

The Jews developed their idea of a tribal god into a universal and righteous creator, to whom all nations would turn at last; in their later thought this universal God is almost identified with the spirit of Wisdom. Later this universal note—which implies the fatherhood of God and therefore the brotherhood of man—was explicitly proclaimed both by Christianity and Islam, but from the start the vaccine and the antibody were at war; within Judaism, Christianity and Islam, a contrary spirit was rigid, nationalist or exclusive.

And while Athens produced the idea of equality before the law, and a highly egalitarian society—in which lots were drawn for public offices and the richer citizens were expected to build warships for the state at their own expense—it was a limited society. It excluded immigrants, slaves, foreigners and women; its greatest thinker, in that study of justice which is the foundation of European political thought, reached the conclusion that the essence of a civilized state lay in specialization of function and in each man attending to his own essential craft. This, Plato thought, was justice. He even argued that if the state was to preserve justice, the people—the ordinary citizens—must be persuaded by a myth to believe that the law-givers were a different creation, in whose composition gold was mixed, while in themselves the corresponding element was iron or brass. His conclusions were aristocratic and the reverse of egalitarian.

Ideally—and if I were writing ten Toynbean volumes—I should

sketch here the history of these universalist Greek and Jewish ideas. All I can do here is to emphasize that the idea of man's ultimate equality in the religious sphere never quite died. But it lay dormant; it had little social reality. Men of humble birth did rise in Tudor England to high positions, but it was rare. Until the end of the eighteenth century, there was an assumption implicit in society, though it might be questioned by intellectuals and a few eccentrics, that birth indicated an inherent difference between human beings. This held good in almost every society of Europe, Africa and Asia, and in the Spanish and British possessions in the New World. Whatever philosophers might say, there were no doubts about this in practice until the American and French Revolutions suddenly expressed the idea of equality in two sovereign states. I need hardly stress that if you think of men as divided by birth into classes, even though they look outwardly much as you look yourself, you find it easy to have even more exclusive ideas about people who *look* different as well.

But American liberty, like Athenian, excluded slaves. And if one takes a quick look at the main societies of the world as they existed in the first half of the nineteenth century, it is clear that the kind of liberty embodied in the United Nations declaration was a very rare exception. Englishmen had the right to trial by a jury of "equals," slavery had been declared incapable of existing on the soil of England and the slave trade had been prohibited, but the right to vote was tied to property and "the laboring poor"—as the horrible phrase ran—had no freedom to combine for bargaining purposes. Jews and Roman Catholics could not vote; a man could be transported for life for poaching. There was nominal equality before the law—but judge and lawyers belonged to the ruling class. In Eastern Europe there was not even a pretence of equality before the law; serfs were still tied to the land and a Russian landowner would reckon the size of his estate not by its area but by the number of "souls"—that is, of serfs. Throughout Asia, society was authoritarian and stratified and in Africa the same was true of those societies which had progressed beyond the stage of tribal consultation and rule by elders. In the Spanish-speaking parts of the New World, a feudal system of land-tenure was general and the laborers on the estate were frequently so tied by debt that they were virtually serfs. In the Andean areas, the hierarchical structure of society was linked with race; the more Indian a man's features, the greater the expectation that he would be at the bottom of the social scale. Slavery was still legal in the Southern States and Brazil.

Almost everywhere, a rigid framework kept men in their place—
a network of inequality, defined by caste, by class, by religion, by
race. And do not forget that Plato's ideal state had been stratified
like this. There was therefore a rational model for inequality as
well as the psychological and economic forces already mentioned.

The forms taken by inequality were very varied. Caste in India
lasted longer than any other system of institutionalized stratification, and relations at the lower end of the scale involved an extreme
of humiliation; a Brahman was polluted not merely by the touch
but by the neighborhood of people from one of the many groups
of untouchables. But the untouchable could not be sold by auction
and parted from his children like the American slave. I cannot
attempt to decide which degradation is deeper.

Varied as these systems of exploitation have been, the point that
really needs explaining is that for so much of the time, the exploited
have acquiesced in it. Of course, there were peasants' risings in
Europe, slave rebellions in the Caribbean, colonial wars, insurrec-
tions put down by dragoons. But the risings were the exceptions.
For a great part of history, people acquiesced, and perhaps the most
damaging effect of inequality is that the justifying myth of inferior
status has so often come to be taken as a fact by the subordinate
group—by the American Negro, by the Andean Indian, by untouchables, by Victorian women.

Many here will know more than I do of the work done in the
United States on reference groups. One of the earliest studies concerned American soldiers; its essence was the discovery that in a
corps where chances of promotion were poor, the men were more
contented than in another where chances of promotion were good.
Where promotion was rare, men were reasonably satisfied because
they compared themselves only with each other and were all
equally deprived. This simple point has been elaborated and confirmed in many contexts; the relationship between actual inequality
experienced and resentment of it is very complex. In Britain, in the
thirties, unemployment was on the whole accepted with singularly
little resentment because on the whole the depression was thought
to be unavoidable. But there were sharp exceptions to this; "the
miners for example, who felt cheated of governmental promises of
reform and victimized by wage-cuts which differed arbitrarily from
district to district, felt progressively more aggrieved as the Depression wore on."[2]

It is a historical commonplace that rebellions have seldom occurred when people were at the lowest ebb of misery but rather
just when improvement began. One might be tempted to think that

the consciousness of inequality grew as the inequality itself was reduced—but it is nothing like so simple as that. There is an armor of insensitivity worn by the dominant group so habitually that they do not think of the subordinate group as persons and this may be reciprocated for a long time so completely that the subordinates do not think of the dominant as people either and simply do not compare their own situation with their masters. But once the idea is introduced that *I* could have what *he* has, then resentment begins. Habit of mind, the possibility of change, any stress on common humanity—will therefore be high on our list of factors in the relationship between actual inequality and the conscious resentment of it. Again, any expectations that are roused and then thwarted will be an immediate irritant. A year spent in discussing Human Rights will sharpen expectations considerably.

We may say then that the passivity of the masses through most of history has been due to the limited range of groups with whom people compare themselves and their limited expectations. And very often their religion or the philosophy of their society has led them to believe that their deprivations were due to divine ordinance or divine displeasure or that it was a moral duty to endure them with resignation.

Let us go back to the point in human history when equality became not merely something that prophets and philosophers talked about, but a social principle proclaimed by two sovereign states and enshrined in their constitutions. We have seen that at one stage human progress depended on specialization, obedience, order, stratification; now progress comes to depend on invention, inspiration, on individual insight, all that is at enmity with regimentation. I spoke of great regimented empires which seemed an essential stage in progress; there were other societies in whose case regimentation was necessary to combine military efficiency with racial supremacy —Sparta, Prussia, South Africa. But one can in the broadest terms say that by 1789 the ideological tide had turned, the curve had passed its apogee, and it became increasingly difficult—at least, in public—to defend inequality and hierarchical organization on a basis of status by birth.

The open society had been proclaimed—and its enemies were forced to declare themselves too. Change in terms of men's lives was slow to take effect and contrary movements still occurred. In the realm of ideas, Darwin's discoveries provided useful ammunition to the enemies of the open society; if natural selection was the method of evolution, it was justifiable by analogy with nature to exploit and even exterminate any population that you could, because the very fact that you could do it demonstrated that you were better fitted to survive. Such ideas are false because man is not in a state of nature but must live in society; they were however reinforced by ideas about the breeding of domestic animals. In the seventy-five years or so before *The Origin of Species,* selective breeding had more than doubled the weight of domestic sheep— and facts of this kind helped people to attach an importance to hereditary distinction which was convenient for those who had it. This idea too was quite erroneous, because the mating choices of aristocrats have not always been directed to socially valuable qualities.

Another counter-movement was the colonial expansion of the late nineteenth century, which carried automatically the germs that were bound to destroy it. Colonial expansion was possible because the nations of Northwestern Europe had begun to evolve a new kind of society that was more individualist and self-reliant than any that had yet existed. Unless they solved the colonial problem by extermination, they could not help teaching the people they dominated the Greco-Judaist idea on which their own society was based; the settlers they exported took it with them. So in one colony after another leaders sprang up who in the name of liberty claimed national equality. But these new societies were sometimes at a stage of development in which much greater specialization was still needed; sometimes they were confronted by natural obstacles which demanded a high degree of cooperation—and therefore regimentation; often they were divided ethnically into groups at different levels of development and between whom there was little communication. However heroic an idealist the leader, he could seldom achieve internal unity, let alone equality. George Washington could not achieve equality for the Negro or unite with the Indian; Simon Bolivar could achieve neither for the peon on the hacienda, nor Nehru for the untouchables. There will long be a temptation in the new states of Africa to put the requirements of material progress, of mastering the environment, of defeating poverty and disease, before the ideals of liberty and social justice. But this is not likely to diminish the leaders' insistence on liberty from foreign interference or social justice *between* nations.

We are concerned not with one but with two curves—one showing the trend of human societies as between stratification and the principles of the French Revolution, the other between actual inequality and conscious resentment of it. Resentment on the whole tends to grow as extreme poverty is left behind but by no means in a smooth curve; even more important elements in its growth are wider comparisons and any indication that change is possible. And at the moment everything points to increasing comparison between the lot of the ordinary man in different societies. There is radio and television. Leaders are bound to travel; Asian and African leaders are constantly in New York, London or Paris. They know what medical care, nutritional standards, education, are like at home. And we bring it home to them; we build a steel and glass three-million-pound teaching hospital at Ibadan while a hundred miles away in the bush people have to make a twelve-hour journey for any medical help—and even then there are no anaesthetics, primitive sterilization of instruments, no light but a smoky paraffin lamp. And the villagers of Africa and Asia, who crowd in to the new sprawling cities, no longer believe that their hardships occur because they have offended a tribal god, or even that they are the result of sins in a previous life. They believe increasingly that they can be avoided, while their leaders have every motive for uniting them in a common purpose and distracting them from present misery by comparisons with peoples elsewhere.

So far I have been deliberately vague in speaking about "equality" and "liberty." These have usually been vague ideas. One cannot suppose that sansculotte mobs defined liberty, fraternity or equality more precisely than Swahili-speakers defined *uhuru* in the 1950's. But it is quite clear that there is, first, a whole group of "just rights" which, when they become "legal rights," constitute what the more comfortable in Britain and America would call freedom—freedom of movement, speech, marriage, religion, freedom from arbitrary arrest and interference by the police; these may almost be defined as what is denied to an African in South Africa. The only *equality* here implied is equality before the law and I suspect that even in Britain and America the less equal among us today regard this as a rather hollow kind of freedom. In Harlem or the East End of London, equality before the law is not much help if you live in a room infested with bugs, where rats bite your baby in the cradle, where the roof leaks and you have to share the privy with several other families.

Can you have *both* freedom and equality? And if not, which do you prefer? Citizens of the United States, as a people, are interested in freedom, but inequality of wealth is tremendous; the U.S.S.R. is a society which lays great stress, at least in its professions, on equality—but not so much on freedom.

We all know today that freedom—in the sense of "civil rights," "human rights," "independence," *uhuru*—is only the beginning. If the lion and the lamb are equally free before the law, it will go hard with the lamb. Can we go a little further towards defining the kinds of inequality that are most intolerable? The first step is to achieve the human rights—negative though we now see them to be—that were fought for from Magna Carta to the march on Washington—the rights that the laissez-faire philosophers would have demanded. But you may have all these and still suffer from inequality in esteem, in wealth and in power.

Clearly, the relative importance of these three dimensions of inequality will vary with the circumstances. If rats are biting the baby and the roof leaks, your first rational choice—one might suppose—will be to get better quarters. In fact of course your choice is unlikely to be rational and, if the rational course is difficult, you are likely to fall back on drugs or drink. But once you are over the worst—with a sound roof over your head and enough to eat—I believe that the order in which these three kinds of inequality should be put in terms of rousing resentment is esteem, wealth, power.

During the ill-fated experiment of the Federation of Rhodesia and Nyasaland, I used to meet many white men who stressed the economic advantages that Federation would produce—gross domestic product, national income, personal income, wages—all these would rise and surely Africans could see—they would say—that this is the prelude to all progress. But Africans from Zambia and Malawi, without exception, used different language. We prefer freedom to gold, they would say. We know that, in the Federation, Southern Rhodesia is the boss; we know that there is no black man in the Southern Rhodesian Parliament; we know, when we go there, that we are looked down on; the country is divided into two parts and in one part we are on sufferance; we are allowed to work but that is about all. This was the kind of thing they said. What they wanted was parity of esteem and Nkrumah's saying about seeking the political kingdom first is not inconsistent with this. He believed that political independence was the first necessary step—but the *goal* was equality of esteem. The desire for power is of course immensely strong in some people but in my view is much less widely distributed than the desire for esteem. Many people are content to be led; few indeed are content to be despised.

In the United States, where there is great inequality in wealth, there is something much nearer parity of esteem—among white people that is—than in Britain and this is probably one reason why there is not more resentment among white people about inequality in wealth. But this very fact adds steam to the Negro's resentment that *he* is left out. There is a growing impatience even in Britain—

and still speaking of white people—at inequality in esteem; but as soon as we turn to nonwhites and to the so-called developing countries, the demand becomes a torrent.

It lies behind the talk of African socialism, of Nègritude, of Black Power and of the "search for an identity." And I ask you to note specially two features of it. First, it is not merely that reference groups are widening—that is, people are comparing their lot with that of people with whom they would never have made any comparison fifty years ago. It is also that there is a determination to construct one's own norms and values rather than take them at second-hand from someone else. I have argued elsewhere at greater length that the Black Muslims and Black Power are symptoms of something that is likely to grow and that will not be confined to the United States—a revolt against the nineteenth century assumption —made by British and French colonialists as well as American whites—that it was all a matter of time and education and that gradually the rest of the world would come to behave just like people of Northwest European stock. Some Negro intellectuals are now saying passionately that they have no intention of doing anything of the kind; other Negroes, in a variety of less sophisticated ways, are showing by action a similar determination. So are the new nations of Africa. This is the appeal of Communism in Asia. Whatever we may think, I believe that there is a widespread feeling in Asia that Russia and China *stand* for social justice and that America and Britain do not.

And the second point, arising from this, is that there is likely to be, as I have already hinted, a great deal of what to comfortable people will seem irrational expression of this emotional protest and demand. Sometimes it is little more than a wail of anguish that is voiced; it suggests no solution, it sees no way out. It utters its pain, its humiliation; that is all. But that the expression is irrational does not mean that the grievance is illegitimate.

Through all I have said runs an implication that in many people's minds there is such a concept as social injustice and that most societies fall short of achieving it. I am not going to try to define social justice, but I do want to refer to one theory or model of social justice; it seems to me inadequate for reasons I shall give, but it does provide an imaginative exercise which is worth making. What is suggested is that one should imagine a group of rational beings who are about to enter into a contract with each other to found and operate a state—for which they will draw up a blueprint in advance with stations in life for all. But no one knows which will be *his* station in life until after the plans are made. It is just if you would be ready to take the station your enemy would allot you. I do not think this makes a complete model because it is based on the idea of "rational beings in a state of nature" and I doubt whether this expression has any meaning. No human being is wholly rational and every human being has been brought up in a society; the assumptions of that society are bound to color his views. The judgments I think would be made by a "rational being in a state of nature" are in fact my judgments. They are subjective. Still, as an imaginative exercise, it is worth using the model. And it is easy to be sure that if there was any likelihood of my being assigned to Harlem—or say, to being a Pakistani carder in the woolen mills of Bradford in Yorkshire—I should stipulate for a good many changes in the society I was about to join. I should also want changes in British society if I knew I was to be transformed into a Durham coalminer or indeed to almost any other category than that to which I belong—professional middle-class with a knack when young for passing useful examinations and therefore with some freedom of choice about working at things which interest me.

As I have said, I am not satisfied with this model of social justice, but I believe—and I emphasize that the judgment is subjective—that whatever criterion we adopt for social justice, neither Britain nor America can yet be regarded as socially just societies, while it is still less possible to suppose that there is social justice in the society of nations, as between the ex-untouchable in the slums of Calcutta and the Harvard graduate.

There are some rather unpalatable consequences to this. I have already suggested that every step towards reducing inequality is liable to increase resentment at what remains. But one can be more specific than this. The very institutions that need to be done away with if society is to be just are often those which have maintained its stability. That is why the French and Russian Revolutions had to destroy so much of value and take so many lives. That is why African leaders today are so impatient with us—the comfortable—when we talk about law and order in South Africa and Rhodesia, when we shudder at the thought of violence. What you call law and order, they say, is brutal violence enthroned and the time is past when it can be dethroned by anything but violence. Peru again is a society where it is hard to see gradualism succeeding. And I am constantly hearing that in the United States there is growing agreement that progress occurs only where there is conflict and confrontation.

It is sometimes assumed that the dominant culture—Spanish in most of South America, Anglo-Saxon in most of North America—

will spread steadily in the course of time and that with advancing industrialization racial barriers will diminish. But there is evidence to suggest the contrary. In industry, management follows local custom rather than leading it and increasing competition for jobs may well exacerbate opposition between races rather than reduce it. There are also grounds for supposing that color consciousness is likely to increase in the cities of Latin America as other criteria for personal status disappear. Nor is it a safe assumption that two societies which have been long in contact will fuse or that it will become increasingly easier to integrate members of one into the other; the reverse may well be the case and it may be much easier to integrate detached representatives of a wholly unknown culture. Consider the relations of Yoruba, Ibo and Hausa in Nigeria; of French and English speaking Canadians; of Creole and East Indian in Guyana.

It remains to ask three questions, with two of which I can only deal in a form so condensed as to be almost ludicrous. First, what kind of society do we regard as just? And what is likely to be the cost of moving towards it—and perhaps even more important— what is the cost of *not* moving towards it?

As to the first, this is a question on which judgments have to be subjective. But it seems to me clear that "human rights"—the basic laissez-faire rights of a legal equality, freedom of speech and move- ment—are not enough. True, it is a first step in each sovereign society to translate them from "just rights" into "legal rights." And as we know, this is a big enough step; to get these bare minimum rights for women, slaves, ethnic minorities, refugees, immigrants, in every sovereign state is a wild enough dream. But, I repeat, it is not enough. The centuries of humiliation, the conviction of inferior- ity, cannot be overcome in a weekend; equality in law does not mean equality in esteem, in wealth, or in power. In these three dimensions, too, certain minimum levels have to be established in a just society.

Even in the England of the Speenhamland Poor Laws, a century and a half ago, it was not believed to be just that a man should die in the streets of hunger. Today we go further and say that there are certain minimum standards of education, of legal help when in trouble, of medical care, of support in old age, which the state ought to provide for everyone. And there is a certain minimum of outward esteem too which we must enforce by laws against gross discrimination; there is a minimum share in power which we insist on too, the chance of registering approval or disapproval for the national government *and* the local unit of government and at least a formal opportunity to be elected to posts of responsibility. Emphasis differs and democratic governments in Europe tend to put the economic minimum relatively higher than the United States, where so high an emphasis is put on incentive and individual competition; in esteem the minimum—for white people—is lower in Europe. But I think that a minimum in all three dimensions is basic to any modern concept of a just state. It implies that there will have to be benevolent discrimination; in an attempt to undo two thousand years of injustice, the Government of India, for example, has now given half a million scholarships to the former untouchables.

But what happens *above* these minimum standards? Here I suggest that there is commonly a gross over-simplification in the picture commonly presented of any complex society. "All the many colored beads are strung up on one vertical string whereas the data and relevant questions indicate the need for several strings, each for one color of bead," wrote Wright Mills in 1963 [3]—but I would go further and suggest that the beads change color and move from one string to another. To change the metaphor, the two societies I know best—England and India—are often described as though they consisted of static tiers or layers, like geological formations, but are in fact more like a shoal of fish, in three dimensions not one, the whole group moving as a body, within which one fish moves up or down or sideways, forward relative to the whole or back; further, the fish in my picture are groups of human beings who may come together for a particular purpose but dissolve and form new groups for different purposes.

If a man's ranking is high in every grouping or dimension, that is a stratified society, but in a complex modern society this is increasingly seldom the case. Fifty years ago in Southern India, the ownership of land in many villages was concentrated in the hands of a group of Brahmans who had also a virtual monopoly of education and government employment and the highest social and ritual prestige. Today they have lost their monopoly of land and education and in respect of political power are at a definite disadvantage. Something similar is happening to the former English aristocracy, who enjoy a kind of ritual prestige in certain contexts, which is beginning to be something of a disability in politics and for certain kinds of employment; something of the kind, again, is taking place for white people in Barbados, where to be white is a disadvantage in politics but still an advantage in some other circumstances.

It may seem fanciful to compare this with the President of a Bank who at his golf club is a rabbit; he will not be treated with so little esteem as a rabbit who is not a Bank President, but he does surely for this one purpose of golf accept a different ranking. And it seems to me healthy and just if there are many such systems of ranking and if the same person is not always at the top. But the society is still unjust if one system of reckoning overrides all others and is not related to contribution to the common good and personal effort.·

A just society, then, is one in which there will be enforceable minimum standards in esteem, in wealth and in power, and a variety of ways of winning esteem and admiration beyond the minimum.

What is the cost of moving towards such a society? And of *not* moving? The two are almost inseparable. The years of acquiescence are over and the price we are going to pay—whatever we do—will be to see, *within* the sovereign state, the symptoms of social disease increasing as every layer of society compares its lot with wider and wider circles and increasingly rejects the norms and values which have held together the unjust society. And the deprived will throw out a great many lively and healthy babies with the bath water. *Between* sovereign states, even more searching comparisons will be made by the leaders; it will often be in their interest to divert attention from internal problems by encouraging jealousy against an outside target. Racial hostility, as the most emotional of all divisions between human groups, will provide the easiest antagonism to encourage. In a world in which the bomb has made international cooperation vital to survival, the work not only of the United Nations, but of its technical agencies, will be hindered at every turn by jealousy and suspicion. We have only to look at the Middle East to see how easily and how dangerously envy of the technically advanced can bedevil international affairs.

No one can tell how world events will develop; one extreme view is to emphasize poverty in the nonwhite world, hunger, growing population, increasing resentment at white wealth, and to see in the future either a world war on racial lines or an epidemic of revolutions. At the other extreme of the ideological spectrum, it is possible to argue, with more cynicism and perhaps more realism, that Russia and the United States will be driven closer to each other by fear of nuclear war and by hostility to China, and will establish a working truce as regards nuclear war. But this may not exclude a succession of peripheral wars between puppets.

The first of these views underestimates the importance of power and of modern weapons; the second underestimates the psychological consequences of continued inequality in human rights and parity of esteem. But the policy of the United States and of Britain at the moment surely pays insufficient attention to the latter factors. All the probabilities suggest that to raise the minimum of wealth in the poor nations will increase their resentment, particularly as the rich nations get richer still.

All I have said underlines the need for a long-sighted thoughtful approach, for much sympathy and forbearance. I cannot pretend that these are likely to be forthcoming. It seems far more probable that for some time to come, bitterness will grow on both sides; the intemperate expression of just grievances will breed angry recriminations; isolated acts of violence will lead to riots. "Increasing polarization" is the jargon phrase. It will be increasingly difficult to remember that the "just rights" which Britain and America have both stood for—although they are not enough—are yet something of which we must not lose sight in trying to get more.

The enemies of the open society are still powerful and the cards are stacked heavily against any easy assumptions that time will solve our problems. This does not mean that there is nothing we can do; it does mean that our outlook has to be radical. All that we are doing increases the likelihood of instability if we do it *slowly*. We have to move very fast to beat the tide of resentment and much hard thinking is needed as to *how* we can move fast. Human rights are not enough without enforceable minimum standards of esteem, of standards of living, of share in power. This means, within the sovereign state, far more social security than most of the free world has yet been ready to contemplate. And between sovereign states there is another tremendous consequence. Justice at present only has meaning within a sovereign state and international justice can only have meaning within a world state.

To achieve either of these goals involves great risk to the freedom of the individual human spirit. But it is a risk that has to be taken.

## References

1. Sir Henry Maine, *Ancient Law* (London: Oxford University Press, 1931), last words of Chapter V.
2. W. G. Runciman, *Relative Deprivation and Social Justice* (London: Routledge and Kegan Paul, 1966).
3. C. Wright Mills, "Social Life of a Modern Community," in *Power, Politics and People*, I. Horowitz, ed. (New York: Ballantine Books, 1963).

# NEGRO, JEWISH, AND ITALIAN HAIR: A SLIGHTLY BRISTLY REPLY TO THE AMERICAN BARBER'S MOST BARBAROUS COMPLAINT

*Milton Mayer*

Milton Mayer, journalist and teacher, has written *What Can a Man Do?*

I left my *Britannica* in my other suit, but it says here in the *Columbia Encyclopedia* that "age, illness or worry lessens the pigmentary secretion and the hair becomes gray or white." That is not what I wanted to know. (And I'll bet that the worry part is spurious.) What I wanted to know is why the barber in Madison, New Jersey, finds it so difficult to cut a Negro's hair or, as the barber puts it, Negro hair. Maybe the *Britannica* defines Negro hair, or even Italian hair; the barber's name is Mr. Gatti.

Mr. Gatti says he doesn't have the necessary special tools. Besides, he says, he doesn't know how.

I have heard tell of several other barbers in the North—where we wag our heads over the barbarousness of the Mississippians—who confess the same melancholy lack of equipment and knowhow. Is the Madison barber barbarous, or do you need a tinsnips or a combine to cut a Negro's hair, plus an M.A. in Negro Hair-Cutting from a Barber University?

I don't really want to know, to be perfectly frank and tell you the honest truth. The reason I don't really want to know is that my own hair is a little kinky (besides being gray or white from age, illness, or worry). More than a little.

Ma used to say, "I declare, that boy's hair is like sofa-stuffing." Then she would turn fondly, and with fond reproach, to my big brother Howard and say, "I don't know why you have to put that awful grease on that nice *straight* hair of yours."

My very own big brother, same genes and jeans as I; why was his hair straight and mine kinky?

By the time I was working at Mandel Brothers on Saturdays,

and reading the works of their grandfather Gregor the rest of the week and learning about dominants and recessives in the common or garden variety of pea, I was thinking about other things. I still am. Other things are kinky, too, but they're no reflection on me or my ancestry.

My ancestry is Jewish. I am, or would be, ashamed to say so, if my big brother's weren't, too; I don't mind making it rough for him, him and his nice straight hair.

Most of the Jews I know have kinky tendencies—and not just in the hair. But my mother didn't and my big brother didn't. Why, my mother was President of Lincoln Lodge, United Order of True Sisters, and my big brother was Student Colonel of the Chicago ROTC. Can you get any unkinkier than that?

I even know some Jewesses (as the *goyim* call Jews of the female persuasion) whose hair is so miserably straight and *goyish* that they cry into their pillows.

Nearly all of the Negroes I know have hair like mine, or like (or as) mine used to be. More so. And the Negro press is full of ads for hair straighteners and empty of ads for hair curlers. So, while I'm willing to concede nothing against the Jews, I think I'd have to plead the Negroes guilty to kinky hair on the whole. I just don't see Old Black Joe with a ducktail cut, and though I hesitate, with Burke, to draw an indictment against an entire people, I'm afraid that the grizzled poll is a characteristic trait of the Negroes, as *Kadavergehorsamkeit** is of the Germans.

I don't know why Negroes' hair is like that, or why mine is. I know why Negroes are supposed to have dark skins and wide nostrils (and why they perspire freely, if they do), because I'm an old Equatorialist and I know that a dark skin and a wide nostril or two (and a well-developed set of sweat glands) stand a man in good stead at the Equator and would play hob with him at the Pole; a physiological adaptation. I savvy the white pith helmet, too, and would not be found dead (by the British) without one. But why the hair? What's it an adaptation to? Maybe it's simply that kinky hair has a proclivity to mat and provide a salubrious air space between the hair and the head; but thermodynamics is not my Equatorial line.

Funny: the barber at Fifty-first and Calumet never boggled at cutting my hair when Pa took me in and sat me on the board the barber put over the arms of the common man's throne. The barber did say he couldn't cut my hair and, what was more, he threatened

---

*"Dead man's obedience,"—*The Editors.*

to cut my ear off, but not because it (or I) was Jewish but because I wouldn't stop squirming. (The reason I wouldn't stop squirming was that I was afraid he'd cut my ear off. You can't do anything with grown-ups.)

Now I'm a grown-up myself, and as grown as I shall ever be, and the price of a store-bought haircut has risen in inverse proportion to the quantity of hair I bring to the barber, and Pa is no longer here to pay the two dollars or two-and-a-quarter (plus a stiletto in the back if you don't leave a tip). The barbers have priced me out of the market. And themselves; the one special tool they do have is the petard. The one special tool I don't have is the money.

So along about fifteen or twenty years ago I impressed my darling Little Julie into child labor. I got a mail-order clippers which was advertised for hair generically; I couldn't find an advertisement for a special tool for Negro, Italian, or Jewish hair. Little Julie charged me what the traffic would bear, which was a quarter. Every so often, as she whisked the clippers, she'd say, "Oops—nicked ya." There was blood on the saddle and blood on the ground and a great big puddle of blood all around. But the price was right.

Then Little Julie took off—as don't they all?—and a neighbor lady undertook to shear me for half-a-dollar and no contusions and abrasions. That was the best deal I ever had, except for Germany after the war (one DM, or twenty-four cents). And the German barber had been taught by the Nazis to keep his mouth shut. (Under the Nazis the Germans even learned to keep their mouths shut at the dentist's.) The next-best deal was, and is, Prague, where for five Kcs (or thirty-five cents) you get the full treatment plus the lowdown on conditions, Czech barbers being slower to learn than German barbers.

The full treatment in my case consists of plenty short all around, and bone dry. It's been years since I've used a comb and/or brush. And you can't tell whether my hair is—or in places was—kinky or straight. The saving on time and money, and on overt anti-Semitism, is considerable. Sometimes I'd scrounge an extra half-dollar's worth out of the neighbor lady by letting it go for a couple of months and getting two haircuts for the price of one. On those long-haired occasions she'd say, "Why, you're almost shaggy," and then, "You know, your hair's really kinky, what there is of it." But she never said it was hard to cut.

The neighbor lady died a little while back. She was a very dear friend, and I remembered that my ancestors let their hair grow in mourning for the dead; but I knew that the neighbor lady, who wouldn't stand for any such antics in life, would resist them even in death. I dismissed the temptation. But I was then confronted by the appalling vision of the words above the portal of the barber shop: "Abandon All Hope of Getting Out for Under Two-Fifty, Ye Who Enter Here."

I submitted myself, as laboratory material, to a Barber College. Short and snappy all around, and the kind of rough work you expect of graduate students these days. It's a clip joint—I have to pay *them* seventy-five cents—but what can a man do?

There's an inner conflict besides. A man of a certain age or condition *doesn't* want to have to get a haircut and *does* want to have a little more hair grow on top. A fellow I met in Europe told me to rub Pantene for the Hair into my hair to make it grow "just a little." There is plain Pantene and Pantene *gras* (or greasy); he recommended the greasy. Putting great store, as I do, by the ancient wisdom of the East, I now rub Pantene into my hair (or scalp). It does not reduce the total area of my tonsure, but it makes me feel that I'm doing something to offset age, illness, and worry, and once in a while a hair comes out. Kinky.

Why do Jews tend to be bald? Why do Negroes tend not to be, except for Old Black Joe who had no hair on the top of his head in the place where the hair ought to be?

What is there about Negroes?

There must be something wrong with them.

Don't tell me there's something wrong with Jews and nothing wrong with Negroes.

And if the *Columbia Encyclopedia* can get away with saying that worry lessens the pigmentary secretion, why can't I get away with saying that the pigmentary secretion keeps the hair straight? I think that my hair is kinky from worry. I worried a great deal as a very small child. Jews are worriers. Italians aren't worriers and their hair is straight; I'll bet that Mr. Gatti's hair is straight. But why should Negroes' hair be kinky? What have *they* got to worry about?

The American Indian, now—there's a man with worries, as any man would be who was disappearing altogether. But his hair is straight. And black. At Mandel Brothers we'd have called him a Mandelian sport and sent him to the Sportswear Section.

*Why are Negroes such good barbers?*

(And where do they go for haircuts?)

The hair line recedes, the color line abides. I'm glad I'm at least white, but I wish I were a white Aryan gentile Protestant native-born red-blooded American. With a hood to cover my hair.

# Chapter Thirteen

# The Possibilities

# of Directing

# Human Evolution

Technological competence has put man in the uncomfortable position of being able to control phenomena he still incompletely understands. Although there is no logical necessity or obligation to intervene in a given natural process simply because it is now possible to do so, there does seem to be a very great cultural compulsion to apply technological and scientific capabilities as soon as they are developed. The hazard of such practice stems from the fact that the scientific disciplines are quite clearly separate from the humanities and social sciences. In the real world such a distinction of course does not exist, so that technological or applied science can have vast socio-cultural repercussions. Man has always tampered with nature—tools, fire, clothing, shelter, etc., are examples—so that the only difference between this practice in the past and in the present is that today our power is greater and the effects of its use are far more rapid and far-reaching.

The fact is we have arrived at a point where we are increasingly capable of directing our own evolution—at least the technological means for doing so exist. Whether the social skills are equal to the task is another problem. And whether we fully understand the consequences of what can be done technologically is also in doubt. Yet one thing seems eminently clear: once started on the road to control of nature—a road embarked on by our ancestors millions of years ago—there is no stopping. The fact of culture has forever excluded the possibility that the species can survive by "letting nature take its course." The question is not whether we *should* regulate biological and ecological processes. The question is how we should exercise our control, a question that requires an answer framed in a multi-disciplinary context, a synthesis which for the present, at any rate, we seem not to be able to create. Anthropology, with feet in both the natural and social sciences and an insistence on a cross-cultural perspective, ought to have something to offer. It should be concerned with the future of man.

# ON RE-DOING MAN: THE ETHICS OF GENETIC ENGINEERING

*Kurt Hirschhorn*

Kurt Hirschhorn is chief of the Division of Medical Genetics at the Mount Sinai School of Medicine in New York.

The past 20 years and, more particularly, the past five years have seen an exponential growth of scientific technology. The chemical structure of the hereditary material and its language have essentially been resolved. Cells can be routinely grown in test tubes by tissue culture techniques. The exact biochemical mechanisms of many hereditary disorders have been clarified. Computer programs for genetic analysis are in common use. All of these advances and many others have inevitably led to discussions and suggestions for the modification of human heredity, both in individuals and in populations: genetic engineering.

One of the principal concerns of the pioneers in the field is the problem of the human genetic load, that is, the frequency of disadvantageous genes in the population. Each of us carries between three and eight genes which, if present in double dose in the off-

From *Commonweal*, May 17, 1968, pp. 257–61. Reprinted by permission.

spring of two carriers of identical genes, would lead to severe genetic abnormality, or even to death, of the affected individual before or after birth. In view of the rapid medical advances in the treatment of such diseases, it is likely that affected individuals will be able to reproduce more frequently than in the past. Therefore, instead of a loss of genes due to death or sterility of the abnormal, the mutant gene will be transmitted to future generations in a slowly but steadily increasing frequency. This is leading the pessimists to predict that we will become a race of genetic cripples requiring a host of therapeutic crutches. The optimists, on the other hand, have great faith that the forces of natural evolution will continue to select favorably those individuals who are best adapted to the then current environment. It is important to remember in this context that the "natural" environment necessarily includes manmade medical, technical and social changes.

Since it appears that at least some of the aspects of evolution and a great deal of genetic planning will be in human and specifically in scientific hands, it is crucial at this relatively early stage to consider the ethical implications of these proposed maneuvers. Few scientists today doubt the feasibility of genetic engineering, and there is considerable danger that common use of this practice will be upon us before its ethical applications are defined.

A number of different methods have been proposed for the control and modification of human hereditary material. Some of these methods are meant to work on the population level, some on the family level and others directly on the affected individual. Interest in the alteration of the genetic pool of human populations originated shortly after the time of Mendel and Darwin in the latter part of the nineteenth century. The leaders were the English group of eugenicists headed by Galton. Eugenics is nothing more than planned breeding. This technique, of course, has been successfully used in the development of hybrid breeds of cattle, corn and other food products.

Human eugenics can be positive or negative. Positive eugenics is the preferential breeding of so-called superior individuals in order to improve the genetic stock of the human race. The most famous of the many proponents of positive eugenics was the late Nobel Prize-winner Herman J. Muller. He suggested that sperm banks be established from a relatively small number of donors, chosen by some appropriate panel, and that this frozen sperm remain in storage until some future panel had decided that the chosen donors truly represented desirable genetic studs. If the decision is favorable, a relatively large number of women would be inseminated with these samples of sperm; proponents of this method hope that a better world would result. The qualifications for such a donor would include high intellectual achievement and a socially desirable personality, qualities assumed to be affected by the genetic makeup of the individual, as well as an absence of obvious genetically determined physical anomalies.

A much more common effort is in the application of negative eugenics. This is defined as the discouragement or the legal prohibition of reproduction by individuals carrying genes leading to disease or disability. This can be achieved by genetic counseling or by sterilization, either on a voluntary or enforced basis. There are, however, quite divergent opinions as to which genetic traits are to be considered sufficiently disadvantageous to warrant the application of negative eugenics.

A diametrically opposite solution is that of euthenics, which is a modification of the environment in such a way as to allow the genetically abnormal individual to develop normally and to live a relatively normal life. Euthenics can be applied both medically and socially. The prescription of glasses for nearsighted individuals is an example of medical euthenics. Special schools for the deaf, a great proportion of whom are genetically abnormal, is an example of social euthenics. The humanitarianism of such efforts is obvious, but it is exactly these types of activities that have led to the concern of the pessimists who assume that evolution has selected for the best of possible variations in man and that further accumulations of genes considered abnormal can only lead to decline.

One of the most talked about advances for the future is the possibility of altering an individual's genetic complement. Since we are well on the way to understanding the genetic code, as well as to deciphering it, it is suggested that we can alter it. This code is written in a language of 64 letters, each being determined by a special arrangement of three out of four possible nucleotide bases. A chain of these bases is called deoxyribonucleic acid or DNA and makes up the genetic material of the chromosomes. If the altered letter responsible for an abnormal gene can be located and the appropriate nucleotide base substituted, the corrected message would again produce its normal product, which would be either a structurally or enzymologically functional protein.

Another method of providing a proper gene, or code word, to an individual having a defect has been suggested from an analysis of viral behavior in bacteria. It has long been known that certain types of viruses can carry genetic information from one bacterium to another or instruct a bacterium carrying it to produce what is essentially a viral product. Viruses are functional only when they live in a host cell. They use the host's genetic machinery to translate their own genetic codes. Viruses living parasitically in human cells can cause diseases such as poliomyelitis and have been implicated in the causation of tumors. Other viruses have been shown to live in cells and be reproduced along with the cells without causing damage either to the cell or to the organism. If such a harmless virus either produces a protein that will serve the function of one lacking in an affected individual, or if it can be made to carry the genetic material required for such functions into the cells of the affected individual, it could permanently cure the disease without additional therapy. If carried on to the next generation, it could even prevent the inheritance of the disease.

## Transplanting Nuclei

An even more radical approach has been outlined by Lederberg. It has become possible to transplant whole nuclei, the structures which carry the DNA, from one cell to another. It has become easy to grow cells from various tissues of any individual in tissue culture. Such tissue cultures can be examined for a variety of genetic markers and thereby screened for evidence of new mutations. Lederberg suggests that it would be possible to use nuclei from such cells derived from known human individuals, again with favorable genetic traits, for the asexual human reproduction of replicas of the individuals whose nuclei are being used. For example, a nucleus from a cell of the chosen individual could be transplanted into a human egg whose own nucleus has been removed. This egg, implanted into a womb, could then divide just like a normal fertilized egg to produce an individual genetically identical to the one whose nucleus was used. One of the proposed advantages of such a method would be that, as in positive eugenics, one could choose the traits that appear to be favorable, and do so with greater efficiency by eliminating the somewhat randomly chosen female parent necessary for the sperm bank approach. Another advantage is that one can mimic what has developed in plants as a system for the preservation of genetic stability over limited periods of time. Many plants reproduce intermittently by such vegetative or parthenogenetic mechanisms, always followed by periods of sexual reproduction for the purpose of elimination of disadvantageous mutants and increase in variability.

Another possibility derives from two other technological advances. Tissue typing, similar to blood typing, and some immunological tricks have made it possible to transplant cells, tissues and organs from one individual to another with reasonably long-term success. Over the past few years scientists have also succeeded in producing cell hybrids containing some of the genetic material from each of two cell types either from two different species or two different individuals from the same species. Very recently Weiss and Green at New York University have succeeded in hybridizing normal human culture cells with cells from a long established mouse tissue culture line. Different products from such fusions contain varying numbers of human chromosomes and, therefore, varying amounts of human genes. If such hybrids can be produced which carry primarily that genetic information which is lacking or abnormal in an affected individual, transplantation of these cultured cells into the individual may produce a correction of his defect.

These are the proposed methods. It is now fair to consider the question of feasibility. Feasibility must be considered not only from a technical point of view; of equal importance are the effects of each of these methods on the evolution of the human population and the effect of evolution upon the efficacy of the method. In general, it can be stated that most of the proposed methods either are now or will in the not too distant future be technically possible. We are, therefore, not dealing with hypothesis in science fiction but with scientific reality. Let us consider each of the propositions independently.

Positive eugenics by means of artificial insemination from sperm banks has been practiced successfully in cattle for many years. Artificial insemination in man is an everyday occurrence. But what are some of its effects? There is now ample evidence in many species, including man, of the advantages for the population of individual genetic variation, mainly in terms of flexibility of adaptation to a changing environment. Changes in environment can produce drastic effects on some individuals, but a population which contains many genetic variations of that set of genes affected by the particular environmental change, will contain numerous individuals who can adapt. There is also good evidence that individuals who carry two different forms of the same gene, that is, are heterozygous, appear to have an advantage. This is even true if that gene in double dose, that is, in the homozygous state, produces a severe disease. For example, individuals homozygous for the gene coding for sickle cell hemoglobin invariably develop sickle cell anemia which is generally fatal before the reproductive years. Heterozygotes for the gene are, however, protected more than normals from the effects of the most malignant form of malaria. It has been shown that women who carry the gene in single dose have a higher fertility in malarial areas than do normals. This effect is well known to agricultural geneticists and is referred to as hybrid vigor. Fertilization of many women by sperm from few men will have an adverse effect on both of these advantages of genetic variability since the population will tend to be more and more alike in their genetic characteristics. Also, selection for a few genetically advantageous factors will carry with it selection for a host of other genes present in the same individuals, genes whose effects are unknown when present in high numbers in the population. Therefore, the interaction between positive eugenics and evolution makes this method not feasible on its own.

## Abnormal Offspring

Negative eugenics is, of course, currently practiced by most human geneticists. It is possible to detect carriers of many genes, which when inherited from both parents will produce abnormal offspring. Parents, both of whom carry such a gene, can be told that they have a one in four chance of producing such an abnormal child. Individuals who carry chromosomal translocations are informed that they have a high risk of producing offspring with congenital malformations and mental retardation. But how far can one carry out such a program? Some states have laws prescribing the sterilization of individuals who are mentally retarded to a certain degree. These laws are frequently based on false information regarding the heredity of the condition. The marriage of people with reduced intelligence is forbidden in some localities, again without adequate genetic information. While the effects of negative eugenics may be quite desirable in individual families with a high risk of known hereditary diseases, it is important to examine its effects on the general population.

These effects must be looked at individually for conditions determined by genes that express themselves in a single dose (dominant), in double dose (recessive) and those which are due to an interaction of many genes (polygenic inheritance). With a few exceptions, dominant diseases are rare and interfere severely with reproductive ability. They are generally maintained in the population by new mutations. Therefore, there is either no need or essentially no need for discouraging these individuals from reproduction. Any discouragement, if applicable, will be useful only within that family but not have any significance for the general population. One possible exception is the severe neurological disorder, Huntington's chorea, which does not express itself until most of the patient's children are already born. In such a situation it may be useful to advise the child of an affected individual that he has a 50 per cent chance of developing the disease and a 25 per cent chance of any of his children being affected. Negative eugenics in such a case would at least keep the gene frequency at the level usually maintained by new mutations.

The story is quite different for recessive conditions. Although detection of the clinically normal carriers of these genes is currently possible only for a few diseases, the techniques are rapidly developing whereby many of these conditions can be diagnosed even if the gene is present only in single dose and will not cause the disease. Again, with any particular married couple it would be possible to advise them that they are both carriers of the gene and that any child of theirs would have a 25 per cent chance of being affected. However, any attempt to decrease the gene frequency of these common genetic disorders in the population by prevention of fertility of all carriers would be doomed to failure. First, we all carry between three and eight of these genes in single doses. Secondly, for many of these conditions, the frequency in the population of carriers is about one in 50 or even greater. Prevention of fertility for even one of these disorders would stop a sizable proportion of the population from reproducing and for all of these disorders would prevent the entire human population from having any children. Reduction in fertility of a sizable proportion of the population would also prevent the passing on to future generations of a great number of favorable genes and would, therefore, interfere with the selective aspects of evolution which can only function to improve the population within a changing environment by selecting from a gene pool containing enormous variability. It has now been shown that in fact no two individuals, with the exception of identical twins, are likely to be genetically and biochemically identical, thereby allowing the greatest possible adaptation to changing environment and the most efficient selection of the fittest.

The most complex problem is that of negative eugenics for traits determined by polygenic inheritance. Characteristics inherited in this manner include many measurements that are distributed over a wide range throughout the population, such as height, birth weight and intelligence. The last of these can serve as a good example of the problems encountered. Severe mental retardation in a child is not infrequently associated with perfectly normal intelligence or in some cases even superior intelligence in the parents. These cases can, *a priori*, be assumed to be due to the homozygous state, in the child, of a gene leading to mental retardation, the parents representing heterozygous carriers. On the other hand, borderline mental retardation shows a high association with subnormal intelligence in other family members. This type of deficiency can be assumed to be due to polygenic factors, more of the pertinent genes in these families being of the variety that tends to lower intelligence. However, among the offspring of these families there is also a high proportion of individuals with normal intelligence and a sprinkling of individuals with superior intelligence.

All of these comments are made with the realization that our current measurements of intelligence are very crude and cannot be compared between different population groups. It is estimated that, on the whole, people with superior intelligence have fewer offspring than do those of average or somewhat below average intelligence. If people of normal intelligence were restricted to producing only two offspring and people of reduced intelligence were by negative eugenics prevented from having any offspring at all, the result, as has been calculated by the British geneticist, Lionel Penrose, would be a gradual shift downward in the mean intelligence level of the population. This is due to the lack of replacement of intellectually superior individuals from offspring of the majority of the population, that is, those not superior in intellect.

## Current Possibilities

It can be seen, therefore, that neither positive nor negative eugenics can ever significantly improve the gene pool of the population and simultaneously allow for adequate evolutionary improvement of the human race. The only useful aspect of negative eugenics is in individual counseling of specific families in order to prevent some of the births of abnormal individuals. One recent advance in this sphere has important implications from both a genetic and a social point of view. It is now possible to diagnose genetic and chromosomal abnormalities in an unborn child by obtaining cells from the amniotic fluid in which the child lives in the mother. While the future may bring further advances, allowing one, then, to start treatment on the unborn child and to produce a functionally normal infant, the only currently possible solution is restricted to termination of particular pregnancies by therapeutic abortion. This is, of course, applied eugenics in its most extreme form.

Euthenics, the alteration of the environment to allow aberrant individuals to develop normally and to lead a normal life, is currently in use. Medical examples include special diets for children with a variety of inborn errors of metabolism who would, in the absence of such diets, either die or grow up mentally retarded. Such action, of course, requires very early diagnosis of these diseases, and programs are currently in effect to routinely examine newborns for such defects. Other examples include the treatment of diabetics with insulin and the provision of special devices for children with skeletal deformities. Social measures are of extreme importance in this regard. As has many times been pointed out by Dobzhansky, it is useless to plan for any type of genetic improvement if we do not provide an environment within which an individual can best use his strong qualities and obtain support for his weak qualities. One need only mention the availability of an environment conductive to artistic endeavor for Toulouse-Lautrec, who was deformed by an inherited disease.

The feasibility of alteration of an individual's genes by direct chemical change of his DNA is technically an enormously difficult task. Even if it became possible to do this, the chance of error would be enormous. Such an error, of course, would have the diametrically opposite effect of that desired; in other words, the individual would become even more abnormal. The introduction of corrective genetic material by viruses or transplantation of appropriately hybridized cells is technically predictable and, since it would be performed only in a single affected individual, would have no direct effect on the population. If it became widespread enough, it could, like euthenics, increase the frequency in the population of so-called abnormal genes, but if this treatment became a routine phenomenon, this would not develop into an evolutionarily disadvantageous situation. It must also be constantly kept in mind that medical advances are occurring at a much more rapid rate than any conceivable deterioration of the genetic endowment of man. It is, therefore, very likely that such corrective procedures will become commonplace long before there is a noticeable increase in the load of disadvantageous genes in the population.

The growing of human beings from cultured cells, while again possibly feasible, would on the other hand interfere with the action of evolutionary forces. There would be an increase, just as with positive eugenics, of a number of individuals who would be alike in their genetic complement with no opportunity for the high degree of genetic recombination which occurs during the formation of sperm and eggs and which is evident in the resultant progeny. This would diminish the adaptability of the population to changes in the environment and, if these genetic replicas were later permitted to return to sexual reproduction, would lead to a marked increase in homozygosity for a number of genes with the disadvantages pointed out before.

## Who Will Be the Judges?

We see, therefore, that many of the proposed techniques are feasible although not necessarily practical in producing their desired results. We may now ask the question of which of these are ethical from a humanistic point of view? Both positive and negative eugenics when applied to populations presume a judgment of what is genetically good and what is bad. Who will be the judges and where will the limit be between good and bad? We have had at least one example of a sad experience with eugenics in its application in Nazi Germany. This alone can serve as a lesson on the inability to separate science and politics. The most difficult decisions will come in defining the borderline cases. Will we breed against tallness because space requirements become more critical? Will we breed against nearsightedness because people with glasses may not make good astronauts? Will we forbid intellectually inferior individuals from procreating despite their proven ability to produce a number of superior individuals? Or should we rather provide an adequate environment for the offspring of such individuals to realize their full genetic potential?

C. C. Li, in his presidential address to the American Society of Human Genetics in 1960, pointed out the real fallacy in eugenic arguments. Man has continuously improved his environment to allow so-called inferior individuals to survive and reproduce. The movement into the cave and the putting on of clothes has protected the individual unable to survive the stress of the elements. Should we then consider that we have reached the peak of man's progress, largely determined by environmental improvements designed to increase fertility and longevity, and that any future improvements designed to permit anyone to live a normal life will only lead to deterioration? Nineteenth century scientists, including such eminent biologists as Galton, firmly believed that this peak was reached in their time. This obviously fallacious reasoning must not allow a lapse in ethical considerations by the individual and by humanity as a whole, just to placate the genetic pessimists.

The tired axiom of democracy that all men are created equal must not be considered from the geneticist's point of view, since genetically all men are created unequal. Equality must be defined purely and simply as equality of opportunity to do what one is best equipped to do. When we achieve this, the forces of natural evolution will choose those individuals best adapted to this egalitarian environment. No matter how we change the genetic make-up of individuals, we cannot do away with natural selection. We must always remember that natural selection is determined by a combination of truly natural events and the artificial modifications which we are introducing into our environment in an exponentially increasing number.

With these points in mind, we can try to decide what in all of these methods is both feasible and ethical. I believe that the only logical conclusion is that all maneuvers of genetic engineering must be judged for each individual and, in each case, must take primary consideration of the rights of the individual. This is impossible by definition in any attempt at positive eugenics. Negative eugenics in the form of intelligent genetic counseling is the answer for some. Our currently unreasonable attitude about practicing negative eugenics by means of intelligent selection for therapeutic abortion must be changed. Basic to such a change is a more accurate definition of a living human being. Such restricted uses of negative eugenics will prevent individual tragedies. Correction of unprevented genetic disease, or that due to new mutation, by introduction of new genetic material may be one answer for the future; but until such a new world becomes universally feasible, we must on the whole restrict ourselves to environmental manipulations from both the points of view of allowing affected individuals to live normally and permitting each individual to realize his full genetic potential. There is no question that genetic engineering will come about. But both the scientists directly involved and, perhaps more important, the political and social leaders of our civilization must exercise utmost caution in order to prevent genetic, evolutionary and social tragedies.

# THE UNCOMPLETED MAN

*Loren Eiseley*

Loren Eiseley is a professor of anthropology at the University of Pennsylvania. Among his books are *Darwin's Century, The Firmament of Time,* and *The Immense Journey.*

The nature into which Shakespeare's Macbeth dabbles so unsuccessfully with the aid of witchcraft, in the famous scene on the heath, is unforgettable in literature. We watch in horrified fascination the malevolent change in the character of Macbeth as he gains a dubious insight into the unfolding future—a future which we know to be self-created. This scene, fearsome enough at all times, is today almost unbearable to the discerning observer. Its power lies in its symbolic delineation of the relationship of Macbeth's midnight world to the realm of modern science—a relationship grasped by few.

The good general, Banquo, who, unlike Macbeth, is wary of such glimpses into the future as the witches have allowed the two companions, seeks to restrain his impetuous comrade. " 'Tis strange," Banquo says,

> And oftentimes, to win us to our harm
> The instruments of darkness tell us truths,
> With us with honest trifles, to betray's
> In deepest consequence.

Macbeth who, in contrast to Banquo, has immediately seized upon the self-imposed reality induced by the witches' prophecies, stumbles out of their toils at the last, only to protest in his dying hour:

> And be these juggling fiends no more believ'd . . .
> That keep the word of promise to our ear
> And break it to our hope!

Who, we may now inquire, are these strange beings who waylaid Macbeth, and why do I, who have spent a lifetime in the domain of science, make the audacious claim that this old murderous tale of the scientific twilight extends its shadow across the doorway of our modern laboratories? These bearded, sexless creatures who possess the faculty of vanishing into air or who reappear in some ultimate flame-wreathed landscape only to mock our folly, are an exteriorized portion of ourselves. They are projections from our own psyche, smoking wisps of mental vapor that proclaim our subconscious intentions and bolster them with Delphic utterances—half-truths which we consciously accept, and which then take power over us. Under the spell of such oracles we create, not a necessary or real future, but a counterfeit drawn from within ourselves, which we then superimpose, through purely human power, upon reality. Indeed one could say that these phantoms create a world which is at the same time spurious and genuine, so complex is our human destiny.

Every age has its style in these necromantic projections. The corpse-lifting divinations of the Elizabethan sorcerers have given way, in our time, to other and, at first sight, more scientific interpretations of the future. Today we know more about man, where he has come from, and what we may expect of him—or so we think. But there is one thing, in my belief, which identifies Macbeth's "juggling fiends" in any age, whether these uncanny phantoms appear as witches, star readers, or today's technologists. This quality is their claim to omniscience—an omniscience only half-stated on the basis of the past or specious present, and always lacking in genuine knowledge of the future. The leading characteristic of the future they present is its fixed, static, inflexible quality.

Such a future is fated beyond human will to change, just as Macbeth's demons, by prophecy, worked in him a transformation of character which then created inevitable tragedy. Until the appearance of the witches on the heath gave it shape, that tragedy existed only as a latent possibility in Macbeth's subconscious. Similarly, in this age, one could quote those who seek control of man's destiny by the evocation of his past. Their wizardry is deceptive because their spells are woven out of a genuine portion of reality—which, however, has taken on this always identifiable quality of fixity in an unfixed universe. The ape is always in our hearts, we are made to say, although each time a child is born something totally and genetically unique enters the universe, just as it did long ago when the great ethical leaders—Christ, the Buddha, Confucius—spoke to their followers.

Man escapes definition even as the modern phantoms in militarist garb proclaim—as I have heard them do—that man will fight from one side of the solar system to the other, and beyond. The danger, of course, is truly there, but it is a danger which, while it lies partially in what man is, lies much closer to what he chooses to believe about himself. Man's whole history is one of transcendence and of self-examination, which have led him to angelic heights of sacrifice as well as into the bleakest regions of despair. The future is not truly fixed but the world arena is smoking with the caldrons of those who would create tomorrow by evoking, rather than exorcising, the stalking ghosts of the past.

Even this past, however, has been far deeper and more pregnant with novelty than the short-time realist can envisage. As an evolutionist I never cease to be astounded by the past. It is replete with more features than one world can realize. Perhaps it was this that led the philosopher Santayana to speak of men's true natures as not adequately manifested in their condition at any given moment, or even in their usual habits. "Their real nature," he contended, "is what they would discover themselves to be if they possessed self-knowledge, or as the Indian scripture has it, if they became what they are." I should like to approach this mystery of the self, which so intrigued the great philosopher, from a mundane path strewn with the sticks and stones through which the archaeologist must pick his way.

## Contemplating the Fish

Let me illustrate what I mean by a very heavy and peculiar stone which I keep upon my desk. It has been split across; carbon black, imprinted in the gray shale, is the outline of a fish. The chemicals that composed the fish—most of them at least—are still there in the stone. They are, in a sense, imperishable. They may come and go, pass in and out of living things, trickle away in the long erosion of time. They are inanimate, yet at one time they constituted a living creature.

Often at my desk, now, I sit contemplating the fish. It does not have to be a fish. It could be the long-horned Alaskan bison on my wall. For the point is, you see, that the fish is extinct and gone, just as our massive-faced and shambling forebears of the Ice Age have vanished. The chemicals still about us here took a shape that will never be seen again so long as grass grows or the sun shines. Just once out of all time there was a pattern that we call *Bison regius,* a fish-like amphibian called *Ichthyostega,* and, at this present moment, a primate who knows, or thinks he knows, the entire score. In the past there has been armor; there have been bellowings out of throats like iron furnaces; there have been phantom lights in the dark forest, and toothed reptiles winging through the air. It has all been carbon and its compounds, the black stain running perpetually across the stone.

But though the elements are known, nothing in all those shapes is now returnable. No living chemist can shape a dinosaur, no living hand can start the dreaming tentacular extensions that characterize the life of the simplest ameboid cell. Finally, as the greatest mystery of all, I who write these words on paper, cannot establish my own reality. I am, by any reasonable and considered logic, dead. This may be a matter of concern to you reading these words, but if it is any consolation, I can assure you that you are as dead as I. For, on my office desk, to prove my words is the fossil out of the stone, and there is the carbon of life stained black on the ancient rock.

There is no life in the fossil. There is no life in the carbon in my body. As the idea strikes me—and believe me it comes as a profound shock—I run down the list of elements. There is no life in the iron, there is no life in the phosphorus, the nitrogen does not contain me, the water that soaks my tissues is not I. What am I then? I pinch my body in a kind of sudden desperation. My heart knocks, my fingers close around the pen. There is, it seems, a semblance of life here.

But the minute I start breaking this strange body down into its constituents, it is dead. It does not know me. Carbon does not speak, calcium does not remember, iron does not weep. Even if I hastily reconstitute their combinations in my mind, rebuild my arteries, and let oxygen in the grip of hemoglobin go hurrying through a thousand conduits, I have a kind of machine, but where in all this array of pipes and hurried flotsam is the dweller?

From whence, out of what steaming pools or boiling cloudbursts did he first arise? What forces can we find which brought him up the shore, sealed his body into an antique, reptilian shape and then cracked it like an egg to let a soft-furred animal with a warmer heart emerge? And we? Would it not be a good thing if man were tapped gently like a fertile egg to see what might creep out? I sometimes think of this as I handle the thick-walled skulls of the animal men who preceded us, or ponder over those remote splay-footed creatures whose bones lie deep in the world's wastelands at the very bottom of time.

## A Question at Night

With the glooms and night terrors of those vast cemeteries I have been long familiar. A precisely similar gloom enwraps the individual life of each of us. There are moments in my bed at midnight, or watching the play of moonlight on the ceiling, when this ghostliness of myself comes home to me with appalling force, when I lie tense, listening as if removed, far off, to the footfalls of my own heart, or seeing my own head on the pillow turning restlessly with the round staring eyes of a gigantic owl. I whisper "Who?" to no one but myself in the silent, sleeping house—the living house gone back to sleep with the sleeping stones, the eternally sleeping chair, the picture that sleeps forever on the bureau, the dead, also sleeping, though they walk in my dreams. In the midst of all this dark, this void, this emptiness, I, more ghostly than a ghost, cry "Who? Who?" to no answer, aware only of other smaller ghosts like the bat sweeping by the window or the dog who, in repeating a bit of his own lost history, turns restlessly among nonexistent grasses before he subsides again upon the floor.

"Trust the divine animal who carries us through the world," writes Emerson. Like the horse who finds the way by instinct when the traveler is lost in the forest, so the divine within us, he contends, may find new passages opening into nature; human metamorphosis may be possible. Emerson wrote at a time when man still lived intimately with animals and pursued wild, dangerous ways through primeval forests and prairies. Emerson and Thoreau lived close enough to nature to know something still of animal intuition and wisdom. They had not reached that point of utter cynicism—that distrust of self and of the human past which leads finally to total entrapment in that past, "man crystallized," as Emerson again was shrewd enough to observe.

This entrapment is all too evident in the writings of many concerned with the evolutionary story of man. Their gaze is fixed solely upon a past into which, one begins to suspect, has been poured a certain amount of today's frustration, venom, and despair. Like the witches in *Macbeth*, these men are tempting us with seeming realities about ourselves until these realities take shape in our minds and become the future. It is not necessary to break the code of DNA in order to control human destiny. The tragedy is that men are already controlling it even while they juggle retorts and shake vials in search of a physical means to enrich their personalities. We would like to contain the uncontainable future in a glass, have it crystallized out before us as a powder to swallow. All then, we imagine, would be well.

As our knowledge of the genetic mechanism increases, both scientists and journalists bombard our ear with ingenious accounts of how we are to control, henceforth, our own evolution. We who have recourse only to a past which we misread and which has made us cynics would now venture to produce our own future out of this past alone. Again I judge this self-esteem as a symptom of our time, our powerful, misused technology, our desire not to seek the good life but to produce a painless mechanical version of it—our willingness to be good if goodness can, in short, be swallowed in a pill.

Once more we are on the heath of the witches, or, to come closer to our own time, we are in the London laboratory where the good Doctor Jekyll produced a potion and reft out of his own body the monster Hyde.

Nature, as I have tried to intimate in this little dissection, is never quite where we see it. It is a becoming as well as a passing, but the becoming is both within and without our power. It is this lesson, with all our hard-gained knowledge, that is so difficult to comprehend. All along the evolutionary road it could have been said, "This is man," if there had then been such a magical self-delineating and mind-freezing word. It could have immobilized us at any step of our journey. It could have held us hanging to the bough from which we actually dropped; it could have kept us cowering, small-brained and helpless, whenever the great cats came through the reeds. It could have stricken us with terror before the fire that was later to be our warmth and weapon against Ice Age cold. At any step of the way, the word *man,* in retrospect, could be said to have encompassed just such final limits.

## Not Starry Influences

Each time the barrier has been surmounted. Man is not man. He is elsewhere. There is within us only that dark, divine animal engaged in a strange journey—that creature who, at midnight, knows its own ghostliness and senses its far road. "Man's unhappiness," broded Carlyle, "comes of his Greatness; it is because there is an Infinite in him, which with all his cunning he cannot quite bring under the Finite." This is why hydrogen, which has become the demon element of our time, should be seen as the intangible dagger which hung before Macbeth's vision, but which had no power except what was lent to it by his own mind.

The terror that confronts our age is our own conception of ourselves. Above all else this is the potion which the modern Dr. Jekylls have concocted. As Shakespeare foresaw:

> It hath been taught us from the primal state
> That he which is was wished until he were.

This is not the voice of the witches. It is the clear voice of a great poet almost four centuries gone, who saw at the dawn of the scientific age what was to be the darkest problem of man: his conception of himself. The words are quiet, almost cryptic; they do not foretell. They imply a problem in free will. Shakespeare, in this passage, says nothing of starry influences, machinery, beakers, or potions. He says, in essence, one thing only: that what we wish will come.

I submit to you that this is the deadliest message man will ever encounter in all literature. It thrusts upon him inescapable choices. Shakespeare's is the eternal, the true voice of the divine animal, piercing, as it has always pierced, the complacency of little centuries in which, encamped as in hidden thickets, men have sought to evade self-knowledge by describing themselves as men.


# GENETICS AND THE SURVIVAL OF THE UNFIT

*Lucy Eisenberg*


Lucy Eisenberg is a graduate of Radcliffe College and Oxford University. Her interest in hereditary diseases grew out of lectures at Oxford by Sir Hans Krebs, one of the first biochemists to study them.


At the end of a conference on human genetics last year, a biologist rose to summarize the proceedings. "I have visions," he said, "of a future genetic clinic in which a person will have not one, but

From *Harper's* Magazine, Feb. 1966, pp. 53–8. Copyright © 1966 by Lucy Eisenberg. Reprinted by permission of William Norris Agency, Inc.

hundreds, of his proteins analyzed completely in short order. The results will be run through a computer, and a license to reproduce will then be issued on the basis of a passing grade with respect to his (or her) genes." The prospective spouse would also have to be tested, he added, "but as my vision begins to assume the proportions of a nightmare I shall abstain from further speculation along these lines."

Eugenic proposals like this are commonplace at scientific meetings nowadays. After twenty years of ill repute, eugenics is again the subject of respectable scientific investigation. But while most eugenicists agree that eventually we will have to put together some kind of eugenic plan, they do not agree on two basic questions. First, will our descendants be feebler and less fit if we do not practice eugenic planning? Second, is eugenics really possible? Do techniques exist *at the present time* for improving the human race by means of selective breeding?

While opinion varies widely, there is a large group of scientists today who answer the first question affirmatively. Among its most eminent members are Linus Pauling, the eternal controversialist, and P. B. Madewar, Fellow of the Royal Society. Pauling has written several short articles about genetic deterioration, and Medawar, who like Pauling is a Nobel Prize winner, made it the subject of his lecture at the Mayo Centennial Symposium last year. The spokesman for the group is the geneticist and popular author Hermann Muller, another Nobel laureate. Muller has been predicting genetic disaster since 1935 and today, at seventy-five, he is still a persuasive and articulate prophet of doom.

The disaster which Muller fears is a result of gene mutations. These are small structural changes in the genes (he calls them "submicroscopic accidents") which are usually harmful to the organism. Because Muller believes that mutations are accumulating, he concludes that the human race is beginning to decline. In the end, the whole world will become a hospital, "and even the best of us will only be ambulatory patients in it."

This propect has worried Muller for many years. But few scientists worried with him so long as the only gene mutations that occurred were spontaneous ones which could not be avoided. Then in 1945 the United States exploded three atomic bombs. Thereafter —because radiation is known to cause a large increase in the gene mutation rate—a number of scientists were converted to Muller's point of view. Seized of apocalyptic visions, geneticists by the hundreds rushed into their labs to study radiation effects. Others set off for Japan to find out if radiation really had increased the mutation rate and what its effects would be on children born after the bomb. Throughout the 1950s, the customary calm of scientific conventions was shattered by technical arguments about experimental results, by emotional discussions of nuclear testing and what we should adopt as an "acceptable level" of radiation fallout.

Tension has been further heightened by the more recent discovery that certain chemicals such as formaldehyde and boric acid can cause gene mutations, and that these chemicals are being incorporated into all sorts of manufactured products, from lipstick to cold-cereal packaging. Furthermore, doctors are learning how to arrest or cure a mounting number of hereditary diseases that are caused by mutant genes. In saving the victims of these maladies they are not, of course, increasing the mutation rate as does radiation or a chemical mutagen. They are, however—by scientific cunning—foiling nature's plan for eliminating mutants. As a result, defective genes that were once eliminated by the death of their carriers are now being maintained and passed on to future generations.

The newly "conquered" hereditary diseases are still rare and even their names are unfamiliar to most people. From a genetic standpoint however, the problem posed is the same as that involved in diabetes (which is also a hereditary disease although the exact method of inheritance is somewhat obscure). Doctors have been treating diabetes successfully since 1921 and the result of this treatment, like those now being developed for other hereditary diseases, is to increase the frequency of defective genes.

Before the discovery of insulin in 1921, all young diabetics died before they could grow up and reproduce. Their genes were thus removed from the pool. (Geneticists often refer to an imaginary pool which contains the genes of every living person). Since 1921 however, many child diabetics have survived, married, and produced children (although the incidence of stillbirth and miscarriage is high among them). The result has been an increase in the frequency of diabetic genes and a consequent increase in the incidence of diabetes. The precise effect is hard to measure since diabetes has also become more prevalent simply because people live longer. There is no doubt however that the survival of diabetic genes is contributing to the effect.

Another group of hereditary diseases for which doctors have lately developed tests and therapies are all fatal if untreated. One of these is Wilson's disease. In its victims a defective gene causes faulty copper metabolism, which leads in turn to insanity and death. However, if the disease is spotted early enough and correctly treated, the symptoms never develop. (The therapy consists of a simple prescription taken by mouth, and removal from the diet of foods with a high copper content such as oysters, chocolate, and nuts.) I talked with one expert, Dr. Herbert Scheinberg at Bronx Municipal Hospital in New York. He sees no reason why the youngsters who are now growing up under treatment for Wilson's disease should not be able to have children of their own one day. Thus his patients will in due course pass on their defective genes.

To be sure, many—perhaps most—of the babies now born with Wilson's disease are not surviving. But this is only because not all doctors as yet know how to test for the malady while it is still mild enough to be treated. However, legislation has been proposed in New York State to ensure that this test will be done on all children. Similar legislation is in committee to insure testing for galactosemia, another hereditary disease whose victims cannot digest sugar, especially milk sugar. A test is already required by law for phenylketonuria—a blood disease that causes idiocy (40 per cent of those untreated have IQ's under 10). The law guarantees that babies who inherit phenylketonuria (PKU) will be spotted early, treated, given a chance to grow up and bear children of their own.

## A Little Abnormality May Be a Good Thing

The prospect of gene mutations being increased by radiation and chemicals, while at the same time science makes the victims of hereditary disease more fertile, has caused the Mullerian faction of geneticists to close ranks and sound the cry of doom. Another group of scientists, however, have questioned their conclusions. The latter, including Theodosius Dobzhansky at the Rockefeller Institute in New York, are much less apprehensive about an increase in mutation rate; nor do they believe that even if all mutant, "abnormal" genes could be eliminated, the race would become healthier and more fit. They are far more optimistic about our future than Muller's group because they have placed their faith in a concept called "heterosis" which holds that "defective" genes are not nearly as defective as they seem.

Because "heterosis" is a rallying cry in this controversy, I made a deliberate effort to understand what it means. (Many scientists are convinced that it is much too complex for the layman. A British biologist has even proposed to start a course in genetics for members of the Cabinet and other interested politicians.)

Actually, the pertinent facts are not complex at all. One need know only that chromosomes are threadlike structures in the nucleus which determine the genetic characteristics of the cell. The

chromosomes themselves are differentiated into more or less discrete regions called genes, which have genetically distinct properties. Each chromosome has hundreds, perhaps thousands, of genes,
each of which has its own special position, or "locus," on the
chromosome. (The chromosomes themselves come in pairs; 46
chromosomes, 23 pairs.)

If we remember that for every trait we inherit *two* genes, heterosis turns out to be a simple idea. It means that if both genes are
exactly the same, the organism will be normal (a fitness of 1). If,
however, a mutation takes place and one gene is slightly different
from the other, the organism will be supernormal (with a fitness of
1.1 or even 1.5). Hence, the fortunate creature who carries two
slightly different (*i.e.*, "polymorphic") genes enjoys what geneticists call "heterotic vigor."

The paradox of heterosis appears when we consider that a pair
of mutant genes can cause serious diseases such as diabetes, cystic
fibrosis, and the others I have mentioned earlier. (Almost all mutant genes are "recessive," which means that the disease does not
appear unless we inherit *two* defective genes.) Nevertheless, if the
theory of heterosis is true, the person who carries one defective
gene and one normal gene is more fit than the person who struggles
along with two normal genes.

At first glance, the theory seems highly unlikely. But studies of
a disease called sickle-cell anemia have proved it can be true.
Babies who inherit two sickle-cell genes have a severe case of
anemia and usually die soon after birth. Doctors have found, however, that a single dose of the sickle-cell gene confers a specific
kind of heterotic vigor on its carriers, namely, resitance to malarial
infection. Thus wherever malaria is endemic, people who carry a
single sickle-cell gene are fortunate. They live longer and have more
children. This means, of course, that the gene is "selected for" in
the course of evolution and that it spreads. The result of this evolutionary process can be clearly seen in Central Africa, where malaria
is extremely common, and where the sickle-cell gene is carried by
at least 20 per cent of the population.

Sickle-cell anemia is a marvelous topic for cocktail-party conversation (if one is drinking with geneticists) not only because it is the
classic example of heterosis, but also because it illustrates the close
relationship between proteins and genes.

Scientists had long suspected that genes are responsible for man-
ufacturing proteins, but they could not be certain until Linus Pauling, who was studying sickle-cell anemia, demonstrated that a
structurally deficient (*i.e.*, mutant) gene produces a structurally
deficient molecule of protein. Pauling discovered that in sickle-cell

anemia the hemoglobin protein is malformed, and that all the symptoms of the disease (including the peculiar, sickle-shaped red blood
cells which give it its name) can be traced to this one "molecular"
defect.

There is no doubt that heterosis explains the prevalence of the
sickle-cell gene. It is also conceivable that "diabetic" genes have
spread for a similar reason. Very possibly one "diabetic" gene
(coupled with one normal gene) confers resistance against chronic
malnutrition by altering the mechanism for digesting sugar. "Diabetic" genes would, according to this theory, have been particularly
useful to cavemen who in the best of times ate in excess, and the
rest of the time ate nearly nothing. According to one geneticist, a
doctor practicing eight thousand years ago might have examined
his patient and said, "You're doing just fine; just enough diabetes
to keep you in the pink of condition."

Though the correlation between diabetes and resistance to malnutrition has not been proven a large number of geneticists believe
that the theory of heterosis applies to a great many, if not a majority, of genes. They believe that for any given locus on a chromosome there are two, or perhaps more, genes which vary slightly
owing to some past mutation. These "polymorphic" genes, as they
are called, are maintained in the population because of the "vigor"
they bring.

Adherents to this theory are forced to a rather startling conclusion: if "defective" genes are taken out of the pool, then future generations will be less rather than more fit, since getting rid of all the
defective genes would also eliminate the extra vigor that results
from a single dose of a faulty gene. Hence, even if one could control marriage and reproduction it will never be possible to breed a
super-race, free from hereditary disease.

One wants to know, of course, why such theories cannot be
tested and one or another proved true. Either we are as a race
declining, or we are not. Either defective genes are an advantage
when present in a single dose, or they are not. Unfortunately, however, in the field of human genetics, facts are hard to find. It is difficult to measure the rate of spontaneous mutation, much less find
out whether the rate is increasing because of radiation. It is hard
to put together enough case histories for a given disease because
many of them are so rare. And it is usually impossible to detect the
people who carry a single defective gene in order to find out
whether they really are more vigorous or not. *Two* recessive genes
can be spotted because all the protein they produce is defective
(like the defective hemoglobin in sickle-cell anemia) or because the
protein they are supposed to produce is missing altogether (lack of

a protein called phenylalanine hydroxylase produces PKU). But when only one gene is defective, its effects are often hidden by the activity of the other, normal gene.

## Poetry, Politics, and Genes

Human beings are peculiar; when they are not sure that what they are saying is true, they say it louder and with greater conviction. This is a weakness which most scientists try to avoid. The genetic controversy, however, has moved some of its participants to an unusual lack of discretion. "It is clear," Sir Julian Huxley said recently, "that the general quality of the world's population is not very high, is beginning to deteriorate, and should and could be improved." In fact, it has not been proved that we are deteriorating and it is not at all clear that the means to improve us exist.

Predictably, the scientists most concerned about genetic deterioration are the same ones who believe improvement is possible if society will only adopt a eugenic plan. Herman Muller, who has worried longest and loudest about deterioration, is also the acknowledged spokesman for eugenic planning. Similarly, Muller's opponents in the deterioration controversy also argue that far too little is yet known to justify deliberate action. "It's not that improvement isn't possible," said one British physiologist of this school, "but I do not think we know much more about how to bring it about than Galileo or Newton knew about how to fly."

One essentially negative goal of the eugenicists is to prevent the spread of hereditary disease. To accomplish this they would forbid people who carry a dangerous dominant gene to have children. Those with two faulty but recessive genes, on the other hand, would be allowed to reproduce, as would healthy people carrying a single dose of the undesirable gene. However a man and woman who carry the *same* dangerous recessive gene would be barred from marrying each other. Thus a man with Wilson's disease could marry whomever he wants as long as she too does not carry the gene for Wilson's disease. Their children will carry the Wilson's gene but none of them would actually have the disease. In this fashion, hereditary diseases would be wiped out in a single generation—if this program were adopted.

However, eugenicists are notoriously vague on the question of implementation. At the Mayo Clinic Centennial proceedings last year, one of them—Peter Brian Medawar—was asked how he would put such a plan into effect. "Of course," he replied, "I do not propose to do it myself, rushing around and forbidding the banns." But, he added, there is no reason why "sensible" people could not be dissuaded from marrying if they know that one out of four of their children is likely to inherit a disease.

Actually, a positive eugenic program would require much more radical steps. Muller's program for example involves a total departure from our present ideas and conventions about marriage and children. Like all believers in positive eugenics, his great hope is that society will improve its genetic stock by adopting the techniques of animal husbandry and breeding only from the best sires and dams.

To this end, he has evolved a plan called AID, Artificial Insemination from Donors. He proposes that banks be established where the sperm of various extraordinary men will be stored. When a woman decides to have children, she will then choose sperm from the donor whose qualities she most admires. "How many women," Muller cried when he launched his plan in 1935, "would be eager and proud to bear and rear a child of Lenin or Darwin! Is it not obvious that restraint, rather than compulsion, would be called for?"

Because of this chance remark Muller has been taunted for years, even by his friends. For the fact is that choosing a sire from among many more or less celebrated men is fraught with complications. As one scientist put it to me, "The trouble with Muller's bank is that he's always having to take people out of it. If it's not politics, it's something else." The latest reject, he mentioned, is Abraham Lincoln, who is now suspected of having had something called Marfan's syndrome (a hereditary condition characterized by excessively long fingers and a cardiac defect). Muller's own solution is to store the sperm for twenty years. In two decades, he thinks, "a better appraisal of the donors will be possible and personal biases and entanglements will fade away."

But Muller still finds little support for his plan. The real obstacle is that as yet we know desperately little about man's genetic endowment and about the interaction between genes and environment which shapes the final human product. Although man carries an estimated 20,000 pairs of genes, scientists know the function of only a very small fraction, 500 at most. They have still to discover how genes interact, and whether some combinations of genes are possible and others are not. There also is a great deal more to be learned about gene linkage and function before the results of a "breeding program" can be predicted with success.

J. B. S. Haldane tells a cautionary tale about positive genetics and directed breeding. It concerns a recessive gene which lowers resistance to tubercular infection. According to Haldane, both John Keats and Emily Brontë inherited a pair of these genes, and as a result they both died prematurely. But he also believes that the poetic and literary talent of both these geniuses was inherited and that it was carried by the same rare and "defective" genes which made them susceptible to TB. The moral—that defective genes are not always what they seem—should surely give pause to those who would tamper with genes without being sure of their function.

### "Genetic Alert"

It is not easy to discover the function of any particular gene. They are too small to be seen with most microscopes and even under the electron microscope they all look exactly alike. Nor is there any chemical test which can distinguish between different ones. One way to study a gene is to investigate inherited traits (as Mendel studied the size and shape of generations of peas in the nineteenth century). A better way is to study the protein that a gene is responsible for making. If a geneticist finds that a protein (like sickle-cell hemoglobin) is inherited according to Mendelian law, he infers that a gene is responsible for the manufacture of hemoglobin and that a mutant form of the gene produces a defective molecule of hemoglobin.

Until recently geneticists have concentrated their efforts on small animals like fruit flies and mice. They also know a great deal about the genes of a red mold called *Neurospora crassa*. But human beings take so long to breed and are so hard to control that geneticists have only recently begun to investigate and catalogue man's genes.

This is now being done systematically and on a large scale by a group of doctors at the Albert Einstein College of Medicine, under the code name "Genetic Alert." With funds from the National Foundation for Neuromuscular Disease they have set up laboratory facilities at the Bronx Municipal Hospital in New York, Children's Hospital in Boston, St. Christopher's Hospital for Children in Philadelphia, and Stanford University Hospital in California. At these hospitals a sample of blood is taken from every well baby brought into the clinic and examined for a possible abnormality in each of three proteins. The results of these tests are read into a computer and then punched onto cards which are automatically filed.

If the tests show that a child does have an abnormal protein, then the doctors can start treatment early enough to prevent the onset of a hereditary disease (or at least to prevent its most serious symptoms). This is however only one of the goals of "Genetic Alert." The other objective is to accumulate information about human genes systematically, so that it can be used for future research. When this is done, a doctor who wants to investigate a certain hereditary condition will only have to push a button to collect the subjects for his study. The computer will type out the names of all the people previously tested by the hospital who inherited the gene that interests him. The information will also be used to make reliable estimates of gene frequencies and for complicated genetic studies called chromosome "mapping."

### Hideous Memories

The purposes of "Genetic Alert" are both clinical—that is, to cure disease—and to advance genetic research. But the directors of the project have no interest in its eugenic implications. Still, these cannot be altogether ignored. If, for example, the project were expanded to cover every child born in the country, it could provide all the information needed to eliminate hereditary disease—which is the goal of negative eugenics.

Scientists do not agree that we should apply eugenic techniques to eliminate hereditary disease or attempt, on the positive side, to improve the human race. And few if any responsible political leaders are prepared even to discuss a question freighted with hideous memories of the "eugenics" of Hitler's Third Reich. Nonetheless, it seems inevitable that—as with the splitting of the atom—scientific progress in genetics will in the foreseeable future raise issues of public policy which scientists alone cannot resolve.

# THE FUTURE OF *HOMO SAPIENS*

*Jean Hiernaux*

Jean Hiernaux is a professor of anthropology at the Free University of Brussels.

It takes considerable presumption to foretell the future, yet it is a task that the research worker cannot evade, although he may admit that his forecasts are based on incomplete knowledge and on hypotheses which are colored by his own personality.

Reproduced from the *UNESCO Courier*, Vol. 18 (April 1965), pp. 12–15.

Man is the product of the evolution of animate matter; and his future can be foretold only by projecting into the future evolutionary trends which are perceptible today. Throughout the natural history of life on our planet, we may trace a series of forms, rising from the simplest to the most complex—from giant molecules, not yet completely differentiated from inert matter, to mammals.

The main stages in this evolution reveal an increasing degree of freedom from close dependence on the environment. For example, by acquiring the ability to maintain the body temperature irrespective of the temperature of external environment, which scientists call "horiothermy," the higher forms of animate matter have entered regions in which previously they could not live.

As life became increasingly complex, the structure and role of the brain grew larger. The maximum development of the brain and the maximum freedom from the power of the external environment were to be achieved by man; and, having acquired that freedom, he gained increasing control over the forces of nature, which he harnessed to suit his needs.

Man is unquestionably the spearhead of evolution, but he does not follow its course in the same way as did those forms which lived before him; at least, it may be said that an evolutionary mechanism not previously in operation came into being with man. Before his coming, evolution was genetic in character; it consisted in changing the qualities inherited by the various species—in other words, changing the stock of genes borne by them. It had nothing to do with the will or with consciousness.

With the coming of man and, no doubt, as a necessary condition for his emergence, an entirely different evolutionary mechanism came into being and developed—the transmission from one individual to another and from one generation to the next of knowledge, inventions, and ways of life which are not inherited, and which can be perpetuated only through constant effort.

This is a less stable form of evolution, but it enables man to advance along the path of freedom and to gain control over his environment much more rapidly than he can through genetic evolution. This is probably the reason why, after a period of interaction between the two evolutionary mechanisms (lasting from the emergence of man, some two million years ago, until his appearance in his present form as *Homo sapiens* about 50,000 years ago), evolution towards a higher state now takes place essentially in the sphere of acquired ability, which we may call the cultural sphere.

There is no perceptible difference between the anatomical development of the skull of fossilized *Homo sapiens* and our skull, but man's control over the forces of nature has grown tremendously, and knowledge and techniques are progressing with ever-increasing speed; cultural evolution has taken the place of genetic evolution.

If this explanation of the lack of change in the brain over tens of thousands of years is correct, we must not expect man in the future to have an enormous head; the brain he has now is large enough for him, and in any case he is already extending its range by means of electronic computers.

It is true that, judging by the bone-structure, *Homo sapiens* usually had coarser features in the stone age than today (as have the modern representatives of that cultural stage, the Australian aborigines). A certain refining of the bony projections has accompanied cultural evolution. Yet it is not to be expected that this trend will continue until the head is markedly different; the ridges of the brow may vanish, but the frontal bone cannot. There is also a tendency for the teeth to become smaller, and even for the third molar to be missing. Here again, there is no reason to think that this situation will ultimately produce a toothless human being. In any case, these processes are extremely slow compared with cultural evolution.

A process still in operation today in the genetic sphere and there is no sign that it is nearing its end, is the modification of the inherited traits of populations so as to secure from the genetic point of view, the best possible adaptation to a changing environment. Our adaptation to our environment, too, is increasingly cultural in character (take, for instance, our clothing, heating and air-conditioning), and advances in medicine are helping to lessen the importance of natural selection; but we are constantly creating new environments (such as that of the great metropolises) which give rise to fresh biological problems. It will be a long time no doubt, before cultural measures make genetic adaptation to local conditions unnecessary, and so put an end to it.

All that has been said so far concerns the spontaneous biological evolution of man. Now, man has acquired knowledge and technical ability which enable him to influence his inherited traits. The branch of science which deals with this process is eugenics. It is based on the theory that, for each inherited characteristic in which men differ from each other (such as the A, B and O blood groups, in which individuals are divided into four groups), there is a determining factor (a gene) which is the best of its kind, and which is found in all parts of the world.

Natural selection will tend to eliminate all alternatives except the best. If a new gene appears, as a result of mutations, either it will be better than the existing genes, and will supersede them, or else it will be weaker, and will be eliminated.

The aim of eugenics is to assist what is good in nature, by discouraging deleterious genes (through preventing individuals possessing them from reproducing) and by encouraging the best gene (for instance by advocating artificial insemination by semen which bears that gene). The tendency is, therefore, for eugenics to produce a human race composed of genetically identical individuals.

In many cases (when it is recessive), the elimination of a deleterious gene, even by total eugenics (the complete prevention of reproduction by those who bear it), requires many generations. Apart from this practical aspect there is a serious argument against the general application of eugenics: recent research has revealed that in very many cases natural selection does not move towards a state of uniformity through the elimination of all genes except one, but rather towards a state of balance between the frequencies of different genes.

Mankind has always exhibited considerable diversity in respect of many hereditary traits, which is a good thing. This is not only because the vitality of each population depends upon such diversity (or polymorphism), but because a gene may be beneficial in certain environmental conditions and harmful in others. We know of genes, for instance, a certain frequency of which is benefical in malarial regions, but which are by no means desirable in other regions.

Men have settled in all parts of the globe; they live in widely differing natural environments which they are constantly modifying in ways that are not always predictable. This being so, the genetic idea is to maintain diversity—the opposite of the aim of eugenics. Eugenics is unjustifiable except insofar as it can eradicate very serious hereditary diseases, of which there are few; if an apparently unfavorable trait occurs frequently in a population, it is very likely to be desirable in some respect at present unknown to us. If a gene is really undesirable in all respects, natural selection will keep its frequency very low.

This criticism applies to positive eugenics, the object of which is to increase the number of "good" genes, as well as to negative eugenics, which aims to eradicate the "bad" ones; underlying both is the same ideal—uniformity. We have no reason to hope that a Superman will be produced in the eugenists' test tubes; any highly

gifted beings they might produce would not constitute a biologically
viable human race.

We should do better to devote our energies to providing populations and individuals with living conditions in which their inherited potentialities can best be realized, rather than manipulating
genes; and that is not eugenics, but what has been called euthenics.

There are hundreds of millions of human beings who, through
hunger or disease, are prevented from realizing their physical potentialities as they would have done under better conditions. Differences between the intellectual achievements of the various human
populations appear to be due entirely to the fact that their food,
health and educational conditions are different. Euthenics opens
up much broader and safer avenues for the betterment of mankind
than does eugenics.

The processes in operation today—especially selection, which
has the effect of differentiating populations by genetic adaptation
to their living conditions, and cross-breeding which produces
greater homogeneity, while at the same time putting a premium
on polymorphism—can, of themselves, produce the state which
appears to meet the biological needs of our race, that is, unity in
diversity. Individual adaptations are never very marked, and they
are much less characteristic of man than his genetic capacity for
general adaptation to varied conditions.

It would seem, therefore, that man is not destined to undergo
any striking biological transformation through either spontaneous
or induced evolution. He is, however, undergoing an ever more
rapid cultural evolution; it took him hundreds of thousands of
years—the palaeolithic era—to bring his stone-cutting technique
to a moderately high standard, but only a few thousand years to
advance from the stone age to the atomic age. It is in the sphere of
cultural achievements that man can undergo a profound evolution
which, though different in kind from genetic evolution, as we have
seen, is moving in the same direction, and is the specifically human
form of evolution.

This kind of evolution has become self-conscious; it is dependent
upon man's desire to advance and on the effectiveness of the
measures he adopts to do so. It requires of men a sustained effort
to improve, both as individuals and as a society. It does not appear
to be necessarily inevitable; our present state of knowledge, indeed,
provides mankind with the means of total self-destruction.

Are we then justified in predicting that the cultural evolution
will continue to progress? We may be somewhat prejudiced on the
side of optimism, but not without reason. Under pressure of the

forces of selection, the genetic evolution has gone on, passing through numerous phases, for over a thousand million years; and in every case the more complex, more highly developed form has supplanted the lower form when they have been present together and in a competitive situation.

True mammals, for example, have supplanted marsupials in all parts of the world except Australia, where they have been but recently introduced. We may reasonably expect that by a similar mechanism a more highly-developed cultural form, when brought into contact with a less highly-developed one, will supersede it. Examples of this may be found in our past. One case is the extremely rapid expansion of the neolithic revolution, i.e., the invention of agriculture and cattle-breeding.

Biological evolutionary forces (using the word "biological" in the narrow sense) altered inherited traits; but cultural evolutionary forces preserve whatever is felt to be an incentive towards mankind's advancement. These include the desire for knowledge, which leads to scientific progress, and the desire of individuals and human societies to draw closer together, which impels us to love our neighbor, to feel ourselves involved in whatever affects mankind as a whole, and to strive for greater social justice.

It is true that, as in the case of genetic evolution, these forces produce nothing more than trends, and do not exclude the possibility of periods of retrogression and partial failure; but, if we look at history from a sufficiently high vantage-point, it seems reasonable to think that they will succeed.

Where can this sort of evolution take mankind? In some fields, it is moving very quickly; knowledge is advancing with great rapidity; and, amidst storm and stress, men are seeking for new forms of social morality consonant with their increasing awareness of their unity and of the interdependence of the elements of which the race is composed.

When we observe the rate of our progress we may wonder whether animate matter inhabiting the earth is not about to undergo, in man, one of those changes of state which dialectical thinking entitles us to visualize. It would seem that, in biology as in physics, slight but accumulated quantitative changes may somewhat suddenly lead to qualitatively new states (consider, for example, the changes undergone by a block of ice which is heated gradually).

Thus, the increasing complexity of inert matter gave rise to life, which had new properties, but within which chemical particles retain their ordinary characteristics; it is the interaction and organization of these particles which is characteristic of life. The increasing complexity of animate matter led to the emergence of man, a qualitatively new creature in certain ways, as in his capacity for abstract thinking, but whose cells possess the same general biological properties as the amoeba.

If we try to apply this principle still further, we shall see that the next critical threshold will bring us to a state in which men differing but little from present-day men will, by virtue of their desire to draw closer together and the intensity and nature of their interaction, constitute a qualitatively new stage of animate matter.

So, if we see the matter aright, we are advancing towards a Supermankind, and not towards Supermen. We may be unable at our stage in evolution to gain a complete picture of this future state, but already we know the paths that lead to it. It may sometimes be difficult to abandon an untroubled immobility but if we are to accept our responsibilities as human beings and respond to the forces of progress, we must move forward along these paths—the ways that lead to knowledge and amity.

# BIOLOGICAL MAN AND THE YEAR 2000

*Ernst Mayr*

Ernst Mayr is a professor at the Museum of Comparative Zoology at Harvard University.

A biologist feels rather out of place in a conference dominated by economists, government experts, historians, and sociologists. The year 2000 is only thirty-three years away, and the physical appearance of man has not changed materially in more than one hundred thousand years so far as one can infer from the fossil record. Biological man in the year 2000 will not be different in any appreciable way from what he is today.

Reprinted by permission from *Daedalus*, Journal of the American Academy of Arts and Sciences, Boston, Massachusetts, Vol. 96, No. 3, pp. 832–36.

Much of the first conference of the Commission was devoted to crystal-ball gazing, guessing, and predicting. Indeed, this is a major concern for city planners, engineers, and economists. When thinking of the future, the biologist tends to be more ambitious. He is not satisfied with merely describing some future condition; he actually would like to make suggestions as to what to do in order to make this a better world. There are two attitudes we can take with reference to the future. We can assume the attitude of the watchers of a Greek tragedy. Without raising a finger, they let the play drift inexorably toward its blood-stained conclusion. Or we can behave like utopians, to a greater or lesser degree, and propose measures that will better the fate of mankind and hopefully better mankind itself. Anyone familiar with the fantastically rapid evolution of the brain from the ape level to the *Homo sapiens* level is entitled to the fond hope that the apparent standstill in man's evolution is only a temporary phase and that a way can be found to initiate a trend toward an even greater future. Biologically, this is not an impossible utopia, since the enormous amount of genetic variability in man would, indeed, permit considerable response to selection pressures. Whether or not this is socially, politically, and morally feasible is an entirely different matter.

Let us forget for the moment the tantalizing problem of man's evolutionary future and turn to the question of coping with biological man as he is now. I pointed out in the conference in October how poorly we have solved the problems posed by man's biological inequality. Nothing is more undemocratic or more apt to destroy equal opportunity than forcing human beings with exceedingly different aptitudes and motivations through identical social institutions. There is only one way to cope with man's genetic diversity, and that is to diversify man's environment. We need more kinds of schools, more curricula within each school, more diversity in economic and moral rewards, and so forth. It is almost unbelievable to the biologist that it has taken so long for the promoters of educational theories to grasp this simple point. To adjust our institutions to the final realization that no two human beings are biologically identical because every individual is genetically unique will occupy us well beyond the year 2000. To a biologist these thirty-three years are no more than a moment in the evolutionary history of mankind. When we deal with this moment, we can well afford to make the simplifying assumption that man is biologically unchanging.

This simplifying assumption is, of course, not correct. The genetic composition of the gene pool of every species of animals and plants changes from generation to generation. Man is no exception.

When we consider the long-term evolution of man we cannot ignore such changes. They happen all around us and right before our eyes. If it is true, as all the facts seem to indicate, that those with below-average intelligence have a higher reproductive rate than those with above-average intelligence, this would document an evolutionary change·(considering the indications for high heritability of intelligence). Shall we stand by passively and let such changes happen for better or for worse, or shall we start thinking again in terms of man's evolutionary future?

Lawrence K. Frank said quite rightly at our last meeting that nothing is so powerful as ideas. This has surely been demonstrated by the American, the French, and the Russian Revolutions, as well as by the ideas of civil disobedience, representative government, and free enterprise. These famous ideas have dramatically changed human institutions; they have changed man's environment and, indeed, man himself. Biology in the last fifty years has developed many ideas that have a similar potential to change not only man's environment but man himself. This to me is a frightening thought. It is doubly frightening when one thinks of the Nazi horrors perpetrated under the guise of improving man. We hear increasingly of sperm banks, of selective sterilization, of genetic engineering, and of other ways to usher in a brave new world.

Our natural reaction to all this is—Down with it! Surely we will not make a mistake if we do nothing, if we adopt a *laissez-faire* policy. Why not maintain the *status quo*? Unfortunately there is no *status quo* so far as the genetic composition of natural populations is concerned. They always change, no matter what we do. Right now an amazingly strong natural selection is going on among the industrial populations of the Western world. Some segments of this population contribute to the gene pool of the next generation two, three, four, or more times as many genes as other segments. As James F. Crow has shown, reproductive advantage has largely replaced survival advantage as far as natural selection in man is concerned.[1] The evolutionist measures fitness in terms of the contribution made to the gene pool of the next generation. The person who has six surviving children has three times as large a fitness as the person with two children. This reproductive differential is now by far the most important component of natural selection in man. It has replaced prereproductive mortality as the principal component of fitness. Under these circumstances it is obvious that a simple *laissez-faire* policy would hardly be an ideal strategy on a long-term basis.

Is there an alternative? I am afraid the honest answer is—Not right now. The reason for this is our enormous ignorance. Fortunately unequal reproduction is not a pressing problem so long as the population explosion continues.

As soon as population control is exercized, it inevitably tends to be qualitative rather than purely quantitative. Even under current conditions, the most responsible segments in our population are the ones that are most successful in controlling family size. If part of their intelligence or self-discipline has a genetic basis, it would mean that these very genes are being discriminated against in our population. Can one do something about this, and if so, what? The answer must be an ambiguous yes and no. It is extremely difficult to approach this subject without falling into the same traps as the racists and naïve eugenicists. Before we can propose any meaningful program for a genetic improvement of mankind, we must satisfy two prior conditions, and it is almost certain that it will require several generations for these conditions to be met.

The first of these prerequisites is a thorough reexamination of some of our most widely accepted, I might almost say sacred, concepts—the role of the individual in society, the consequences of population structure (versus typological essentialism), the question of personal rights in an interdependent cooperative society. As Karl Popper and others have pointed out perceptively, we are still suffering from the heritage of Platonian (essentialist) misconceptions. It will take a long time before they are properly recognized and eliminated. Much that was objectionable in past eugenic proposals was due to this unfortunate heritage. When evaluating human contributions to the gene pool of the next generation, we must rigorously exclude all traces of typological thinking. We are not concerned with human types or races; we are not concerned with black or white skin, with straight or curly hair, with the rich or the poor. We are simply concerned with individuals and their genetic potential. The correlations between different kinds of traits, physical and nonphysical, are so slight that it would be not only unfair but actually misleading to adopt a typological approach. Yet typological thinking is still dominant in much of psychology, anthropology, economics, sociology, and even biology. It will have to be eradicated totally before we can seriously consider the future of mankind.

The second prerequisite is research on the nature of the genetic contribution to human traits. If the time should ever come when we are emotionally ready to allow a reproductive premium for above-average genotypes, we would have to be able to determine what makes a genotype "valuable." At present we are unable to do this. We all remember the great controversy of the past generation over nature versus nurture. Fortunately this argument is now dead except in the minds of a few who have not kept track of the developments in genetics in the past thirty years. We now know that the phenotypes of almost all traits are the result of both a genetic predisposition and its response to the environment. Students of selection have demonstrated that successful selection is possible even when the genetic contribution to a trait (its heritability) is less than 20 per cent, indeed less than 10 per cent.

Enormous advances have been made in recent generations in the control of the nurture component of human traits through improved public health, child care, nutrition, a better educational system, and other measures that help to bring out the full potential contained in the genotype. There is, however, an obvious limit to the effectiveness of such measures. One can improve an I.Q. measure by twenty points and in exceptional cases perhaps by thirty points, but one cannot turn an 80 I.Q. into a 150 I.Q. no matter what one does. Once we have exhausted all the possibilities of improvement through improved nurture, we must start thinking about positive eugenics; there is no third alternative. We have little knowledge of the genetics of important human traits at the present time, and the field is cluttered up with old wives' tales. Research on identical twins (in comparison with same-sexed dizygotic twins) has made important contributions, as have longitudinal family studies, such as those of Sheldon C. and Elizabeth W. Reed on mental retardation. The obstacles to research are formidable. Experimentation is nearly always impossible, as is the setting up of proper controls. Yet the information needed is of such importance that research will have to be stepped up.

I have stressed the need for reconceptualization. Most people have been raised with the belief that equality equals biological identity, and this early conditioning still dominates much of our thinking and our emotions. J. B. S. Haldane and others have pointed out that the human achievements—those things that distinguish man from the animals and are responsible for man's civilization, art, literature, and science—were achieved by less than 1 per cent of the human population, by those in the upper tail of the curve of human variation in inventiveness, imagination, perserverance, and ability to think clearly. A rather small downward shift in the mean value of the curve of human variability might obliterate much of this highest class of potential achievers. A slight upward shift of the curve might double the size of this class. Perhaps this is not a legitimate calculation, but such considerations help us to focus on an important but badly neglected challenge to mankind.

Man, along with all other sexually reproducing species, undergoes slight genetic change from generation to generation. Such change is negligible on a short-range basis, and no appreciable change in biological man is to be expected between now and the year 2000 or, indeed, for the next several hundred years. Nevertheless, a genetic change is inevitable over the centuries, and man must ask himself whether he wants to adopt a *laissez-faire* attitude toward these changes or to be the master of his own fate. If he should adopt the second alternative, he must not only rebuild much of his conceptual framework, but start an extensive research program that would give substance to what are now purely subjective and largely arbitrary value judgments concerning human characteristics.

Reference

1. James F. Crow, "Mechanisms and Trends in Human Evolution," *Daedalus* (Summer, 1961) pp. 416–31.

# MAN AND HIS ENVIRONMENT—BIOMEDICAL KNOWLEDGE AND SOCIAL ACTION

*René Dubos*

René Dubos, professor of pathology at The Rockefeller University in New York, is greatly concerned with the effect of the environment on man and of man's effect on the environment. Two of his recent books are *Man Adapting* and *So Human an Animal*.

## I. The University and Diversity of Mankind

Any medical problem presents itself under two aspects which are sharply different, but complementary. On the one hand, all phenomena of health and disease reflect the biological unity of

From Perspectives in Biology and Medicine, Vol. 9 (Summer 1966), pp. 523–36. Reprinted by permission of the University of Chicago Press and the author. This speech was delivered at the inauguration of the new Pan American Health Organization building in Washington, D.C.

mankind; on the other hand, all are conditioned by the diversity of the social institutions and ways of life. The duality of man's nature —unity and diversity—creates a medical paradox that is responsible for the complexities of the problems faced by the Pan-American Health Organization (PAHO). The paradox is that all men, irrespective of origin, have fundamentally the same biological constitution, physiological requirements, and responses to stimuli; yet despite this biological uniformity, their diseases and medical needs differ profoundly acording to their habitats, social institutions, and ways of life. Anyone concerned with problems of health and disease must, therefore, keep in mind both the universal aspects of human biology and the social diversity of medical problems.

The dedication of a new building provides an opportunity to reexamine the goals of the institution that it serves. For this reason, I shall take the liberty to make a few general statements that may help to sharpen the contrast between the universal requirements of man's life and the special medical needs of his societies. This contrast will bring into relief some unsolved health problems which are in the province of PAHO.

The prehistorical and historical events of the human adventure in the Americas constitute perhaps the most convincing evidence for the unity of mankind. As far as can be judged, various populations of ancient man began to move into the Americas during the late Paleolithic period. After their initial penetration, they rapidly spread over the whole American continent, but they appear to have remained almost completely isolated from the rest of mankind for more than 10,000 years. During that period, they progressively developed several great civilizations profoundly different from those of Asia and Europe, yet very meaningful to those of us whose cultural evolution took place on other continents. Obviously, the most fundamental and universal characteristics of the human mind were already fully developed by the time ancient man first penetrated the Americas.

During the past five centuries, many waves of immigration brought other human races from all parts of the earth into intimate contact with the various tribes of Amerindians. These mass migrations resulted in an immense number of highly varied and successful racial mixtures. The genetic and physiological compatibility of human races that had been separated for so many thousand years thus confirms the cultural evidence that all human beings originally derive from the same evolutionary stock.

Because of their biological similarity, all men are potentially liable to the same kinds of diseases—a fact well documented by anthropological studies and by recent medical surveys of primitive tribes. Furthermore, all men can derive benefits from the same kinds of medical care, as proven by the uniformity of their response to the prophylactic and therapeutic procedures of modern medicine. But despite these medical similarities, experience shows that each geographical area, each type of society, and each economic group is characterized by its own pattern of diseases and has special medical needs. For example, the control of disease in tropical lowlands obviously presents theoretical and practical problems far different from those encountered on arid plateaus or on high mountains. The contrast is even greater between the disease problems most prevalent in impoverished rural communities and those emerging at present in prosperous industrial agglomerations.

Individual persons differ, of course, in their genetic constitution and, consequently, in their innate resistance to disease. But in most cases, genetic endowment and racial origin play only a very small role in determining the types and severity of the diseases characteristic of a particular region, or a particular social group. Whether they be of African, Amerindian, European, or Oriental origin, and whatever the complexity of the racial mixtures of which they are constituted, human populations usually acquire the burden of diseases characteristic of the geographical area and social group in which they are born and live. Medically speaking, man is, in general, more the product of his environment than of his genetic endowment. The health of the people is determined not by their race but by the conditions of their life. I feel justified in emphasizing these obvious truths because they are fundamental to the formulation of practical medical policies as well as to the development of research programs in biomedicine.

## II. The Diseases of Scarcity

Irrespective of race and climate, the incidence of most nutritional, infectious, and even degenerative diseases is closely related to the economic status. In fact, social factors are of such obvious importance in the causation and control of disease, that many sociologists and even medical scientists are inclined to believe that political and social reforms are the most promising approach to health improvement among destitute people. There is no doubt concerning the factual validity of the observations on which this belief is based, but its unconditioned and uncritical acceptance would probably lead to the formulation of national policies unfavorable, in the long run, both to health improvement and to social development. It seems worthwhile, therefore, to focus our attention on the comparative merits and limitations of the social and medical approaches to disease control. To discuss this problem, I shall briefly consider a few examples illustrating the complex interplay between economic conditions, the health of the people, and biomedical knowledge.

As we all know, malnutrition is certainly responsible for a very large percentage of the disease problems in the world and especially in the Americas. There is no doubt, furthermore, that shortages of food and bad nutritional habits are usually the outcome of economic limitations and of unwise social practices. It would seem to follow from these premises that the solution to the problem of nutritional diseases is more likely to come from political and social reforms than from the application of scientific knowledge. But, in reality, both approaches are equally essential. Experience has shown that political and social measures cannot be effective unless they are based on very sophisticated scientific information concerning nutritional needs and the chemical constitution of foodstuffs.

Nutritional surveys have revealed, for example, that deficiencies in proteins and in certain vitamins constitute a more frequent cause of severe malnutrition than does the shortage of calories. Modern analytical methods have shown, furthermore, that the various proteins differ greatly in nutritional value because they do not all have the same amino acid composition. Thus, it has become clear that malnutrition cannot be corrected merely by producing more food, for example, more beans or more corn. Just more protein will not necessarily solve the problem either. What is needed is a regimen having the proper chemical composition. In practice, mixtures of foodstuffs providing a correct balance of all essential nutrients, especially of all essential amino acids, constitute the nutritional formulas most favorable to health and best suited to the economics of developing countries.

Precise chemical knowledge of food composition is thus necessary for the formulation of nutritional requirements and of agricultural programs. But this knowledge is not sufficient to produce the kind of food readily accepted by the people and therefore beneficial to them. There exist in each region and each culture a number of food habits that cannot be changed without an immense amount of effort. At the end of World War I, for example, corn (maize) was shipped by the American Relief Committee to the famished people of Europe; however, Europeans were not able to use the grain because it was foreign to their nutritional traditions, so much so that they did not even know how to cook it and incorporate it in their diet. Thus, knowledge of the chemical composition of foods and of their theoretical nutritional value must be supplemented not only by a know-how of production methods but also by a sophisticated awareness of what is socially acceptable in a given region.

As we shall see later, other complications arise from the fact that, paradoxically enough, overnutrition also can constitute a form of malnutrition. Furthermore, human beings often develop physiological adjustments to nutritional scarcity or to excessive abundance and thereby acquire food habits and behavior patterns that are unfavorable to health and to social growth.

I realize that everyone here is quite familiar with the problems of malnutrition that I have discussed so superficially in the preceding paragraphs. My purpose in mentioning them was not to convey factual knowledge but merely to illustrate that social action must be guided by biomedical wisdom. Without this guidance, social reforms are likely to be misdirected and fail altogether, or at best to benefit only a very small percentage of the population.

The control of diarrheal diseases constitutes another problem in which social action is likely to fail unless guided by scientific understanding of etiology. There is, of course, good reason to believe that infectious processes play an important role in most kinds of intestinal disorders. For this reason, it has been commonly assumed that medical programs for their control should be based on the widespread distribution of drugs and vaccines against pathogens such as shigellas, salmonellas, amoebae, or various viruses. In fact, large and expensive public health campaigns are being carried out on this assumption. The truth is, however, that the etiology of diarrheal diseases is not at all understood. Prophylactic and therapeutic measures based on such inadequate knowledge are at best of little usefulness; in fact, they probably do more harm than good in many cases. There are indications, indeed, that general dietary improvement, better practices of infant feeding and handling, and simply an abundant supply of water would be a far more effective and less costly approach to the control of many intestinal disorders than are prophylaxis and treatment with drugs and vaccines.

In this case again, it would be out of place to describe here programs of research and action. My purpose is, rather, to emphasize that diarrheal diseases and other infectious processes, including tuberculosis, present biomedical problems peculiar to each geographical area and to each social group. Their control often requires that the living conditions be changed, and this in turn demands a kind of social action based on comprehensive epidemiologic and etiologic understanding.

Both malnutrition and diarrheal diseases create medical problems that are especially dramatic in the young age groups. In fact, these disorders account for a very large percentage of infantile mortality in destitute populations. But the importance of malnutrition and infection greatly transcends the damage revealed by mortality statistics. Children who have suffered from nutritional deficiencies or from prolonged infectious processes during the early stages of their development commonly fail to grow into healthy, vigorous adults. Not only do the pathological experiences of early life tend to depress physical and mental activity during youth and the teenage period, but frequently the unfavorable effects persist through adulthood and appear indeed irreversible.

The irreversibility of the pathological effects resulting from early experiences is not limited to malnutrition and infection: Irreversible damage commonly results from most forms of early deprivations, whether they be physiological, emotional, or social in nature. Some of the effects exerted by early influences are so lasting that they condition most activities during the entire life span and thereby affect the social and economic performance of adults and, therefore, of the whole society. Control of disease during the early phases of life and also the guidance of all aspects of physical and mental development may thus constitute the most far-reaching aspect of medical action.

Allow me to express here my deeply felt conviction that the extent of health improvement that ensues from building ultramodern hospitals with up-to-date equipment is probably trivial in comparison with the results that can be achieved at much lower cost by providing all infants and children with well-balanced food, sanitary conditions, and a stimulating environment. Needless to say, acceptance of this thesis would imply profound changes in medico-social policies and would affect also the selection of problems in scientific research. The aged deserve, of course, all our help and sympathy; the adults obviously constitute the resources of the present—but, more important perhaps, the young represent the future. Much biomedical knowledge, as well as social wisdom, is needed to formulate policy decisions concerning the comparative degrees of emphasis to be placed on the medical care of the different age groups.

## III. The Diseases of Civilization

The examples that I have mentioned so far concern diseases extremely prevalent and destructive in underprivileged populations. But in fact, the diseases that are emerging in the prosperous industrialized countries could have served just as well to illustrate that social planning should always be guided by biomedical knowledge. Had time permitted, I would have discussed at length the disturbing fact that, contrary to general belief, life expectancy past the age of forty-five has not increased significantly anywhere in the world, not even in the social groups that can afford the most elaborate medical care. Vascular diseases, certain types of cancers, chronic ailments of the respiratory tract are among the many conditions that are becoming increasingly frequent among adults in affluent societies. As long as this trend continues, there cannot be any hope for greater longevity.

Epidemiological studies leave no doubt that the increase in incidence of chronic and degenerative diseases in industrialized societies is due, in part at least, and probably in very large part, to environmental and behavioral changes. Many different factors have been incriminated as playing a role in the diseases of adult life in prosperous countries. These factors include aspects of the modern world as different as environmental pollution, overnutrition of adults, latent endogenous infectious processes, and the psychic disturbances associated with competitive behavior, emotional solitude, traffic congestion, or automated work. In reality, there is as yet no convincing knowledge concerning the mechanisms that relate the environment and the ways of life to the increased incidence of chronic and degenerative diseases in affluent societies. But granted the deficiencies in etiological understanding, I must mention, nevertheless, some general aspects of the relation of social health to the total environment which make the problem relevant to all countries of the world, irrespective of their state of economic development.

It can be taken for granted that industrialization and urbanization will soon become almost universal human phenomena. In view of the speed at which social and technologic changes occur, many of the environmental stresses that plague the affluent countries today are likely to spread to the rest of the world in the near future. In this regard, it is hardly an exaggeration to state that the future begins today even in the least developed countries. Wherever a new industry is established, there will soon be pollution of the water and the air, occupational dangers for the workers and their families, changes in nutritional habits and in other social practices, emotional upsets arising from unfamiliar working conditions and from disruption of ancestral customs. Unless carefully watched and controlled, these disturbances will add their deleterious effects to those of malnutrition, tuberculosis, malaria, schistosomiasis, etc., and will create new kinds of physiological misery in the areas of the world undergoing industrialization.

The health problems posed by social and technological changes have determinants that are peculiar to each geographical area, indeed to each community. Smogs differ in composition according to the climate, the topography of the district, the kind of fuel used, and the type of technological operations. Similarly, each industrial process engenders its own kind of occupational dangers and water pollution. Clearly then, the public health problems caused by rapid industrial growth cannot be solved by slavishly applying methods developed under other conditions. Their control will require programs of research and of social action suited to the peculiarities of each local situation.

Even more important is the obvious fact that the so-called diseases of civilization will not be eliminated automatically by improving the economic status since they are, in fact, created by industrial growth. Just as scientific guidance is required for the control of the diseases of scarcity that prevail at present in the "underdeveloped" regions of the world, so a new kind of science must be developed to deal with the medical problems affecting the industrial areas which could be properly called "maldeveloped." Unless the social structure can be managed on the basis of a suitable biomedical knowledge, all countries in the process of becoming industrialized will soon become maldeveloped. They will duplicate the horrible conditions that prevail now in the polluted, congested, and inhuman industrial centers. It would be tragic indeed if technologic and economic growth meant the replacement of the diseases of scarcity in the underdeveloped areas by the diseases of affluence in the maldeveloped countries.

## IV. Adaptation and Its Dangers

While both scarcity and affluence are at the origin of much disease throughout the world, it is also true, on the other hand, that men can survive and multiply under the most wretched and unnatural conditions. After all, many human beings survived the horrors of concentration camps during World War II! And the most polluted, maldeveloped, and traumatic cities are also the most populous! Life in the Americas illustrates, in fact and in a spectacular fashion, the wide range of man's adaptive potentialities, since these potentialities have enabled him to colonize even the least hospitable parts of the continent. For many thousand years, men have maintained themselves against great odds and have created civilizations in tropical lowlands, on semidesertic plateaus, or on the high Andes. They have become adjusted to isolation in remote areas, to crowding in shanty towns, to nutritional scarcity, to intense air and water pollution, even to high doses of radioactive background. It would seem to follow from these facts that mankind can become adapted to almost any type of hostile environment. One could assume, in other words, that mankind will be able to take in stride the stresses of the second Industrial Revolution and of overpopulation, just as it has survived famines, wars, and epidemics in the past.

Adaptability is by definition an asset for survival. But paradoxically, it constitutes in certain cases a heavy handicap against cultural and economic growth. The biological phenomena of adaptation present, therefore, problems that are of immediate relevance, not only to health, but also to social development.

It can be anticipated that the emergence of new technologies and the need to discover and exploit new natural resources will increasingly compel human beings to change their professional occupations and to move rapidly from one place to another. The very process of change creates problems for public health because adults who have to live and to function under physical and social conditions profoundly different from those in which they have developed frequently experience physiological and emotional stresses. The most common cause of disease in the modern world is probably the failure to meet successfully the exacting adaptive demands created by changes of life because these changes are now so frequent and so rapid. For this reason, understanding of the mechanisms through which adaptation takes place, and the development of medical and social techniques to facilitate its achievement, has become one of the large responsibilities of physicians and of medical scientists.

It has become apparent, on the other hand, that adaptative processes can generate dangers of their own—dangers which often remain so completely unnoticed at first that their medical and social consequences are neglected. The dangers originating from some forms of adaptation are indeed so varied and so great that the field deserves an exhaustive study by biomedical and social sciences. For lack of time, I shall limit myself to two examples, namely, the distant consequences of air pollution and of malnutrition.

Air pollution provides tragic evidence of the fact that many of the physiological, mental, and social processes which make it possible to live in a hostile environment commonly express themselves at a later date in overt disease and in economic loss. During the past two centuries, for instance, the inhabitants of the industrial areas of northern Europe have been exposed to large concentrations of many types of air pollutants produced by incomplete combustion of coal, and released in the fumes from chemical plants. Such exposure is rendered even more objectionable by the inclemency of the Atlantic climate. However, long experience with pollution and with bad weather results in the development of physiological reactions and living habits that obviously have adaptive value, since northern Europeans seem to accept almost cheerfully conditions which appear unbearable to a nonexperienced person.

This adaptive response is not peculiar to northern Europeans. It occurs in all heavily industrialized areas where the inhabitants function effectively despite the almost constant presence of irritating substances in the air they breathe. In other words, it would seem at first sight that human beings can readily make a completely adequate adjustment to massive air pollution.

Unfortunately, adaptation to the stresses of the present often has to be paid in the form of physiological misery at some future date. Even among persons who seem to be unaware of the smogs surrounding them, the respiratory tract registers the insult of the various air pollutants. Eventually, the cumulative effects of irritation result in chronic bronchitis and other forms of irreversible pulmonary disease. Generally, however, this does not happen until several years late. In fact, chronic pulmonary disease now constitutes the greatest single medical problem in northern Europe, as well as the most costly. It is increasing in prevalence at an alarming rate in North America also, and it will undoubtedly spread to all areas undergoing industrialization. There is good evidence, furthermore, that air pollution contributes to the incidence of various cancers—not only pulmonary carcinoma. It increases also the number of fatalities among persons suffering from vascular disorders.

The delayed effects of air pollutants constitute a tragic model for the kind of medical problems likely to arise in the future from the various forms of environmental pollution. Unfortunately, the course of events can be predicted with some confidence.

Wherever conditions permit, chemical pollution of air, water, and food soon will be sufficiently controlled to prevent the disabling toxic effects that are immediate and obvious. Human beings will then tolerate without complaints concentrations of environmental pollutants that do not constitute an obvious nuisance and do not interfere seriously with social and economic life. But it is probable that continued exposure to low levels of toxic agents will result eventually in a great variety of delayed pathological manifestations, creating much physiological misery and greatly increasing the medical load. The point of importance here is that the worst pathological effects of environmental pollutants will not be detected at the time of exposure. Indeed, they may not become evident until several decades later. Man readily becomes adjusted to low concentrations of pollutants that do not have an immediate nuisance value, but this apparent adaptation to the conditions of the present will cause much human suffering and create large social burdens in the future.

Adjustment to malnutrition also can have distant consequences of far-reaching importance. Recent physiological and behavioral studies have revealed that people who have been born and raised in an environment where food intake is quantitatively or qualitatively inadequate seem to achieve a certain form of physiological adaptation to low food intake. Unconsciously, they tend to restrict their physical and mental activity so as to reduce their nutritional needs; in other words, they become adjusted to undernutrition by living less intensely. Physical and mental apathy and other forms of indolence have long been assumed to have a racial or climatic origin. But in reality, these behavioral traits often constitute a form of physiological adjustment to malnutrition, especially when nutritional scarcity has occurred during very early life.

Adaptation to an inadequate food intake has obvious merits for survival under conditions of scarcity; indolence may even have some romantic appeal for the harried and tense observer from a competitive society. But the dismal aspect of metabolic and mental adjustment to malnutrition is that it creates a vicious circle. It is responsible for much of the difficulty experienced in several parts of the world by those who attempt to stimulate national economies. Populations that have been deprived during early life remain healthy as long as little effort is required of them, but they commonly exhibit little resistance to stress. For this reason, probably, they find it difficult to make the efforts required to improve their economic status.

Hardly anything is known concerning the physiological mechanisms of adaptation to nutritional scarcity. In fact, ignorance in this field is so great that nutritionists would hardly know how to correct the effects of early food deprivation even if the food supplies in deprived populations became sufficient to provide adults with an optimum diet. The production of more food and of better food is a technological and social problem. But the improvement of the nutritional status demands, in addition, sophisticated biomedical knowledge.

## V. Biomedical Sciences and the Human Condition

I have emphasized in this discussion the adaptive responses of man to his environment, not only because of the immense practical problems that they pose, but also because they illustrate so well the complex interplay among human health, social action, and biomedical knowledge. Admittedly, all aspects of man's life including his health are linked to his history and his social structures. Ortega y Gasset went as far as claiming that "Man has no nature, what he has is history." But it is also true that man's social history is conditioned by his biological responses to his total environment. In order to evaluate the significance and to recognize the implications of this fact, it may be helpful to turn back for a moment to the generalities stated at the beginning of this essay and, in particular, to the medical paradox arising from the biological unity of man's nature and the diversity of his diseases.

Anthropological evidence leaves no doubt that the diseases of modern man were also present in prehistoric man; furthermore, these diseases also exist today in all underdeveloped societies including the most primitive. On the other hand, the relative prevalence of the various diseases has certainly changed during historical times, and it continues to change; the pattern of diseases today differs profoundly from one area to another and in accordance with the social structure and economic status of the group under consideration. The phenomena of disease exhibit universal and unchangeable characteristics because man's fundamental nature has remained essentially the same for the past 100,000 years, whereas the relative incidence of the various types of disease exhibits great diversity because the conditions of human life are so varied and so changeable.

It will be apparent that in my discussion I have hardly mentioned those aspects of the biomedical sciences which bear on the universal aspects of man's nature and of disease, even though such knowledge provides, of course, the basis for many therapeutic procedures of modern medicine. The reason for this neglect is not failure to recognize the importance of classical therapeutic medicine but simply the fact that its scientific basis and its practical applications are given priority both in teaching and in research throughout the countries of Western civilization. In contrast, medical schools and research institutes pay little heed to the effects that environmental factors exert on the life of human societies. Yet there is no doubt that the most important health problems in the world today have their origin in man's responses to his total environment. This is particularly true in the Americas because the continent presents such an immense variety of physical and social conditions and because many of its countries are at present experiencing an industrial and social revolution that will inevitably generate upheavals in the ways of life.

In final analysis, health depends upon successful adaptation to the physical and social environment. The very use of the word "adaptation," however, points to the immense conceptual difficulties faced by those who are concerned with human health. As we have seen, the concept of adaptation can hardly be applied to human beings in a simple way, with a purely biological meaning, because this would often imply the acceptance of a state not desirable in the long run. Neither fitness to the conditions of the present nor comfort or survival of the person concerned will encompass the goals of man and the richness of his nature. Man lives, of course, in the present, but he also wants to preserve the past, and he is concerned with the future. These are not empty words. They refer to complexities of the human condition that must be faced by all physicians, public health officers, and scientists who are really concerned, not only with the physico-chemical operations of the body machine, but with the welfare of human beings.

It was to acknowledge the practical importance of these complexities that I have repeatedly emphasized throughout this discussion the two contrasting but complementary aspects of the health sciences—those dealing with the universal aspects of man's nature and those arising from the diversity of physical and social environments. Biomedical knowledge constitutes one of the highest expressions of culture precisely because it must perforce deal with both these aspects of the human condition.

I realize, of course, that even with the generous facilities symbolized by the building we are dedicating, enormous obstacles that appear almost insuperable stand in the way of those who try to satisfy the universal requirements of man's nature, while functioning within the limits and restrictions imposed by social institutions and historical frameworks. But men of good heart are not discouraged by such difficulties. Indeed they thrive on them and derive from the struggle the inspiration for further adventures of the spirit. You will forgive me for trying to convey to you my faith in the future, and in the success of PAHO, by paraphrasing the French writer Albert Camus, who was, until his untimely death a few years ago, the conscience and the voice of the postwar generations. To believe in the human condition might be regarded as the attitude of a fool, but to despair of it is the act of a coward.